13-3

EXAM PREPARATION & PRACTICE GUIDE

❄ **HAESE MATHEMATICS**

Mathematics
for the international student
Mathematics SL

third edition

Robert Haese
Sandra Haese
Michael Haese
Marjut Mäenpää
Mark Humphries

for use with
IB Diploma Programme

Michael Haese
Robert Haese

third edition

Haese Mathematics

MATHEMATICS FOR THE INTERNATIONAL STUDENT
Mathematics SL
EXAM PREPARATION & PRACTICE GUIDE third edition

Michael Haese   B.Sc.(Hons), Ph.D.
Robert Haese   B.Sc.

Haese Mathematics
3 Frank Collopy Court, Adelaide Airport, SA 5950, AUSTRALIA
Telephone: +61 8 8355 9444, Fax: + 61 8 8355 9471
Email: info@haesemathematics.com.au
Web: www.haesemathematics.com.au

National Library of Australia Card Number & ISBN 978-1-921972-10-2

© Haese Mathematics 2012

Published by Haese Mathematics
3 Frank Collopy Court, Adelaide Airport, SA 5950, AUSTRALIA

First Edition	2006	
Second Edition	2009	
Third Edition	2012	

Artwork by Gregory Olesinski and Piotr Poturaj.
Cover design by Piotr Poturaj.

Typeset in Australia by Charlotte Frost.

Typeset in Times Roman 9/10.

Printed in Malaysia through Bookpac Production Services, Singapore.

The Guide has been developed independently of the International Baccalaureate Organization (IBO). The Guide is in no way connected with, or endorsed by, the IBO.

Acknowledgements: While every attempt has been made to trace and acknowledge copyright, the authors and publishers apologise for any accidental infringement where copyright has proved untraceable. They would be pleased to come to a suitable agreement with the rightful owner.

The authors and publishers would like to thank all those teachers who have read the proofs of this book and offered advice and encouragement.

Special thanks to Susan Cox, Paul Thompson, Sara Brouwer, Dr. Andrzej Cichy who offered to read and comment on the proofs. To anyone we may have missed, we offer our apologies.

The publishers wish to make it clear that acknowledging these teachers does not imply any endorsement of this book by any of them, and all responsibility for the content rests with the authors and publishers.

FOREWORD

The aim of this Guide is to help you prepare for the Mathematics SL final examinations.

In this third edition, the questions throughout are divided into two categories: 'no calculators' and 'calculators' in response to the introduction of a calculator-free examination paper.

This Guide should be used in conjunction with other material suggested by your teacher. Past examination papers, for example, are invaluable aids. Ensure you frequently refer to the information booklet. It is essential that you become familiar with the layout and content of the booklet.

This Guide covers all six Topics in the Mathematics SL syllabus. The main elements within each Topic are summarised in a way that highlights the important facts and concepts. These summaries are intended to complement your textbook and information booklet. When a formula can be found in the information booklet, it may not be repeated in this Guide.

Two sets of Skill Builder Questions appear at the end of each Topic, the first set categorised as 'no calculators', the second as 'calculators'. Skill Builder Questions can be used as a warm-up and should help to consolidate your understanding of each Topic. The best way to consolidate your understanding is to be active: to summarise concepts concisely and accurately, and to practise answering questions.

Following the coverage of all six Topics, the Guide has three Trial Examinations. Each Trial Examination contains two papers: Paper 1, where calculators are not allowed, and Paper 2, where calculators are required. This format is consistent with the Mathematics SL final examination. Full solutions are provided, but it is recommended that you work through a full set before checking the solutions.

Try to complete the Trial Examinations under examination conditions. Getting into good habits will reduce pressure during the examination.

- It is important that you persevere with a question, but sometimes it is a good strategy to move on to other questions and return later to ones you have found challenging. Time management is very important during the examination, and too much time spent on a difficult question may mean that you do not leave yourself sufficient time to complete other questions.

- Use a pen rather than a pencil, except for graphs and diagrams.

- If you make a mistake draw, a single line through the work you want to replace. Do not cross out work until you have replaced it with something you consider better.

- Set out your work clearly with full explanations. Do not take shortcuts.

- Diagrams and graphs should be sufficiently large, well labelled and clearly drawn.

- Remember to leave answers correct to three significant figures unless an exact answer is more appropriate or a different level of accuracy is requested in the question.

Get used to reading the questions carefully.

- Check for key words. If the word "hence" appears, then you must use the result you have just obtained. "Hence, or otherwise" means that you can use any method you like, although it is likely that the best method uses the previous result.

- Rushing into a question may mean that you miss subtle points. Underlining key words may help.

- Often questions in the examination are set so that, even if you cannot get through one part, the question can still be picked up in a later part.

After completing a Trial Examination, identify areas of weakness.

- Return to your notes or textbook and review the Topic.

- Ask your teacher or a friend for help if further explanation is needed.

- Summarise each Topic. Summaries that you make yourself are the most valuable.

- Test yourself, or work with someone else to help improve your knowledge of a Topic.

- If you have had difficulty with a question, try it again later. Do not just assume that you know how to do it once you have read the solution. It is important that you work on areas of weakness, but do not neglect the other areas.

In addition to the information booklet, your graphics display calculator is an essential aid.

- Make sure you are familiar with the model you will be using.

- In trigonometry questions, remember to check whether the graphics calculator should be in degrees or radians.

- Become familiar with common error messages and how to respond to them.

- Important features of graphs may be revealed by zooming in or out.

- Asymptotic behaviour is not always clear on a graphics calculator screen; don't just rely on appearances. As with all aspects of the graphics calculator, reflect on the reasonableness of the results.

- Are your batteries fresh?

We hope this guide will help you structure your revision program effectively. Remember that good examination techniques will come from good examination preparation.

We welcome your feedback:

web: http://haesemathematics.com.au

email: info@haesemathematics.com.au

TABLE OF CONTENTS

1 ALGEBRA   **5**
Sequences and series   5
Exponentials and logarithms   5
The binomial theorem   5
Skill builder questions (no calculators)   5
Skill builder questions (calculators)   6

2 FUNCTIONS AND EQUATIONS   **7**
Functions $f : x \mapsto f(x)$ or $y = f(x)$ 7
Graphs of functions   8
Transformations of graphs   8
Linear functions   8
Quadratic functions   8
Quadratic equations   9
Rational functions   9
Exponential and logarithmic functions   9
Exponential equations   9
Skill builder questions (no calculators)   9
Skill builder questions (calculators)   11

3 CIRCULAR FUNCTIONS AND TRIGONOMETRY   **11**
Non-right angled triangle trigonometry   12
Periodic functions   12
Transforming $y = \sin x$ 12
The general sine function   13
The cosine function   13
The tangent function   13
Trigonometric identities   13
Trigonometric equations   13
Skill builder questions (no calculators)   13
Skill builder questions (calculators)   15

4 VECTORS   **16**
Vectors in geometric form   16
Vectors in component form   16
Position vectors in 2-D   17
Position vectors in 3-D   17
Properties of vectors   17
Lines   17
Skill builder questions (no calculators)   18
Skill builder questions (calculators)   19

5 STATISTICS AND PROBABILITY   **20**
Populations and samples   20
Types of data and its representation   20
The centre of a data set   20
Percentiles   21
The spread of a distribution   21
Outliers   21
Boxplots   21
Two variable statistics   21
Probability   22
Discrete random variables   22
Continuous random variables   22
Skill builder questions (no calculators)   23

Skill builder questions (calculators)   25

6 CALCULUS   **28**
Limits   28
Rates of change   28
Differentiation   28
Properties of curves   28
Kinematic problems   29
Optimisation problems   29
Integration   30
Solids of revolution   31
Skill builder questions (no calculators)   31
Skill builder questions (calculators)   35

TRIAL EXAMINATIONS   **38**
Trial examination 1
    Paper 1 - No calculators   38
    Paper 2 - Calculators   39
Trial examination 2
    Paper 1 - No calculators   40
    Paper 2 - Calculators   40
Trial examination 3
    Paper 1 - No calculators   41
    Paper 2 - Calculators   42

SOLUTIONS   **44**
Topic 1 (Algebra)
    No calculators   44
    Calculators   46
Topic 2 (Functions and equations)
    No calculators   48
    Calculators   53
Topic 3 (Circular functions and trigonometry)
    No calculators   55
    Calculators   60
Topic 4 (Vectors)
    No calculators   63
    Calculators   67
Topic 5 (Statistics and Probability)
    No calculators   70
    Calculators   72
Topic 6 (Calculus)
    No calculators   76
    Calculators   90
Trial examination 1   98
Trial examination 2   101
Trial examination 3   105

TOPIC 1:   ALGEBRA

SEQUENCES AND SERIES

A **number sequence** is a set of numbers defined by a rule. Often, the rule is a formula for the **general term** or **nth term** of the sequence.

A sequence which continues forever is called an **infinite sequence**.

A sequence which terminates is called a **finite sequence**.

Arithmetic Sequences

In an **arithmetic sequence**, each term differs from the previous one by the same fixed number.

$u_{n+1} - u_n = d$ for all n, where d is a constant called the **common difference**.

For an arithmetic sequence with first term u_1 and common difference d, the nth term is $u_n = u_1 + (n-1)d$.

Geometric Sequences

In a **geometric sequence**, each term is obtained from the previous one by multiplying by the same non-zero constant.

$\dfrac{u_{n+1}}{u_n} = r$ for all n, where r is a constant called the **common ratio**.

For a geometric sequence with first term u_1 and common ratio r, the nth term is $u_n = u_1 r^{n-1}$.

For **compound interest** problems we have a geometric sequence. If the interest rate is $i\%$ per time period then the common ratio is $\left(1 + \frac{i}{100}\right)$ and the number of compounding periods is n.

Series

A **series** is the addition of the terms of a sequence.

For a finite series with n terms, its sum is
$S_n = u_1 + u_2 + \ldots + u_n$.

For an infinite series, the sum $u_1 + u_2 + \ldots + u_n + \ldots$ can only be calculated in some cases.

Using **sigma notation** we write

$u_1 + u_2 + u_3 + \ldots + u_n$ as $\displaystyle\sum_{k=1}^{n} u_k$.

For a **finite arithmetic series**, $S_n = \frac{n}{2}(u_1 + u_n)$ or $S_n = \frac{n}{2}(2u_1 + (n-1)d)$.

For a **finite geometric series** with $r \neq 1$, $S_n = \dfrac{u_1(r^n - 1)}{r - 1}$.

The sum of an **infinite geometric series** is
$S = \dfrac{u_1}{1 - r}$ provided $|r| < 1$.

If $|r| > 1$ the series is **divergent**.

EXPONENTIALS AND LOGARITHMS

Exponential and logarithmic functions are inverses of each other. The graph of $y = \log_a x$ is the reflection in the line $y = x$ of the graph of $y = a^x$.

Index or Exponent Laws	
$a^m \times a^n = a^{m+n}$	$a^{-n} = \dfrac{1}{a^n}$ and $\dfrac{1}{a^{-n}} = a^n$
$\dfrac{a^m}{a^n} = a^{m-n}$	$a^{\frac{1}{n}} = \sqrt[n]{a}$
$(a^m)^n = a^{mn}$	$a^{\frac{m}{n}} = \sqrt[n]{a^m} = (\sqrt[n]{a})^m$
$a^0 = 1 \ (a \neq 0)$	

If $a^x = a^k$ then $x = k$. So, if the base numbers are the same, we can **equate indices**.

If $b = a^x$, $a \neq 1$, $a > 0$, we say that x is the **logarithm** of b in base a, and that $b = a^x \Leftrightarrow x = \log_a b$, $b > 0$.

The **natural logarithm** is the logarithm in base e. $\ln x \equiv \log_e x$

Logarithm Laws	
Base c, $c \neq 1$, $c > 0$	**Base e**
$\log_c AB = \log_c A + \log_c B$	$\ln xy = \ln x + \ln y$
$\log_c\left(\dfrac{A}{B}\right) = \log_c A - \log_c B$	$\ln\left(\dfrac{x}{y}\right) = \ln x - \ln y$
$\log_c A^n = n\log_c A$	$\ln x^y = y\ln x$
$\log_c 1 = 0$	$\ln 1 = 0$
$\log_c c = 1$	$\ln e = 1$

To change the base of a logarithm, use the rule $\log_b a = \dfrac{\log_c a}{\log_c b}$.

$x = \log_a a^x$ and $x = a^{\log_a x}$ provided $x > 0$.

THE BINOMIAL THEOREM

$a + b$ is called a **binomial** as it contains two terms.

Any expression of the form $(a + b)^n$ is called a **power of a binomial**.

The **binomial coefficient** $\binom{n}{r} = \dfrac{n!}{r!(n-r)!}$

where $n! = n(n-1)(n-2)\ldots \times 3 \times 2 \times 1$
and $0! = 1$

You should also know how to calculate binomial coefficients from Pascal's triangle and using your calculator.

The **general binomial expansion** is

$(a+b)^n = \binom{n}{0}a^n + \binom{n}{1}a^{n-1}b + \binom{n}{2}a^{n-2}b^2 + \ldots$
$\qquad\qquad\qquad + \binom{n}{r}a^{n-r}b^r + \ldots + \binom{n}{n}b^n$

where $\binom{n}{r}$ is the binomial coefficient of $a^{n-r}b^r$ and $r = 0, 1, 2, 3, \ldots, n$.

The **general term** in the binomial expansion is

$T_{r+1} = \binom{n}{r}a^{n-r}b^r$, so $(a+b)^n = \displaystyle\sum_{r=0}^{n}\binom{n}{r}a^{n-r}b^r$.

SKILL BUILDER QUESTIONS (NO CALCULATORS)

1 The first four terms of an arithmetic sequence are 51, 45, 39, 33.

   a Write down the common difference d.

   b Find the 20th term u_{20}.

   c Find the sum of the first 20 terms.

2 The first four terms of a geometric sequence are 0.125, 0.25, 0.5, 1.

   a Write down the common ratio r.

   b Find the 20th term u_{20}.

   c Find the sum of the first 10 terms.

3 An infinite geometric series has terms $u_1 = 27$ and $u_4 = 8$.

   a Find the common ratio r.

   b Find the 6th term of the series.

   c Using summation notation, write an expression for the sum to infinity S of the series.

   d Evaluate S.

4 An arithmetic series has terms $u_7 = 1$ and $u_{15} = -23$.

   a Find the first term u_1 and common difference d.

   b Find the 27th term u_{27}.

   c Find the sum of the first 27 terms of the series.

5 The first term of a finite arithmetic series is 18 and the sum of the series is -210. The common difference is -3. Suppose there are n terms in the series.

   a Show that $\dfrac{n}{2}(39 - 3n) = -210$.

   b Hence find n.

6 Consider the infinite geometric sequence $x^{-\frac{1}{2}}$, x, $x^{\frac{5}{2}}$, ...

   a Write down the common ratio r.

   b Find the 10th term of the sequence.

   c For what values of x will the sum of the corresponding infinite geometric series converge?

7 A finite geometric series is defined by $\displaystyle\sum_{k=1}^{7} 3 \times 2^{k-1}$.

   a How many terms are there in the series?

   b Find the first term u_1 and common ratio r.

   c Find the sum of the series.

8 **a** An infinite geometric series is defined by $\displaystyle\sum_{k=1}^{\infty} 2\left(\frac{2}{3}\right)^{k}$.

      i Find the first term u_1 and common ratio r.

      ii Find the sum of the series.

   b A finite arithmetic series is defined by $\displaystyle\sum_{k=1}^{n} (k - 4)$.

      i Find the first term u_1 and common difference d.

      ii Find the sum of the series, in terms of n.

   c Find n such that the sums of the series in **a** and **b** are equal.

9 **a** Find the sum to infinity of the infinite geometric series $1 + 0.6 + (0.6)^2 + (0.6)^3 + ...$

   b When a ball is dropped from a height of 1 m, on each bounce it returns to 60% of the height it reached previously. Find the total distance travelled by the ball until it stops bouncing.

10 Solve for x:

   a $9^x - 6(3^x) + 8 = 0$ **b** $8^{2x-3} = 16^{2-x}$

11 Solve for x:

   a $\log_5(2x - 1) = -1$ **b** $25^x - 5^{x+1} + 6 = 0$

12 Solve for x:

   a $4^x + 4 = 17(2^{x-1})$ **b** $\log_3 x + \log_3(x - 2) = 1$

13 **a** Simplify: $\frac{1}{4}\log 81 + \log 12 - \log 4$

   b If $x = \log_a 5$, write in terms of x: $\log_a(5a)$

   c Write without logarithms: $\log_a N = 2\log_a d - \log_a c$

14 **a** If $A = \log_{10} P$, $B = \log_{10} Q$, and $C = \log_{10} R$, express in terms of A, B, and C: $\log_{10}\left(P^2 Q\sqrt{R}\right)$.

   b Write $\dfrac{8}{\log_5 9}$ in the form $a \log_3 b$ where $a, b \in \mathbb{Z}$.

15 **a** How many terms are in the expansion of $\left(x + \dfrac{1}{x}\right)^5$?

   b Use Pascal's triangle to help expand and simplify $\left(x + \dfrac{1}{x}\right)^5$.

16 Consider the binomial expansion of $(a + b)^6$.

   a Write down the general term in the expansion.

   b Given that $\binom{6}{4} = 15$, find the coefficient of $a^4 b^2$.

17 Consider the expansion of $\left(3x - \dfrac{1}{x^2}\right)^4$.

   a How many terms are in the expansion?

   b Use the binomial coefficient $\binom{n}{r} = \dfrac{n!}{r!(n-r)!}$ to find the term in x.

SKILL BUILDER QUESTIONS (CALCULATORS)

1 Consider the arithmetic sequence $100, 130, 160, 190, ...$

   a Write an expression for the general term u_n.

   b Find the first term in the sequence to exceed 1200.

   c The sum of the first k terms of the sequence is $19\,140$. Find k.

2 Consider the geometric sequence with $u_5 = 18$ and $u_8 = 486$.

   a Find the first term u_1 and common ratio r.

   b Find the 12th term of the sequence.

   c Find the sum of the first 10 terms of the corresponding geometric series.

3 Maria invested €800 on Jan 1st 2004.

   a If her investment earns fixed interest of 7% per annum, what was it worth on Jan 1st 2012?

   b How many years will it take for her investment to reach €4000?

4 Ying is training to run a marathon. In one week she ran 10 km on the first day and increased the distance by 10% on each subsequent day.

   a How far did she run on the seventh day?

   b What was the total distance she ran during the week?

5 Find the sum of the series:

   a $10 + 14 + 18 + 22 + ... + 138$

   b $6 - 12 + 24 - 48 + 96 - .... + 1536$

6 The sum of an infinite geometric series is 1.5, and its first term is 1. Find:

   a the common ratio

   b the sum of the first 7 terms, in rational form.

7 A sequence is defined by $u_n = 12\left(\frac{2}{3}\right)^{n-1}$.

   a Prove that the sequence is geometric.

   b Find the 5th term in rational form.

   c Find: **i** $\displaystyle\sum_{n=1}^{\infty} u_n$

                ii $\displaystyle\sum_{n=1}^{20} u_n$ correct to 4 decimal places.

8 Stan invests £3500 for 33 months at an interest rate of 8% p.a. compounded quarterly. Find its maturing value.

9 Consider the series $\displaystyle\sum_{k=1}^{\infty} 12(x-2)^{k-1}$.

   a For what values of x will the series converge?

   b Evaluate the sum of the series when $x = \sqrt{5}$.

10 Twins Pierre and Francesca were each given $100 on their 15th birthday. They immediately put their money into their individual money boxes.

Each week throughout the next year they added a portion of their weekly pocket money. Pierre added $10 each week. Francesca added 50 cents the first week, $1 the next, $1.50 the next, and so on, adding an extra 50 cents each subsequent week.

   a Find the amount that each had added to his or her money box after 8 weeks.

   b How much did Francesca add to her money box in the last week before her 16th birthday?

   c Calculate the total amount they each had in their money boxes after one year.

11 Hayley and Patrick were training for a road cycling race. During the first week they both cycled 60 km. Hayley cycled an additional 20 km each subsequent week, whereas Patrick increased his distance by 20% each subsequent week.

   a How far did each of them cycle in the 5th week of training?

   b Who was the first to cycle 210 km in one week?

   c What total distance did each cycle in the first 12 weeks?

12 Kapil invested 2000 rupees in a bank account on Jan 1st 2002. Each year thereafter, he invested another 2000 rupees into the same account. The account pays 8.25% per annum compounded annually.

   a Find the total value of Kapil's investment immediately after he invested 2000 rupees on Jan 1st 2009.

   b Would it have been a better option for Kapil to invest his money each year into an account paying 9% per annum simple interest? Justify your answer.

13 Paige has €500 to invest in an account that pays 7.2% p.a. compounded monthly. The formula $u_{n+1} = u_1 \times r^n$ can be used to model the investment, where n is the time in months.

   a Explain why $r = 1.006$.

   b How long will it take for Paige's investment to be worth €1000?

14 Solve for x:

   a $5 \times 2^x = 160$ **b** $(1.25)^x = 10$ **c** $7e^x = 100$

15 **a** Solve for t: $200 \times e^{\frac{t}{4}} = 1500$

   b Suppose $A = 125e^{-kt}$, and that $A = 200$ when $t = 3$. Find the value of k.

16 At the beginning of 2000 the number of koalas on an island was 2400. The numbers steadily increase each year according to $N(t) = 2400 + 250t$ where t is the number of years since 2000. The population of kangaroos on the same island is given by $K(t) = 3200 \times (0.85)^t$.

   a What was the kangaroo population at the beginning of 2000?

   b How many kangaroos were on the island at the beginning of 2005?

   c How many koalas were on the island at the beginning of 2005?

   d After how many years will the kangaroo population fall below 1000?

   e When will the number of koalas exceed the number of kangaroos?

17 Consider the expansion of $\left(x + \dfrac{3}{x^2}\right)^9$.

   a How many terms are in the expansion?

   b Find the constant term.

18 Consider the expansion of $\left(x + 2y^3\right)^7$.

   a Write down a formula for the general term.

   b Find the coefficient of $x^4 y^9$.

19 Consider the binomial expansion of $\left(2x - \dfrac{1}{x^2}\right)^{12}$. Find:

   a the general term   **b** the coefficient of x^3

   c the constant term.

20 Consider the binomial expansion of $\left(kx + \dfrac{1}{\sqrt{x}}\right)^9$.

   a Write down a formula for the general term.

   b Given that the constant term is $-10\frac{1}{2}$, find k.

21 Find the coefficient of x^5 in the expansion of $(x + 2)(1 - x)^{10}$.

TOPIC 2:   FUNCTIONS AND EQUATIONS

FUNCTIONS $f : x \mapsto f(x)$ OR $y = f(x)$

A **relation** is any set of points which connects two variables.

A **function** is a relation in which no two different ordered pairs have the same x-coordinate or first member. For each value of x there is only one value of y or $f(x)$. We sometimes refer to y or $f(x)$ as the **function value** or **image** of x.

We **test for functions** using the vertical line test. A graph is a function if no vertical line intersects the graph more than once.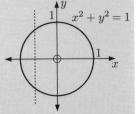

For example, the graph of the circle $x^2 + y^2 = 1$ shows that this relation is not a function.

The **domain** of a relation is the set of values that x can take.

Mathematics SL – Exam Preparation & Practice Guide (3rd edition)

To find the domain of a function, remember that we cannot:
- divide by zero
- take the square root of a negative number
- take the logarithm of a non-positive number.

The **range** of a relation is the set of values that y or $f(x)$ can take.

Given $f : x \mapsto f(x)$ and $g : x \mapsto g(x)$, the **composite function** of f and g is $f \circ g : x \mapsto f(g(x))$.

In general, $f(g(x)) \neq g(f(x))$, so $f \circ g \neq g \circ f$.

The **identity function** is $f(x) = x$.

If $y = f(x)$ has an **inverse function** $y = f^{-1}(x)$, then the inverse function:
- must satisfy the vertical line test
- is a reflection of $y = f(x)$ in the line $y = x$
- satisfies $(f \circ f^{-1})(x) = (f^{-1} \circ f)(x) = x$
- has range equal to the domain of $f(x)$
- has domain equal to the range of $f(x)$.

Any function which has an inverse and whose graph is symmetrical about the line $y = x$, is a **self-inverse function**.

GRAPHS OF FUNCTIONS

The **x-intercepts** of a function are the values of x for which $y = 0$. They are the **zeros** of the function.

The **y-intercept** of a function is the value of y when $x = 0$.

An **asymptote** is a line that the graph *approaches* or begins to look like as it tends to infinity in a particular direction.

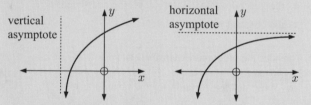

To find vertical asymptotes, look for values of x for which the function is undefined:
- If $y = \dfrac{f(x)}{g(x)}$, find where $g(x) = 0$.
- If $y = \log_a(f(x))$, find where $f(x) = 0$.

To find horizontal asymptotes, consider the behaviour as $|x| \to \infty$.

TRANSFORMATIONS OF GRAPHS

- $y = f(x) + b$ **translates** $y = f(x)$ vertically b units.
- $y = f(x - a)$ **translates** $y = f(x)$ horizontally a units.
- $y = f(x - a) + b$ **translates** $y = f(x)$ by the vector $\binom{a}{b}$.
- $y = pf(x)$, $p > 0$ is a **vertical stretch** of $y = f(x)$ with scale factor p.
- $y = f(qx)$, $q > 0$ is a **horizontal stretch** of $y = f(x)$ with scale factor $\dfrac{1}{q}$.
- $y = -f(x)$ is a **reflection** of $y = f(x)$ in the x-axis.
- $y = f(-x)$ is a **reflection** of $y = f(x)$ in the y-axis.
- If it exists, $y = f^{-1}(x)$ is a **reflection** of $y = f(x)$ in the line $y = x$.

LINEAR FUNCTIONS

A **linear function** has the form $f(x) = ax + b$, $a \neq 0$.

Its graph is a straight line with gradient a and y-intercept b.

Perpendicular lines have gradients which are the negative reciprocals of each other.

QUADRATIC FUNCTIONS

A **quadratic function** has the form $f(x) = ax^2 + bx + c$, $a \neq 0$.

The graph is a parabola with the following properties:
- it is *concave up* if $a > 0$ and *concave down* if $a < 0$
- its axis of symmetry is $x = \dfrac{-b}{2a}$
- its vertex is at $\left(\dfrac{-b}{2a}, f\left(\dfrac{-b}{2a}\right)\right)$.

A quadratic function written in the form:
- $f(x) = a(x - h)^2 + k$ has vertex (h, k)
- $f(x) = a(x - p)(x - q)$ has x-intercepts p and q.

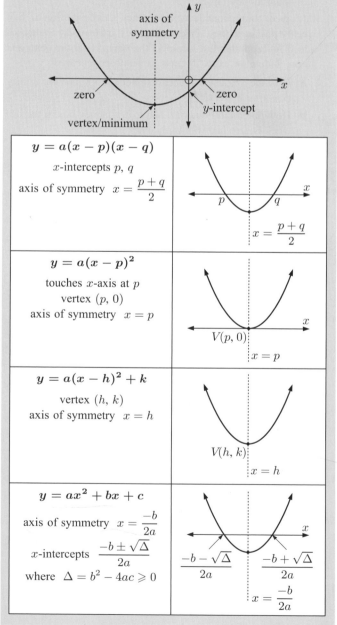

QUADRATIC EQUATIONS

A quadratic equation of the form $ax^2 + bx + c = 0$, $a \neq 0$, can be solved by:

- factorisation
- completing the square
- the quadratic formula $x = \dfrac{-b \pm \sqrt{b^2 - 4ac}}{2a}$.

The **discriminant** of the quadratic equation is $\Delta = b^2 - 4ac$.

The quadratic equation has:

- *no real solutions* if $\Delta < 0$
- *one real (repeated) solution* if $\Delta = 0$
- *two real solutions* if $\Delta > 0$.

The number of solutions indicates whether the graph of the corresponding quadratic function *does not meet*, *touches*, or *cuts* the x-axis.

A quadratic function is **positive definite** if $a > 0$ and $\Delta < 0$.
A quadratic function is **negative definite** if $a < 0$ and $\Delta < 0$.

RATIONAL FUNCTIONS

The **rational functions** we consider in this course can be written in the form $y = \dfrac{ax + b}{cx + d}$, $c \neq 0$.

They are characterised by a vertical and a horizontal asymptote.

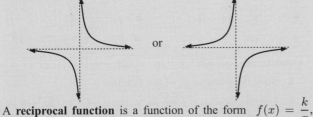

A **reciprocal function** is a function of the form $f(x) = \dfrac{k}{x}$, $k \neq 0$.

All reciprocal functions are self-inverse functions.

EXPONENTIAL AND LOGARITHMIC FUNCTIONS

The simplest **exponential function** is $f(x) = b^x$, $b > 0$, $b \neq 1$.

If $b > 1$ we have *growth*.

If $0 < b < 1$ we have *decay*.

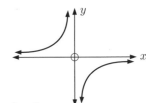

The graph of $y = b^x$ has the horizontal asymptote $y = 0$.

$b^x > 0$ and $b^{-x} > 0$ for all $x \in \mathbb{R}$.

The inverse function of $f(x) = b^x$ is the **logarithmic function** $f^{-1}(x) = \log_b x$, $x > 0$.

The graph of $y = \log_b x$ has the vertical asymptote $x = 0$.

EXPONENTIAL EQUATIONS

- If we can make the base numbers the same then we can equate indices.

  So, if $a^x = a^k$ then $x = k$.

- If the bases cannot be made the same then we take the logarithm of both sides.

  For example:

  $$\text{If } 2^x = 30$$
  $$\text{then } \log(2^x) = \log 30$$
  $$\therefore \ x \log 2 = \log 30$$
  $$\therefore \ x = \frac{\log 30}{\log 2} \approx 4.91$$

SKILL BUILDER QUESTIONS (NO CALCULATORS)

1 The graph alongside shows a relation between x and y.

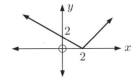

  a Is the relation a function? Explain your answer.

  b State the domain and range of the relation.

  c Sketch the result when the graph is translated through $\binom{-2}{-1}$ and then reflected in the x-axis.

2 The graph alongside shows a relation between x and y.

  a Explain why the relation is a function.

  b State the domain and range of the function.

  c The graph is symmetrical about the line $y = x$. What does this tell us about the function?

3 Given $f : x \mapsto 5x - 2$ and $g : x \mapsto 2x + 7$, find in simplest form:

  a $(f \circ g)(x)$ **b** $(g \circ f)(x)$ **c** $g^{-1}(x)$

4 Consider the functions $f(x) = x - 2$ and $g(x) = 3 - x - 2x^2$. Find:

  a $f^{-1}(x)$ **b** $(g \circ f)(x)$ **c** $(g \circ f)(-1)$

5 Let $f(x) = x^2 - 3$ and $g(x) = 2x + 1$. The graph of $y = h(x)$ is found by a translation of $y = (f \circ g)(x)$ through $\binom{-1}{2}$.

  a Find $(f \circ g)(x)$.

  b Show that $h(x) = 4x^2 + 12x + 8$.

  c Find the coordinates of the vertex of $y = h(x)$.

  d Find the axes intercepts of $y = h(x)$.

  e Hence sketch $y = h(x)$.

6 Functions f and g are defined by $f : x \mapsto 3x + 1$ and $g : x \mapsto 4 - x$.

  Find: **a** $f(g(x))$ **b** $(g \circ f)(-4)$ **c** $f^{-1}\left(\frac{1}{2}\right)$

7 Consider $f(x) = 2^{x-1}$.

  a Find $f(1)$ and $f(2)$.

  b Graph $y = f(x)$ and its inverse function on the same set of axes.

c Find $f^{-1}(x)$.

d State the domain and range of $f^{-1}(x)$.

8 Consider the functions $f(x) = \dfrac{1}{x-1} + \sqrt{x+1}$ and $g(x) = x^2$.

  a State the domain of f.

  b Find $(f \circ g)(x)$.

  c Is the domain of $(f \circ g)$ the same as the domain of either f or g? Explain your answer.

  d Write down the function which is a vertical stretch of f with scale factor 2.

9 Copy this graph of $y = f(x)$.
Draw graphs of:

  a $y = f(x+2)$

  b $y = 2f(x) - 3$

  c $y = 4 - f(x)$

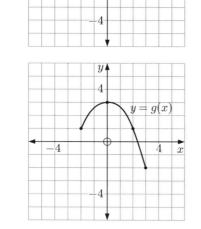

10 Copy this graph of $y = g(x)$.
Draw graphs of:

  a $y = g(-x)$

  b $y = g(2x)$

11 Consider the function $g : x \mapsto 4 - \ln(x-2)$.

  a State the domain and range of g.

  b Write down the equation of the asymptote of $y = g(x)$.

  c Write down the function h which is a horizontal stretch of g with scale factor $\frac{1}{2}$.

  d Write down the equation of the asymptote of $y = h(x)$.

12 For each of the following functions:

  i find the x-intercepts

  ii find the equation of the axis of symmetry

  iii find the coordinates of the vertex

  iv state the y-intercept

  v sketch the function.

  a $y = -4x(x+3)$

  b $y = \frac{1}{2}(x+6)(x-4)$

  c $y = -3(x-2)^2$

  d $y = 2(x+5)^2 - 4$

13 The function f can be written in the form
$f(x) = a(x-p)(x-q)$
where $p > q$.

  a Write down the values of p and q.

  b Find a.

  c Write down the equation of the axis of symmetry.

14 The function f can be written in the form
$f(x) = a(x-p)^2$.

  a Write down the value of p.

  b Find a.

  c Write down the equation of the axis of symmetry.

  d Write down the equation of the quadratic function $g(x)$ whose graph is the reflection of $y = f(x)$ in the y-axis.

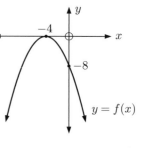

15 The function f can be written in the form
$f(x) = a(x-h)^2 + k$.

  a Write down the equation of the axis of symmetry.

  b Write down the values of h and k.

  c Find a.

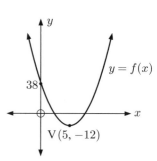

16 For each of the following functions:

  i find the y-intercept

  ii write the function in the form $y = a(x-h)^2 + k$

  iii find the coordinates of the vertex

  iv sketch the function.

  a $y = x^2 - 4x + 9$

  b $y = x^2 - 6x - 2$

  c $y = 4x^2 + 16x + 11$

  d $y = -3x^2 + 12x - 10$

17 Consider the function $y = x^2 + 12x + 8$.

  a State the y-intercept of the function.

  b Use the quadratic formula to solve $x^2 + 12x + 8 = 0$ exactly.

  c Find the coordinates of the vertex of the function.

  d State the range of the function.

  e Sketch the function.

18 **a** Determine the discriminant of $x^2 + 8x + k = 0$.

  b Hence, find the values of k for which the equation has:

    i no real roots

    ii two distinct real roots.

19 For what values of m would the graph of $y = mx^2 + 4x + 6$ lie entirely above the x-axis?

20 Find m given that $mx^2 + (m-2)x + m = 0$ has a repeated root.

21 -2 is a solution of $x^2 + bx + (b-2) = 0$.

  a Find the value of b.

  b Find the other solution to the equation.

22 Consider the function $f(x) = \dfrac{x+2}{x-1}$.

  a Find the domain and range of f.

  b Write down the equations of the asymptotes of $y = f(x)$.

  c Find the axes intercepts.

  d Sketch the function.

23 Consider the function $f(x) = 4 - \dfrac{1}{x-2}$.

  a Find the domain and range of f.

  b Write down the equations of the asymptotes of $y = f(x)$.

c Find the axes intercepts.

d Sketch the function.

24 Consider the function $f(x) = x^2$.

   a On the same set of axes, sketch the graphs of
   $y = f(x - 1) + 2$ and $y = \frac{1}{2}f(x) - 1$.

   b For each graph in **a**, describe the transformations which map $y = f(x)$ onto the graph.

25 Consider the function $f(x) = \sqrt{x}$.

   a On the same set of axes, sketch the graphs of
   $y = -f(x)$, $y = f(-x)$, and $y = f(\frac{1}{2}x)$.

   b For each graph in **a**, describe the transformation which maps $y = f(x)$ onto the graph.

26 Let $f(x) = \ln(1 - x^2)$.

   a State the domain of f.

   b Show that $f(-x) = f(x)$. Explain what this means about the graph of the function.

   c The graph of $y = f(x)$ is shown. How many solutions are there to the equation $\ln(1 - x^2) = -2$?

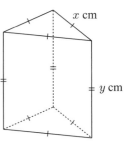

SKILL BUILDER QUESTIONS (CALCULATORS)

1 **a** State the domain and range of the function
   $f : x \mapsto \sqrt{x + 3}$.

   b What transformation maps $y = \sqrt{x}$ onto the function f?

2 **a** State the domain and range of the function
   $f : x \mapsto \ln(x - 2)$.

   b Write down the equation of the asymptote of the function.

   c State the equation of the function which results when f is stretched vertically with scale factor 3, then reflected in the y-axis.

3 **a** State the domain and range of $f(x) = \dfrac{1}{\sqrt{x - 4}} + 3$.

   b What transformation maps $y = \dfrac{1}{\sqrt{x}}$ onto the function f?

   c Write down the equations of the asymptotes of $y = f(x)$.

4 Consider the function $f(x) = e^x$ and $g(x) = 2x + 1$.

   a Find $(f \circ g)(x)$.

   b Find the inverse function of $(f \circ g)$.

   c Hence find $(f \circ g)^{-1}(7)$.

5 On the same axes, sketch the graphs of $y = e^{x-2}$ and $y = 2 - e^x$.
   Hence find, correct to 3 decimal places, any points of intersection of the graphs.

6 Suppose $f : x \mapsto \ln x$ and $g : x \mapsto x^3$. Find the value of:

   a $(f \circ g)(2)$

   b $(g \circ f)(2)$

   c $(f^{-1} \circ g)(1.2)$

   d $(g \circ f)^{-1}(8)$

7 Consider $f : x \mapsto \ln(x + 2) - 5$, $x > -2$.

   a Find the defining equation of f^{-1}.

   b On the same set of axes, sketch the graphs of f and f^{-1}.

   c State the domain and range of f and f^{-1}.

8 Consider the quadratic $y = 2x^2 - 9x + 3$.

   a Find the equation of the axis of symmetry.

   b Find the coordinates of the vertex.

   c Find the axes intercepts.

   d Sketch the function.

9 Let $f(x) = \dfrac{6 - 2x}{x + 4}$.

   a Find the asymptotes.

   b Find the axes intercepts.

   c Sketch the function.

   d Find the inverse function $f^{-1}(x)$.

10 Suppose $f(x) = 25 - x^2$ and $g(x) = \dfrac{2}{\sqrt{x}}$.

   a Find $(g \circ f)(x)$.

   b State the domain of $(g \circ f)$.

   c Find the asymptotes of $y = (g \circ f)(x)$.

11 Consider $y = -1 + 2^{-x}$.

   a Find the axes intercepts.

   b Find any asymptotes of the function.

   c State the domain and range of the function.

   d Hence sketch the function.

12 Consider $y = e^{x-1} + 1$.

   a Find the axes intercepts.

   b Find any asymptotes of the function.

   c State the domain and range of the function.

   d Hence sketch the function.

13 The current in an electrical circuit t milliseconds after it is switched off is given by $I(t) = 40e^{-0.1t}$ amps.

   a What current was flowing in the circuit initially?

   b What current is still flowing in the circuit after $t = 100$ milliseconds?

   c Sketch $I(t)$ and $I = 1$ on the same set of axes.

   d How long will it take for the current to fall to 1 amp?

14 Andreas is making an aquarium in the shape of an equilateral triangular prism. The sum of all side lengths of the prism must be 1.8 m.
Let the equilateral triangle ends have sides of length x cm, and the aquarium have height y cm.

   a Show that the area of the end is $\frac{\sqrt{3}}{4}x^2$ cm^2.

   b Show that $y = 60 - 2x$.

   c Show that the total surface area of the aquarium is given by $A = \left(\frac{\sqrt{3}}{2} - 6\right)x^2 + 180x$ cm^2.

   d What dimensions should Andreas choose for the aquarium to maximise its surface area?

The **unit circle** is the circle centred at the origin O and with radius 1 unit.

Consider point P on the unit circle where [OP] makes angle θ with the positive x-axis. The coordinates of P are $(\cos\theta, \sin\theta)$.

θ is **positive** when measured in an **anticlockwise** direction from the positive x-axis.

From the unit circle we can see that:

- $\cos^2\theta + \sin^2\theta = 1$
- $-1 \leqslant \cos\theta \leqslant 1$ and $-1 \leqslant \sin\theta \leqslant 1$ for all θ
- $\tan\theta = \dfrac{\sin\theta}{\cos\theta}$ provided $\cos\theta \neq 0$.

π radians is equivalent to $180°$.

To convert from degrees to radians, multiply by $\frac{\pi}{180}$.

To convert from radians to degrees, multiply by $\frac{180}{\pi}$.

For θ in radians:

- the length of an arc of radius r and angle θ is $l = \theta r$
- the area of a sector of radius r and angle θ is $A = \frac{1}{2}\theta r^2$.

MULTIPLES OF 45° OR $\frac{\pi}{4}$

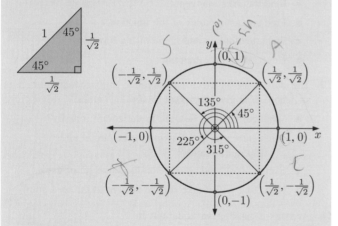

MULTIPLES OF 30° OR $\frac{\pi}{6}$

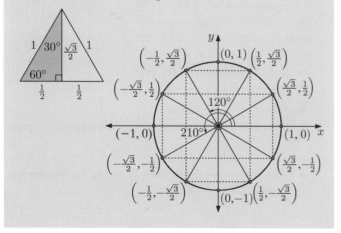

If a straight line makes an angle of θ with the positive x-axis, then its gradient is $m = \tan\theta$.

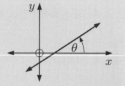

NON-RIGHT ANGLED TRIANGLE TRIGONOMETRY

For the triangle alongside:

Area formula

Area $= \frac{1}{2}ab\sin C$

Cosine rule

$a^2 = b^2 + c^2 - 2bc\cos A$

Sine rule

$\dfrac{\sin A}{a} = \dfrac{\sin B}{b} = \dfrac{\sin C}{c}$

If you have the choice of rules to use, use the cosine rule to avoid the **ambiguous case**.

PERIODIC FUNCTIONS

A **periodic function** is one which repeats itself over and over in a horizontal direction.

The **period** of a periodic function is the length of one cycle.

$f(x)$ is a periodic function with period $p \Leftrightarrow p$ is the smallest positive value such that $f(x+p) = f(x)$ for all x.

For example, a **wave** oscillates about a horizontal line called the **principal axis**.

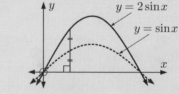

The **amplitude** is the distance between a maximum or minimum point and the principal axis.

TRANSFORMING $y = \sin x$

- $y = a\sin x$ is a **vertical stretch** of $y = \sin x$ with scale factor a.

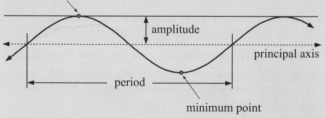

- $y = \sin bx$ is a **horizontal stretch** of $y = \sin x$ with scale factor $\frac{1}{b}$.

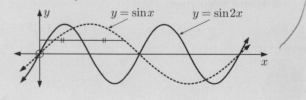

- $y = \sin(x - c)$ is a **horizontal translation** of $y = \sin x$ through c units.
- $y = \sin x + d$ is a **vertical translation** of $y = \sin x$ through d units.

THE GENERAL SINE FUNCTION

If we begin with $y = \sin x$, we can perform transformations to produce the **general sine function** $f(x) = a \sin b(x - c) + d$.

We have a vertical stretch with scale factor a and a horizontal stretch with scale factor $\frac{1}{b}$, followed by a translation with vector $\binom{c}{d}$.

The general sine function has the following properties:

- the **amplitude** is $|a|$
- the **principal axis** is $y = d$
- the **period** is $\frac{2\pi}{b}$.

THE COSINE FUNCTION

Since $\cos x = \sin\left(x + \frac{\pi}{2}\right)$, the graph of $y = \cos x$ is a horizontal translation of $y = \sin x$, $\frac{\pi}{2}$ units to the left.

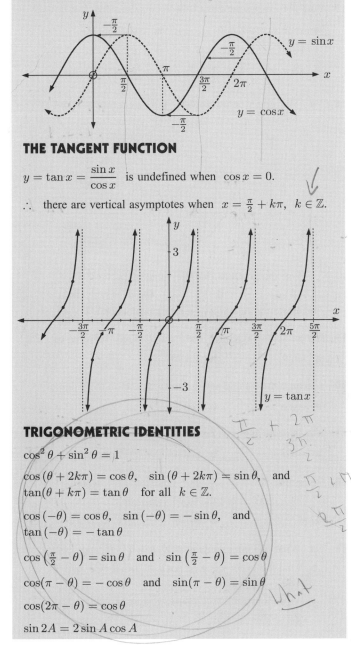

THE TANGENT FUNCTION

$y = \tan x = \dfrac{\sin x}{\cos x}$ is undefined when $\cos x = 0$.

$\therefore$ there are vertical asymptotes when $x = \frac{\pi}{2} + k\pi$, $k \in \mathbb{Z}$.

TRIGONOMETRIC IDENTITIES

$\cos^2\theta + \sin^2\theta = 1$

$\cos(\theta + 2k\pi) = \cos\theta$, $\sin(\theta + 2k\pi) = \sin\theta$, and $\tan(\theta + k\pi) = \tan\theta$ for all $k \in \mathbb{Z}$.

$\cos(-\theta) = \cos\theta$, $\sin(-\theta) = -\sin\theta$, and $\tan(-\theta) = -\tan\theta$

$\cos\left(\frac{\pi}{2} - \theta\right) = \sin\theta$ and $\sin\left(\frac{\pi}{2} - \theta\right) = \cos\theta$

$\cos(\pi - \theta) = -\cos\theta$ and $\sin(\pi - \theta) = \sin\theta$

$\cos(2\pi - \theta) = \cos\theta$

$\sin 2A = 2\sin A\cos A$

$$\cos 2A = \begin{cases} \cos^2 A - \sin^2 A \\ 1 - 2\sin^2 A \\ 2\cos^2 A - 1 \end{cases}$$

TRIGONOMETRIC EQUATIONS

To solve trigonometric equations we can either use graphs from technology, or algebraic methods involving the trigonometric identities. In either case we must make sure to include all solutions on the specified domain.

We use the inverse trigonometric functions to invert sin, cos, and tan.

Equation	Function	Domain	Range
$\sin x = k$	$x = \sin^{-1} k$	$-1 \leqslant k \leqslant 1$	$-\frac{\pi}{2} \leqslant x \leqslant \frac{\pi}{2}$
$\cos x = k$	$x = \cos^{-1} k$	$-1 \leqslant k \leqslant 1$	$0 \leqslant x \leqslant \pi$
$\tan x = k$	$x = \tan^{-1} k$	$k \in \mathbb{R}$	$-\frac{\pi}{2} < x < \frac{\pi}{2}$

Your calculator will only give one answer in the range of the function. For example, when using $\sin^{-1}$ our calculator will always give us an acute angle answer, but the obtuse angle with the same sine may also be valid. Sometimes you need to add or subtract multiples of 2π for cos or sin, or multiples of π for tan.

An equation of the form $a\sin x = b\cos x$ can always be solved as $\tan x = \frac{b}{a}$.

SKILL BUILDER QUESTIONS (NO CALCULATORS)

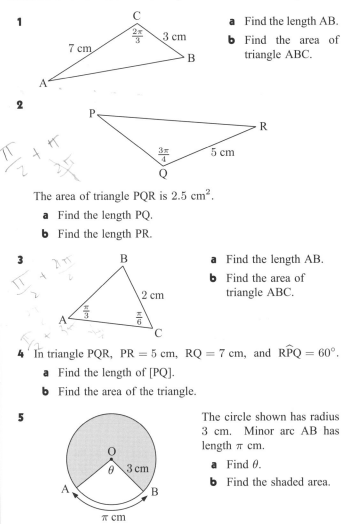

1
- **a** Find the length AB.
- **b** Find the area of triangle ABC.

2
The area of triangle PQR is 2.5 cm^2.
- **a** Find the length PQ.
- **b** Find the length PR.

3
- **a** Find the length AB.
- **b** Find the area of triangle ABC.

4 In triangle PQR, $PR = 5 \text{ cm}$, $RQ = 7 \text{ cm}$, and $R\widehat{P}Q = 60°$.
- **a** Find the length of [PQ].
- **b** Find the area of the triangle.

5
The circle shown has radius 3 cm. Minor arc AB has length π cm.
- **a** Find θ.
- **b** Find the shaded area.

6 A sector of a circle of radius 10 cm has a perimeter of 40 cm.

   a Find the arc length of the sector.

   b Find the area of the sector.

7 A sector of a circle has an arc length of 6 cm and an area of 20 cm².

   a Find the radius of the circle.

   b Find the angle of the sector.

8 **a** Find the length of the minor arc PQ.

   b Find the shaded area.

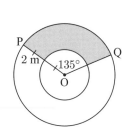

9 **a** Simplify $\cos^2\left(\frac{\pi}{4}\right) - \sin^2\left(\frac{5\pi}{6}\right)$.

   b Find the equation of the straight line illustrated:

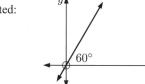

10 **a** Simplify $\tan\left(-\frac{\pi}{6}\right) - \cos\left(\frac{4\pi}{3}\right)$.

   b Find the equation of the straight line illustrated:

11 For each of the following functions:

   i state the amplitude
   ii state the principle axis
   iii state the period
   iv sketch the function.

   a $y = 2\sin(x - \frac{\pi}{3})$ for $0 \leqslant x \leqslant 2\pi$

   b $y = \sin x + 2$ for $-\pi \leqslant x \leqslant \pi$

   c $y = 3\cos 2x$ for $0 \leqslant x \leqslant 2\pi$

   d $y = \cos(\frac{x}{2}) - 1$ for $0 \leqslant x \leqslant 2\pi$

   e $y = \sin 2x + 2$ for $0 \leqslant x \leqslant 2\pi$

   f $y = 10 - 6\sin 3x$ for $0 \leqslant x \leqslant 2\pi$

12 For each of the following functions:

   i state the period
   ii write the equations of the asymptotes
   iii sketch the function.

   a $y = \tan\left(\frac{x}{2}\right)$ for $-2\pi \leqslant x \leqslant 2\pi$

   b $y = 5\tan 3x$ for $0 \leqslant x \leqslant \pi$

13 **a** What consecutive transformations map the graph of $y = \sin x$ onto $y = 2\sin\left(\frac{x}{3}\right)$?

   b Sketch $y = \sin x$ and $y = 2\sin\left(\frac{x}{3}\right)$ on the same set of axes for $0 \leqslant x \leqslant 2\pi$.

14 **a** What consecutive transformations map the graph of $y = \sin x$ onto $y = \sin\left(x + \frac{\pi}{3}\right) - 4$?

   b Sketch $y = \sin x$ and $y = \sin\left(x + \frac{\pi}{3}\right) - 4$ on the same set of axes for $0 \leqslant x \leqslant 2\pi$.

15

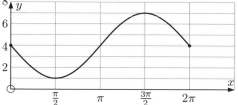

Part of the graph of $y = a + b\sin x$ is drawn above.
Find the value of: **a** a **b** b

16

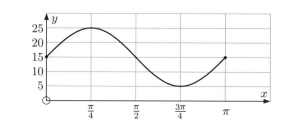

The graph above shows $y = a\sin(bx) + c$ for $0 \leqslant x \leqslant \pi$.
Find the values of a, b, and c.

17 Find the exact solutions of these equations for $0 \leqslant x \leqslant 2\pi$:

   a $\sqrt{2}\cos x + 1 = 0$ **b** $2\sin x = \sqrt{3}$

   c $2\sin^2 x + 3\cos x = 3$ **d** $\sin 2x + \sin x = 0$

   e $\sin x = -\sqrt{3}\cos x$ **f** $\frac{1}{\sqrt{3}}\cos x - \sin x = 0$

18 **a** The graph below shows $y = a\cos(b(x - c)) + d$ for $1 \leqslant x \leqslant 5$.

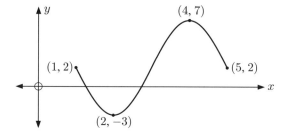

   Use the graph to find the value of:

   i a **ii** b **iii** d **iv** c

   b Write the function in **a** as a sine function.

19 θ is an acute angle and $\cos\theta = \frac{3}{8}$. Find the value of:

   a $\sin\theta$ **b** $\sin 2\theta$

20 α is an obtuse angle and $\sin\alpha = \frac{2}{3}$. Find the value of:

   a $\cos\alpha$ **b** $\cos 2\alpha$

21 If α is acute and $\cos 2\alpha = \frac{5}{13}$, find the value of:

   a $\sin\alpha$ **b** $\cos\alpha$ **c** $\tan\alpha$

22 Given that $\sin\theta = -\frac{1}{2}$ and $\cos\theta = -\frac{\sqrt{3}}{2}$ where $0° < \theta < 360°$, find the exact value of:

   a θ **b** $\tan\theta$ **c** $\tan 2\theta$

23 **a** What quadrant contains θ if $\tan\theta > 0$ and $\cos\theta < 0$?

   b Find the exact value of $\cos\theta$ if $\tan\theta = 2$ and $180° < \theta < 270°$.

   c What transformation maps $y = \tan x$ onto $y = \tan(x + \frac{\pi}{6}) + 2$?

24

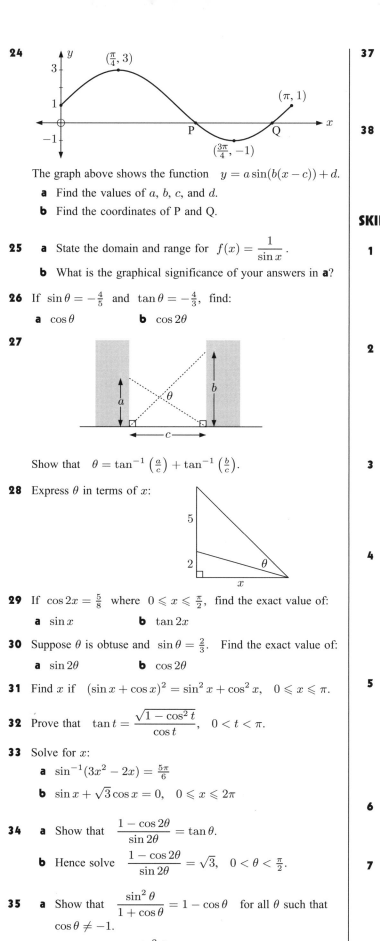

The graph above shows the function $y = a\sin(b(x-c)) + d$.

   a Find the values of a, b, c, and d.

   b Find the coordinates of P and Q.

25 **a** State the domain and range for $f(x) = \dfrac{1}{\sin x}$.

   b What is the graphical significance of your answers in **a**?

26 If $\sin\theta = -\frac{4}{5}$ and $\tan\theta = -\frac{4}{3}$, find:

   a $\cos\theta$ **b** $\cos 2\theta$

27

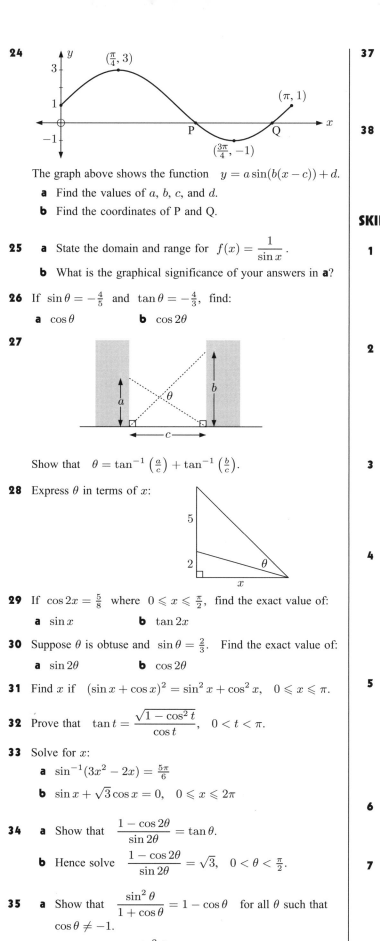

Show that $\theta = \tan^{-1}\left(\dfrac{a}{c}\right) + \tan^{-1}\left(\dfrac{b}{c}\right)$.

28 Express θ in terms of x:

29 If $\cos 2x = \frac{5}{8}$ where $0 \leqslant x \leqslant \frac{\pi}{2}$, find the exact value of:

   a $\sin x$ **b** $\tan 2x$

30 Suppose θ is obtuse and $\sin\theta = \frac{2}{3}$. Find the exact value of:

   a $\sin 2\theta$ **b** $\cos 2\theta$

31 Find x if $(\sin x + \cos x)^2 = \sin^2 x + \cos^2 x$, $0 \leqslant x \leqslant \pi$.

32 Prove that $\tan t = \dfrac{\sqrt{1 - \cos^2 t}}{\cos t}$, $0 < t < \pi$.

33 Solve for x:

   a $\sin^{-1}(3x^2 - 2x) = \frac{5\pi}{6}$

   b $\sin x + \sqrt{3}\cos x = 0$, $0 \leqslant x \leqslant 2\pi$

34 **a** Show that $\dfrac{1 - \cos 2\theta}{\sin 2\theta} = \tan\theta$.

   b Hence solve $\dfrac{1 - \cos 2\theta}{\sin 2\theta} = \sqrt{3}$, $0 < \theta < \frac{\pi}{2}$.

35 **a** Show that $\dfrac{\sin^2\theta}{1 + \cos\theta} = 1 - \cos\theta$ for all θ such that $\cos\theta \neq -1$.

   b Hence solve $\dfrac{\sin^2\theta}{1 + \cos\theta} = \frac{1}{2}$ for $-\pi \leqslant \theta \leqslant \pi$.

36 **a** Show that $-3\cos 2\theta - 14\sin\theta + 11 = 6\sin^2\theta - 14\sin\theta + 8$.

   b Hence solve $-3\cos 2\theta - 14\sin\theta + 11 = 0$ for $-\pi < \theta \leqslant \pi$.

37 **a** Show that $\cos 2\theta + 2\sqrt{2}\cos\theta - 2 = 2\cos^2\theta + 2\sqrt{2}\cos\theta - 3$.

   b Hence solve $\cos 2\theta + 2\sqrt{2}\cos\theta - 2 = 0$ for $-\pi < \theta \leqslant \pi$.

38 Suppose $\tan 2A = \sin A$ where $\sin A \neq 0$.

   a Show that $2\cos^2 A - 2\cos A - 1 = 0$.

   b Hence find $\cos A$ in simplest radical form.

SKILL BUILDER QUESTIONS (CALCULATORS)

1

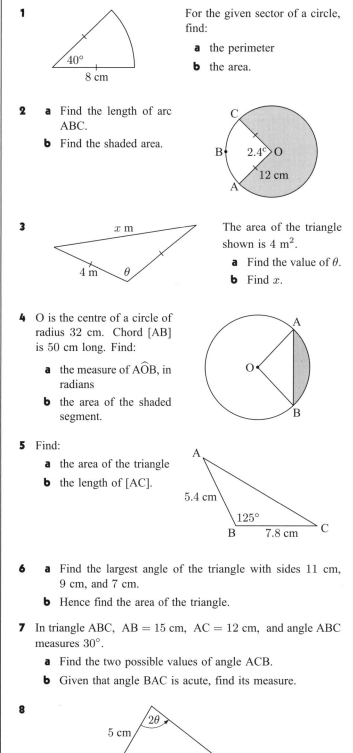

For the given sector of a circle, find:

   a the perimeter

   b the area.

2 **a** Find the length of arc ABC.

   b Find the shaded area.

3 The area of the triangle shown is 4 m².

   a Find the value of θ.

   b Find x.

4 O is the centre of a circle of radius 32 cm. Chord [AB] is 50 cm long. Find:

   a the measure of $A\widehat{O}B$, in radians

   b the area of the shaded segment.

5 Find:

   a the area of the triangle

   b the length of [AC].

6 **a** Find the largest angle of the triangle with sides 11 cm, 9 cm, and 7 cm.

   b Hence find the area of the triangle.

7 In triangle ABC, AB = 15 cm, AC = 12 cm, and angle ABC measures 30°.

   a Find the two possible values of angle ACB.

   b Given that angle BAC is acute, find its measure.

8

Find: **a** $\cos\theta$ **b** the area of the triangle.

9 Solve for x if $0 \leqslant x \leqslant 2\pi$:

   a $\sin x = 0.785$ **b** $2\cos x = 5\sin x$

   c $\tan 3x = 0.9$ **d** $4\sin^2 x = \cos^2 x$

10 **a** Solve for θ exactly: $2\sin\theta = \sqrt{3}, \quad -2\pi \leqslant \theta \leqslant 2\pi$.

    b Hence find θ such that $2\sin\theta \leqslant \sqrt{3}, \quad -2\pi \leqslant \theta \leqslant 2\pi$.

11 **a** Solve for θ exactly: $\sqrt{2}\cos\theta = -1, \quad -2\pi \leqslant \theta \leqslant 2\pi$.

    b Hence find θ such that $\sqrt{2}\cos\theta \leqslant -1, \quad -2\pi \leqslant \theta \leqslant 2\pi$.

12 The depth of water in a tidal river t hours after midnight may be represented by a function of the form

$d = a + b\sin\left(\frac{2\pi t}{k}\right)$ metres where a, b, and k are constants.

The water is at a maximum depth of 12.5 m at 3 am and again at 3 pm. It is at a minimum depth of 8.7 m at 9 am and 9 pm.

   a Find the value of k.

   b Find a and b.

   c At what time after 9 pm will the depth of water first be 10 m?

13 [PT] is a tangent to the circle at T. The circle has radius 9 cm and OP = 30 cm. Find:

   a the angle α

   b the area of the shaded region.

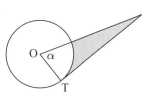

14 An aeroplane averaging 400 km h^{-1} travels directly north from an airport for 45 minutes, then changes its course to north-east for 90 minutes.

   a What is the direct distance between the plane's present position and the airport?

   b How long would it take the plane to return to the airport if it travelled there directly with the same average speed?

15 The electrical impulse from a person's heartbeat is modelled by the function $I = \dfrac{\sin t}{t^2 + 1}$ where t is the time in milliseconds, $-4\pi \leqslant t \leqslant 4\pi$.

   a At what times is there zero electrical impulse in the heartbeat?

   b Find the solutions of $\dfrac{\sin t}{t^2 + 1} = 0.3$ to 3 decimal places.

   c What do the solutions in **b** mean in the context of the heartbeat?

16 Suppose that $\tan\theta = 2\cos\theta, \quad 0 < \theta < \frac{\pi}{2}$.

   a Show that $2\sin^2\theta + \sin\theta - 2 = 0$.

   b Hence find θ.

17

A bicycle wheel sits on the road so its valve is at the bottom. The inner radius of the tyre is 35 cm and the outer radius is 40 cm. The wheel begins to rotate at a constant speed of 4 revolutions per second.

   a Find the height of the valve above the road after:

     i 0 seconds   **ii** $\frac{1}{12}$ second.

   b The height of the valve above the road after t seconds can be modelled by the function

$H(t) = a\sin(b(t - c)) + d$ cm.

   Find:

    i a **ii** d **iii** b **iv** c

   c How long does it take the valve to rise to 60 cm above the road?

TOPIC 4:   VECTORS

A **scalar** is a quantity which has only size or **magnitude**.

A **vector** is a quantity with both **magnitude** and **direction**.

Two vectors are **equal** if they have the same magnitude *and* direction.

VECTORS IN GEOMETRIC FORM

Given two vectors $\mathbf{v}$ and $\mathbf{w}$, to find $\mathbf{v} + \mathbf{w}$ we first start by drawing $\mathbf{v}$, and then from the end of $\mathbf{v}$ we draw $\mathbf{w}$. The vector $\mathbf{v} + \mathbf{w}$ starts at the beginning of $\mathbf{v}$ and ends at the end of $\mathbf{w}$.

To find $\mathbf{v} - \mathbf{w}$ we find $\mathbf{v} + (-\mathbf{w})$. We start by drawing $\mathbf{v}$, then from the end of $\mathbf{v}$ we draw $-\mathbf{w}$.

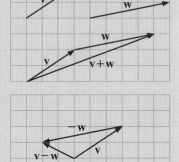

The **zero vector 0**, is a vector of length 0. It is the only vector with no direction.

In the diagram alongside,

      $\mathbf{a} + \mathbf{b} = \mathbf{c}$

or $\mathbf{a} + \mathbf{b} - \mathbf{c} = \mathbf{0}$.

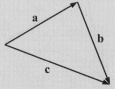

VECTORS IN COMPONENT FORM

The basic unit vectors with magnitude 1 are:

  in 2-D: $\mathbf{i} = \begin{pmatrix} 1 \\ 0 \end{pmatrix}$ and $\mathbf{j} = \begin{pmatrix} 0 \\ 1 \end{pmatrix}$

  in 3-D: $\mathbf{i} = \begin{pmatrix} 1 \\ 0 \\ 0 \end{pmatrix}$, $\mathbf{j} = \begin{pmatrix} 0 \\ 1 \\ 0 \end{pmatrix}$, and $\mathbf{k} = \begin{pmatrix} 0 \\ 0 \\ 1 \end{pmatrix}$.

The **zero vector 0** is $\begin{pmatrix} 0 \\ 0 \end{pmatrix}$ in 2-D and $\begin{pmatrix} 0 \\ 0 \\ 0 \end{pmatrix}$ in 3-D.

The general 2-D vector $\mathbf{v} = \begin{pmatrix} v_1 \\ v_2 \end{pmatrix} = v_1\mathbf{i} + v_2\mathbf{j}$

The general 3-D vector $\mathbf{v} = \begin{pmatrix} v_1 \\ v_2 \\ v_3 \end{pmatrix} = v_1\mathbf{i} + v_2\mathbf{j} + v_3\mathbf{k}$.

In examinations, scalars are written in italics, for example a, and vectors are written in bold type, for example $\mathbf{a}$. On paper you should write vector $\mathbf{a}$ as $\overrightarrow{a}$.

You should understand the following for vectors in component form:

- vector equality
- vector addition
  - ▸ $\mathbf{a} + \mathbf{b} = \mathbf{b} + \mathbf{a}$
  - ▸ $(\mathbf{a} + \mathbf{b}) + \mathbf{c} = \mathbf{a} + (\mathbf{b} + \mathbf{c})$
  - ▸ $\mathbf{a} + \mathbf{0} = \mathbf{0} + \mathbf{a} = \mathbf{a}$
  - ▸ $\mathbf{a} + (-\mathbf{a}) = (-\mathbf{a}) + \mathbf{a} = \mathbf{0}$
- vector subtraction $\mathbf{a} - \mathbf{b} = \mathbf{a} + (-\mathbf{b})$
- multiplication by a scalar k to produce vector $k\mathbf{a}$ which is parallel to $\mathbf{a}$
  - ▸ if $k > 0$, $k\mathbf{a}$ and $\mathbf{a}$ have the same direction
  - ▸ if $k < 0$, $k\mathbf{a}$ and $\mathbf{a}$ have opposite directions
  - ▸ if $k = 0$, $k\mathbf{a} = \mathbf{0}$
- the magnitude of vector $\mathbf{v}$, $|\mathbf{v}| = \sqrt{v_1^2 + v_2^2 + v_3^2}$
- the distance between two points in space is the magnitude of the vector which joins them
- $|k\mathbf{a}| = |k||\mathbf{a}|$
- $k(\mathbf{a} + \mathbf{b}) = k\mathbf{a} + k\mathbf{b}$

POSITION VECTORS IN 2-D

The **position vector** of $A(x, y)$ is $\overrightarrow{OA}$ or $\mathbf{a} = \begin{pmatrix} x \\ y \end{pmatrix}$ or $x\mathbf{i} + y\mathbf{j}$.

The position vector of B relative to A is
$\overrightarrow{AB} = \overrightarrow{OB} - \overrightarrow{OA} = \mathbf{b} - \mathbf{a}$.

Given $A(x_1, y_1)$ and $B(x_2, y_2)$:

- the length of $\overrightarrow{AB}$ is $AB = \sqrt{(x_2 - x_1)^2 + (y_2 - y_1)^2}$
- the midpoint of $\overrightarrow{AB}$ is $\left(\dfrac{x_1 + x_2}{2}, \dfrac{y_1 + y_2}{2} \right)$.

POSITION VECTORS IN 3-D

The **position vector** of $A(x, y, z)$ is $\overrightarrow{OA}$ or $\mathbf{a} = \begin{pmatrix} x \\ y \\ z \end{pmatrix}$ or $x\mathbf{i} + y\mathbf{j} + z\mathbf{k}$.

Given $A(x_1, y_1, z_1)$ and $B(x_2, y_2, z_2)$:

- the length of $\overrightarrow{AB}$ is
  $AB = \sqrt{(x_2 - x_1)^2 + (y_2 - y_1)^2 + (z_2 - z_1)^2}$
- the midpoint of $\overrightarrow{AB}$ is $\left(\dfrac{x_1 + x_2}{2}, \dfrac{y_1 + y_2}{2}, \dfrac{z_1 + z_2}{2} \right)$.

PROPERTIES OF VECTORS

A, B, and C are **collinear** if $\overrightarrow{AB} = k\overrightarrow{BC}$ for some scalar k.

Two vectors $\mathbf{a}$ and $\mathbf{b}$ are parallel if $\mathbf{a} = k\mathbf{b}$ for some constant $k \neq 0$.

The unit vector in the direction of $\mathbf{a}$ is $\dfrac{1}{|\mathbf{a}|}\mathbf{a}$.

A vector $\mathbf{b}$ of length k in the same direction as $\mathbf{a}$ is $\mathbf{b} = \dfrac{k}{|\mathbf{a}|}\mathbf{a}$.

A vector $\mathbf{b}$ of length k which is *parallel* to $\mathbf{a}$ could be
$\mathbf{b} = \pm\dfrac{k}{|\mathbf{a}|}\mathbf{a}$.

The scalar or dot product of two vectors

$\mathbf{v} \bullet \mathbf{w} = |\mathbf{v}||\mathbf{w}|\cos\theta$ where θ is the angle between the vectors.

If $\mathbf{v} = \begin{pmatrix} v_1 \\ v_2 \\ v_3 \end{pmatrix}$ and $\mathbf{w} = \begin{pmatrix} w_1 \\ w_2 \\ w_3 \end{pmatrix}$ then

$\mathbf{v} \bullet \mathbf{w} = v_1 w_1 + v_2 w_2 + v_3 w_3$.

For non-zero vectors $\mathbf{v}$ and $\mathbf{w}$:

- $\mathbf{v} \bullet \mathbf{w} = 0 \Leftrightarrow \mathbf{v}$ is perpendicular to $\mathbf{w}$
- $\mathbf{v} = k\mathbf{w} \Leftrightarrow \mathbf{v}$ is parallel to $\mathbf{w}$
- $|\mathbf{v} \bullet \mathbf{w}| = |\mathbf{v}||\mathbf{w}| \Leftrightarrow \mathbf{v}$ is parallel to $\mathbf{w}$

The angle θ between vectors $\mathbf{v}$ and $\mathbf{w}$ emanating from the same point is given by $\cos\theta = \dfrac{\mathbf{v} \bullet \mathbf{w}}{|\mathbf{v}||\mathbf{w}|}$.

If $\mathbf{v} \bullet \mathbf{w} > 0$ then θ is acute.

If $\mathbf{v} \bullet \mathbf{w} < 0$ then θ is obtuse.

LINES

The **vector equation of a line** is $\mathbf{r} = \mathbf{a} + t\mathbf{b}$ where $\mathbf{a}$ is the position vector of any point on the line, $\mathbf{b}$ is a vector parallel to the line, and $t \in \mathbb{R}$.

For example, if an object has initial position vector $\mathbf{a}$ and moves with constant velocity $\mathbf{b}$, its position at time t is given by $\mathbf{r} = \mathbf{a} + t\mathbf{b}$ for $t \geqslant 0$.

If $\mathbf{r} = \begin{pmatrix} x \\ y \\ z \end{pmatrix}$, $\mathbf{a} = \begin{pmatrix} x_0 \\ y_0 \\ z_0 \end{pmatrix}$, and $\mathbf{b} = \begin{pmatrix} l \\ m \\ n \end{pmatrix}$, the **parametric form** for the equation of a line is $x = x_0 + tl$, $y = y_0 + tm$, $z = z_0 + tn$.

The **acute angle** θ **between two lines** is given by $\cos\theta = \dfrac{|\mathbf{a} \bullet \mathbf{b}|}{|\mathbf{a}||\mathbf{b}|}$ where $\mathbf{a}$ and $\mathbf{b}$ are the direction vectors of the lines.

Lines are:

- **parallel** if their direction vectors are parallel: $\mathbf{a} = k\mathbf{b}$
- **coincident** if they are parallel and have a common point
- **intersecting** if you can solve them simultaneously to find a unique common point that fits both equations
- **skew** if they are not parallel and do not have a point of intersection; there are no solutions when the equations are solved simultaneously.

The shortest distance from point A to a line with direction vector $\mathbf{b}$ occurs at the point P on the line such that $\overrightarrow{AP}$ is perpendicular to $\mathbf{b}$.

SKILL BUILDER QUESTIONS (NO CALCULATORS)

1

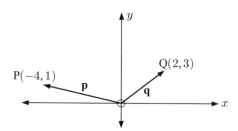

a Write down the vectors **p** and **q**.

b The point R is defined by the vector **p** + **q**. Find the coordinates of R.

c Classify quadrilateral OPRQ.

2

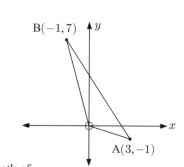

a Find $\overrightarrow{AB}$.

b Find the length of:

    i $\overrightarrow{OA}$ **ii** $\overrightarrow{AB}$.

c Find the measure of $O\hat{A}B$.

d Hence find the area of triangle OAB.

3 Consider the *position vector* $\mathbf{a} = \begin{pmatrix} 1 \\ -2 \\ 3 \end{pmatrix}$.

a Write **a** in terms of the base vectors **i**, **j**, and **k**.

b Find the magnitude of **a**.

c Write down a unit vector in the opposite direction to **a**.

4 Find the value(s) of k for which $\begin{pmatrix} k \\ 1 \\ 3 \end{pmatrix}$ and $\begin{pmatrix} 4 \\ k \\ 3k \end{pmatrix}$ are:

a parallel   **b** perpendicular.

5

a Find $\overrightarrow{BC}$.

b Find the coordinates of D.

c Find the angle between the diagonals [AC] and [BD].

d Hence classify quadrilateral ABCD.

6

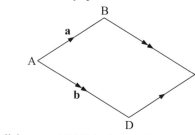

Parallelogram ABCD is formed by vectors $\overrightarrow{AB} = \overrightarrow{DC} = \mathbf{a}$, and $\overrightarrow{AD} = \overrightarrow{BC} = \mathbf{b}$.

a Write the diagonals $\overrightarrow{AC}$ and $\overrightarrow{BD}$ in terms of **a** and **b**.

b Calculate the vector dot product $\overrightarrow{AC} \bullet \overrightarrow{BD}$ in terms of **a** and **b**.

c Show that if ABCD is a rhombus then $\overrightarrow{AC}$ is perpendicular to $\overrightarrow{BD}$.

7 Find t if $\begin{pmatrix} t \\ 1 \end{pmatrix}$ and $\begin{pmatrix} t-4 \\ -5 \end{pmatrix}$ are perpendicular vectors.

8 Consider the points A(1, 3) and B(5, −1). Suppose $\mathbf{a} = \overrightarrow{OA}$ and $\mathbf{b} = \overrightarrow{OB}$, and let M be the midpoint of $\overrightarrow{AB}$.

a Write $\overrightarrow{OM}$ in terms of **a** and **b**.

b *Hence* find the coordinates of M.

c Write a vector equation for the line passing through O and M.

d Find the two points on (OM) which are $2\sqrt{10}$ units from M.

9 Consider vectors $\mathbf{a} = 3\mathbf{i} - 6\mathbf{j}$ and $\mathbf{b} = 7\mathbf{i} + 2\mathbf{j}$.
The point C(5, 22) can be located using the vector $\overrightarrow{OC} = r\mathbf{a} + s\mathbf{b}$. Find the values of r and s.

10 Line L_1 passes through the point $(-5, -2)$ and is parallel to $\begin{pmatrix} 2 \\ 3 \end{pmatrix}$.

a Write a vector equation for the line.

b Find the point on the line with x-coordinate -1.

c The line L_2 is perpendicular to L_1, and passes through $(4, 5)$.

    i Write a vector equation for the line L_2.

    ii Find the point of intersection of L_1 and L_2.

    iii Hence find the shortest distance from $(4, 5)$ to the line L_1.

11 Vectors **v** and **w** are given by $\mathbf{v} = 5\mathbf{i} - 2\mathbf{j}$ and $\mathbf{w} = \mathbf{i} + 3\mathbf{j}$.

a Find scalars r and s such that
$r(\mathbf{v} - \mathbf{w}) = (r + s)\,\mathbf{i} - 20\mathbf{j}$.

b Find the cosine of the angle between **v** and **w**.

12 **a** Find the vector equation of the line through $(-2, -1)$ which is parallel to the vector $3\mathbf{i} + \mathbf{j}$.

b The line in **a** makes an angle of $\frac{\pi}{3}$ with the line $x = 1 + kt$, $y = 2 - t$, $t \in \mathbb{R}$.
Show that k satisfies the equation $13k^2 - 12k - 3 = 0$.

13 Triangle ABC is defined by the following information:
$\overrightarrow{OA} = -2\mathbf{i} + 4\mathbf{j}$, $\overrightarrow{AB} \bullet \overrightarrow{OA} = 0$, $\overrightarrow{CA} = -6\mathbf{i} + 2\mathbf{j}$,
and $\overrightarrow{CB}$ is parallel to **j**.

a Find the coordinates of:

    i A   **ii** C   **iii** B

b Find the point P on [BC] such that $\overrightarrow{AP}$ is perpendicular to $\overrightarrow{BC}$.

c Hence find the area of triangle ABC.

14 Suppose $\mathbf{m} = 3\mathbf{i} + \mathbf{j} + 2\mathbf{k}$ and $\mathbf{n} = -2\mathbf{i} + 5\mathbf{j} - 4\mathbf{k}$. Find:

a $|\mathbf{m} + \mathbf{n}|$ **b** $\mathbf{m} \bullet \mathbf{n}$

c the vector equation of the line passing through $(1, -1, 2)$ which is parallel to **m**.

15 Find t given that $\begin{pmatrix} 2t \\ -4 \\ 7 \end{pmatrix}$ and $\begin{pmatrix} 3 \\ t \\ -8 \end{pmatrix}$ are perpendicular vectors.

16 Write vector equations for these lines:

  a parallel to $\begin{pmatrix} 1 \\ 2 \\ 3 \end{pmatrix}$ and passing through the point $(5, 0, -2)$

  b parallel to $2\mathbf{i} - 3\mathbf{j} + 4\mathbf{k}$ and passing through the point $(-2, 5, 4)$

  c perpendicular to the XOZ plane and passing through the point $(2, -4, 1)$.

17 Find the parametric equations of these lines:

  a passing through $(5, -1, 2)$ and parallel to $\begin{pmatrix} 7 \\ 2 \\ -3 \end{pmatrix}$

  b passing through $(0, 2, -6)$ and parallel to $2\mathbf{i} - 3\mathbf{j} + \mathbf{k}$

  c passing through $(2, 5, 1)$ and $(8, 6, 2)$.

18 Suppose $\mathbf{a} = \begin{pmatrix} 4 \\ -2 \\ 1 \end{pmatrix}$ and $\mathbf{b} = \begin{pmatrix} 3 \\ 2 \\ -4 \end{pmatrix}$.

  a Find $\mathbf{x}$ such that $\mathbf{a} - 4\mathbf{x} = 2\mathbf{b}$.

  b Find constants p and q if $\begin{pmatrix} p \\ q \\ -3 \end{pmatrix}$ is parallel to $\mathbf{a}$.

  c Find the possible values of k if $\begin{pmatrix} -10 \\ k^2 \\ k + 10 \end{pmatrix}$ is perpendicular to $\mathbf{b}$.

19 **a** Line L_1 passes through $A(1, -1, 2)$ and $B(5, -1, -1)$.

    i Write a vector equation for the line.

    ii Find a point on L_1 which is 20 units from A.

    iii At what point does L_1 meet the YOZ plane?

  b Line L_2 passes through $C(4, 1, -\frac{13}{2})$ and is parallel to $-3\mathbf{i} + 2\mathbf{j} - 4\mathbf{k}$.

    i Write a vector equation for the line.

    ii Show that L_1 is perpendicular to L_2.

  c L_1 meets L_2 at the point P.

    i State the y-coordinate of P.

    ii Find the coordinates of P.

  d Find the shortest distance from C to the line L_1.

20 A mountain railway runs straight up a mountainside with the aid of a cable. The train begins at point A with position vector $\mathbf{a}$, and ends at point B with position vector $\mathbf{b}$.

After t minutes, the train is at point P with position vector $\mathbf{p} = \left(1 - \frac{t}{12}\right)\mathbf{a} + \frac{t}{12}\mathbf{b}$.

  a Locate the train at time $t = 0$.

  b How long does it take for the train to reach B?

  c Suppose $\mathbf{a} = \begin{pmatrix} 1 \\ 3 \\ 0 \end{pmatrix}$ and $\mathbf{b} = \begin{pmatrix} 2 \\ 2 \\ 1 \end{pmatrix}$ where the units are kilometres.

    i Find the distance between A and B.

    ii Find the average speed of the train, giving your answer exactly.

21 Suppose $\mathbf{a} = \begin{pmatrix} 1 \\ 3 \\ k \end{pmatrix}$, $\mathbf{b} = \begin{pmatrix} 2 \\ 0 \\ -1 \end{pmatrix}$, $\mathbf{c} = \begin{pmatrix} -1 \\ 2 \\ 3 \end{pmatrix}$, and $\mathbf{b}$ is perpendicular to $\mathbf{c} - 2\mathbf{a}$. Find the value of k.

22 A is $(-1, 2, 1)$ and B is $(0, 1, 3)$.

  a Write a vector equation for the line (AB) in the form $\mathbf{r} = \mathbf{a} + t\mathbf{b}$, $t \in \mathbb{R}$.

  b Find the angle between (AB) and the line L given by $\begin{pmatrix} x \\ y \\ z \end{pmatrix} = \begin{pmatrix} 1 \\ -1 \\ 2 \end{pmatrix} + s \begin{pmatrix} 2 \\ 0 \\ -1 \end{pmatrix}$.

SKILL BUILDER QUESTIONS (CALCULATORS)

1 Consider the points $A(2, 10)$, $B(-2, 2)$, and $C(16, 6)$. Suppose M is the midpoint of [BC]. Find:

  a $\overrightarrow{AC}$ **b** $\overrightarrow{AM}$ **c** the size of angle BAC.

2 For $\mathbf{p} = 4\mathbf{i} - 9\mathbf{j}$ and $\mathbf{q} = -12\mathbf{i} + 5\mathbf{j}$, find:

  a $|\mathbf{q}|$ **b** $\mathbf{p} \bullet \mathbf{q}$

  c the angle between $\mathbf{p}$ and $\mathbf{q}$

  d a unit vector parallel to $\mathbf{q}$.

3

Q(4, 10)

• R(10, 6)

P(6, −4)

  a Show that $\overrightarrow{QR} = \overrightarrow{OP}$. Hence classify quadrilateral OPRQ.

  b Find the midpoint M of [PQ].

  c Show that O, M, and R are collinear.

  d Find a vector equation for the line (OR).

4 Line L_1 passes through $(6, 17)$ and is parallel to $-\mathbf{i} - 2\mathbf{j}$. Line L_2 passes through $(0, 5)$ and $(4, 2)$.

  a Write a vector equation for L_1 in the form $\mathbf{r}_1 = \mathbf{a} + s\mathbf{b}$.

  b **i** Find a direction vector for L_2.

    ii Hence write a vector equation for L_2.

  c Find the acute angle between the lines L_1 and L_2.

5 **a** Given $\mathbf{a} \bullet \mathbf{b} < 0$, what conclusion can you draw about the angle between $\mathbf{a}$ and $\mathbf{b}$?

  b Consider vectors $\mathbf{a} = \begin{pmatrix} -2 \\ 1 \\ 3 \end{pmatrix}$ and $\mathbf{b} = \begin{pmatrix} 3 \\ -1 \\ 1 \end{pmatrix}$.

    i Find $\mathbf{a} \bullet \mathbf{b}$.

    ii Hence find the angle between these vectors in degrees, correct to one decimal place.

    iii Find the area of the triangle defined by $\mathbf{a}$ and $\mathbf{b}$.

6

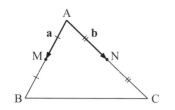

In triangle ABC, M is the midpoint of [AB] and N is the midpoint of [AC].

Suppose $\overrightarrow{AM} = \mathbf{a}$ and $\overrightarrow{AN} = \mathbf{b}$.

a Write in terms of **a** and **b**:

   i $\overrightarrow{AB}$ **ii** $\overrightarrow{AC}$ **iii** $\overrightarrow{MN}$ **iv** $\overrightarrow{BC}$

b Explain why the line segment joining the midpoints of two sides of a triangle is always parallel to the third side and half its length.

7 Quadrilateral ABCD has vertices A(2, 10), B(12, 8), C(11, 5), and D(−1, 2).

Find the acute angle between the diagonals $\overrightarrow{AC}$ and $\overrightarrow{BD}$.

8 A boat moves in a straight line defined by the parametric equations $x = 3 + t$ and $y = 4t − 3$, where t is the time in seconds, $t \geqslant 0$, and x and y are measured in metres.

Find:
   a the initial position of the boat

   b the position of the boat after 3 seconds

   c the velocity vector of the boat

   d the speed of the boat.

9 Suppose **i** represents a 1 km displacement due east and **j** represents a 1 km displacement due north. A lighthouse is located at the point $(0, 10)$. A ship is moving in a straight line with parametric equations $x = 3 − 2t$, $y = 3t + 1$, $t \geqslant 0$, where t is the number of hours after 8:30 am.

a What was the position of the ship at 8:30 am?

b Find the ship's: **i** velocity vector   **ii** speed.

c Find the distance between the ship and the lighthouse at 10:30 am.

d Find the time when the ship is directly west of the lighthouse.

e At what time (to the nearest minute) is the ship closest to the lighthouse?

10 **a** Write vector equations in the form $\mathbf{r} = \mathbf{a} + t\mathbf{b}$ to define the position at time t for these remote controlled toy racing cars. All distances are in metres and time is in seconds.

   i Car A is initially at $(9, −3)$, and is travelling at $\sqrt{13}$ m s^{-1} in the direction $−2\mathbf{i} + 3\mathbf{j}$.

   ii Car B is initially at $(−1, 4)$, and travels at a constant velocity for 3 seconds to $(5, 7)$.

b Show that the paths of the cars intersect at $(3, 6)$.

c Will the cars collide? Explain your answer.

11 For the points A(2, 0, 5), B(−3, 1, 7), and C(4, −2, 9), find:

   a $\overrightarrow{AB}$ **b** $\overrightarrow{AC}$ **c** the size of $\widehat{BAC}$.

12 A(2, −5, 3), B(7, −3, −1), C(1, 3, 0), and D(−4, 1, 4) are vertices of a quadrilateral.

   a Prove that ABCD is a parallelogram.

   b Find the size of the smaller angles of the parallelogram.

13 Consider the points K(4, −2, 7), L(6, 1, −1), and M(3, −2, 5).

   a Find the measure of $\widehat{KLM}$.

b Write parametric equations for the line passing through K and L.

c Show that the shortest distance from M to (KL) is $\dfrac{3\sqrt{33}}{11}$ units.

14 Lines L_1, L_2, and L_3 are defined by:

$$L_1 : \begin{pmatrix} x \\ y \\ z \end{pmatrix} = \begin{pmatrix} 2 \\ 1 \\ -1 \end{pmatrix} + t \begin{pmatrix} 3 \\ -6 \\ -3 \end{pmatrix}$$

$L_2 :$ $x = 5 − r$, $y = −4 + 2r$, $z = 1 + r$

$L_3 :$ $x = 5 − 3s$, $y = 5 + 4s$, $z = 1 + 2s$

a Show that L_1 is parallel to L_2.

b Show that L_1 and L_3 intersect, and find the angle between them.

TOPIC 5:   STATISTICS AND PROBABILITY

POPULATIONS AND SAMPLES

The **population** is the entire collection of individuals about which we want to draw conclusion.

In a **census** we collect information from the whole population.

In a **survey** we collect information from a **sample** of the population.

A **random sample** is a sample for which each member of the population has an equal chance of being selected. Random samples are used to ensure the sample reflects the true population.

TYPES OF DATA AND ITS REPRESENTATION

Discrete data can take any of a set of distinct values x_1, x_2, x_3, ... It is normally **counted**.

Continuous data can take any value within a certain continuous range. It is normally **measured**.

Grouped data refers to data which is collected in groups or classes, often for presentation purposes. The **interval width** of a class is its upper score minus its lower score.

For both discrete and continuous data we can plot the data value on the horizontal axis and the frequency on the vertical axis.

A **column graph** is used for discrete data. The columns have spaces between them.

A **frequency histogram** is used for continuous data. The classes are of equal width, and there are no spaces between the columns.

A **relative frequency histogram** uses relative frequency on the vertical axis. It enables us to compare distributions of different sample size.

Data may be symmetric, positively skewed, or negatively skewed.

    symmetric   positively skewed   negatively skewed

We use a **cumulative frequency graph** or **ogive** to display the cumulative frequency for each data value in a distribution. This enables us to read off the values at each percentile.

THE CENTRE OF A DATA SET

The **mean** of a set of scores is their arithmetic average.

For a large population, the **population mean** μ is generally unknown. The **sample mean** $\overline{x}$ is used as an **unbiased estimate** of μ.

For ungrouped data, $\quad \overline{x} = \dfrac{\sum\limits_{i=1}^{n} x_i}{n}$

For grouped data, $\quad \overline{x} = \dfrac{\sum fx}{\sum f}$ where f is the frequency of each value.

The **median** is the middle score of an ordered sample.

For an **odd number** of data, the median is one of the original data values.

For an **even number** of data, the median is the average of the two middle values, and may not be in the original data set.

The **mode** is the most frequently occurring score. If there are two modes we say the data is **bimodal**. For continuous data we refer to a **modal class**.

If a data set is symmetric, both the mode and the median should accurately measure the centre of the distribution.

PERCENTILES

The **kth percentile** is the score a such that $k\%$ of the scores are less than a.

The **lower quartile** Q_1 corresponds to the 25th percentile.

The **median** Q_2 corresponds to the 50th percentile.

The **upper quartile** Q_3 corresponds to the 75th percentile.

You should know how to generate a **cumulative frequency graph** and use it to estimate Q_1, Q_2, and Q_3.

THE SPREAD OF A DISTRIBUTION

The **range** measures the spread from the highest to lowest score.

The **interquartile range** $\text{IQR} = Q_3 - Q_1$.

The **sample variance** s_n^2 measures the **spread** of the scores about the sample mean.

The **sample standard deviation** s_n is the square root of the variance. You will find formulae for the standard deviation in your information booklet.

OUTLIERS

Outliers are extraordinary data that are separated from the main body of the data. We test for outliers by calculating upper and lower boundaries:

$$\text{Upper boundary} = Q_3 + 1.5 \times \text{IQR}$$
$$\text{Lower boundary} = Q_1 - 1.5 \times \text{IQR}$$

Any data outside of these boundaries is considered an outlier.

BOXPLOTS

A **boxplot** includes the **5-number summary** of a data set: minimum value, Q_1, Q_2, Q_3, maximum value.

An outlier is indicated by an asterisk $*$.

TWO VARIABLE STATISTICS

Correlation refers to the relationship or association between two variables.

We can use a **scatter diagram** of the data to help identify **outliers** and to describe the correlation. We consider **direction**, **linearity**, and **strength**.

LINEARITY

These points are roughly linear.

These points do not follow a linear trend.

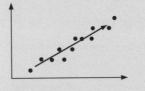

STRENGTH

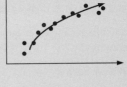

strong positive   strong negative

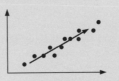 

moderate positive   moderate negative

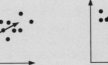

weak positive   weak negative

If a change in one variable *causes* a change in the other variable then we say there is a **causal relationship** between them.

To measure the strength of the relationship between two variables, we use **Pearson's product-moment correlation coefficient** r.

The correlation coefficient always lies in the range $-1 \leqslant r \leqslant 1$.

- The sign of r indicates the direction of correlation.
- The size of r indicates the strength of correlation.

$r = 1$	perfect positive correlation
$0.95 \leqslant r < 1$	very strong positive correlation
$0.87 \leqslant r < 0.95$	strong positive correlation
$0.5 \leqslant r < 0.87$	moderate positive correlation
$0.1 \leqslant r < 0.5$	weak positive correlation
$-0.1 < r < 0.1$	no correlation
$-0.5 < r \leqslant -0.1$	weak negative correlation
$-0.87 < r \leqslant -0.5$	moderate negative correlation
$-0.95 < r \leqslant -0.87$	strong negative correlation
$-1 < r \leqslant -0.95$	very strong negative correlation
$r = -1$	perfect negative correlation

The straight **line of best fit** drawn by eye should pass through the **mean point** $(\overline{x}, \overline{y})$.

To get an accurate line of best fit we use a method called **linear regression**. The line obtained is called the **least squares regression line**. You should be able to find this line using your calculator.

When using a line of best fit to estimate values, **interpolation** is usually reliable, whereas **extrapolation** may not be.

PROBABILITY

A **trial** occurs each time we perform an experiment.

The possible results from each trial of an experiment are called its **outcomes**.

The **sample space** U is the set of all possible outcomes from one trial of the experiment.

Experimental Probability

In many situations, we can only measure the probability of an event by experimentation.

Experimental probability = relative frequency

Theoretical Probability

If all outcomes are equally likely, the probability of event A occurring is $P(A) = \dfrac{n(A)}{n(U)}$.

For any event A, $0 \leqslant P(A) \leqslant 1$.

For any event A, A' is the event that A does not occur. A and A' are **complementary events**, and $P(A) + P(A') = 1$.

The **union** A *or* B is $A \cup B$.

The **intersection** A *and* B is $A \cap B$.

$P(A \cup B) = P(A) + P(B) - P(A \cap B)$

$A \cup A' = U$ and $A \cap A' = \varnothing$

For **disjoint** or **mutually exclusive** events, $P(A \cap B) = 0$.

Compound events

Two events are **independent** if the occurrence of each of them does not affect the probability that the other occurs. An example of this is sampling **with replacement**. For independent events A and B, $P(A \cap B) = P(A) P(B)$.

Two events are **dependent** if the occurrence of one of them *does* affect the probability that the other occurs. An example of this is sampling **without replacement**.

You should be able to use **Venn diagrams** and **tree diagrams** to calculate probabilities. You should also be able to use Venn diagrams to verify set identities.

Conditional Probability

For any two events A and B, $P(A \mid B) = \dfrac{P(A \cap B)}{P(B)}$.

For independent events: $P(A) = P(A \mid B) = P(A \mid B')$

$$P(A \cap B) = P(A) P(B).$$

$P(B) = P(0.3)$

DISCRETE RANDOM VARIABLES

A **random variable** represents the possible numerical outcomes of an experiment.

A **discrete random variable** can take any of a set of distinct values, each of which corresponds to exactly one outcome in the sample space.

For a discrete random variable where p_i is the probability of the ith outcome: $0 \leqslant p_i \leqslant 1$ and $\sum p_i = 1$.

The probabilities p_i may be given as a **probability distribution function** $P(x)$ where x can take discrete values.

If there are n trials of an experiment, and an event has probability p of occurring in each of the trials, then the number of times we **expect** the event to occur is np.

The **expectation** of a random variable is $E(X) = \mu = \sum\limits_{i=1}^{n} p_i x_i$.

In a gambling game, suppose X represents the gain of a player from each game. The game is **fair** if $E(X) = 0$.

The Binomial Distribution

In a **binomial experiment** there are two possible results: success and failure.

Suppose there are n independent trials of the same experiment with the probability of success being a constant p for each trial. If X represents the number of successes in the n trials, then X has a **binomial distribution**, and we write $X \sim B(n, p)$.

The **binomial probability distribution function** is
$P(X = r) = \binom{n}{r} p^r (1 - p)^{n-r}$ where $r = 0, 1, 2, ..., n$.

You should be able to use your calculator to find:

- $P(X = r)$ using the binomial probability distribution function
- $P(X \leqslant r)$ or $P(X \geqslant r)$ using the binomial cumulative distribution function.

In a binomial experiment:

- $E(X) = \mu = np$
- $\sigma = \sqrt{np(1 - p)}$
- $\text{Var}(X) = \sigma^2 = np(1 - p)$

CONTINUOUS RANDOM VARIABLES

A **continuous random variable** takes on all possible *measured* values. We consider measurements that are in a particular *range* rather than taking a particular value. For example, we do not consider $X = 3.7\,\text{kg}$ but rather $3.65 \leqslant X < 3.75\,\text{kg}$.

A **probability density function** is a function $f(x)$ such that $f(x) \geqslant 0$ on a given interval $a \leqslant x \leqslant b$, and $\int_a^b f(x)\, dx = 1$. So, the area under the graph of $f(x)$ is 1.

$P(c \leqslant X \leqslant d) = \int_c^d f(x)\, dx$

The Normal Distribution

If the random variable X has a normal distribution with mean μ and variance σ^2, we write $X \sim N(\mu, \sigma^2)$.

The probability density function is $f(x) = \dfrac{1}{\sigma\sqrt{2\pi}} e^{-\frac{1}{2}\left(\frac{x-\mu}{\sigma}\right)^2}$ for $x \in \mathbb{R}$.

$f(x)$ is a bell-shaped curve which is symmetric about $x = \mu$. It has the property that:

- $\approx 68\%$ of all scores lie within one σ of μ
- $\approx 95\%$ of all scores lie within two σs of μ
- $\approx 99.7\%$ of all scores lie within three σs of μ.

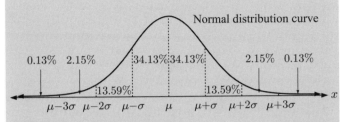

The Standard Normal Distribution

Every normal X-distribution can be transformed into the **standard normal distribution** or **Z-distribution** using the transformation $z = \dfrac{x - \mu}{\sigma}$.

The standard normal distribution has mean 0 and variance 1, so $Z \sim N(0, 1)$.

The probability density function is $f(z) = \dfrac{1}{\sqrt{2\pi}} e^{-\frac{1}{2}z^2}$ for $z \in \mathbb{R}$.

We use Z-distributions when:
- we are looking for an unknown mean μ or variance σ^2
- we are comparing scores from two different normal distributions

You should be able to use your calculator to find normal probabilities for the situations:

- $P(Z \leqslant a)$
- $P(Z \geqslant a)$
- $P(a \leqslant Z \leqslant b)$

You should also be able to use your calculator to find the scores corresponding to particular probabilities, or **quantiles**.

SKILL BUILDER QUESTIONS (NO CALCULATORS)

1 A frequency table for the speeds of 72 cars travelling through a country town one Sunday morning is given alongside.

Speed (km h^{-1})	Frequency
$30 \leqslant v < 40$	4
$40 \leqslant v < 50$	11
$50 \leqslant v < 60$	x
$60 \leqslant v < 70$	18
$70 \leqslant v < 80$	12
$80 \leqslant v < 90$	6
$90 \leqslant v < 100$	4
$100 \leqslant v < 110$	2

   a Find the value of x.

   b What is the modal class?

   c Construct a cumulative frequency graph for the data, and use it to estimate:

     i the median
     ii the interquartile range
     iii the 40th percentile of the data.

2 After seven netball matches, Kai has averaged 11 goals per game.

Score	7	9	x	13	16
Frequency	1	2	1	2	1

   a Find the value of x.

   b How many goals will she need to score in the next game to improve her overall average to 12?

3 After a 10 minute run, a class of 24 students measured their pulse rates. The results were:

85 106 148 112 105 96 100 108 135 126 144 156
98 108 112 128 148 140 120 123 133 144 118 125

   a Find:

     i the lower quartile
     ii the median

     iii the upper quartile
     iv the interquartile range

     v the range of the data.

   b Are there any outliers?

   c Draw a box and whisker plot to represent the data.

4 A cumulative frequency graph for the selling price of units sold at Sunset Beach last year is given below.

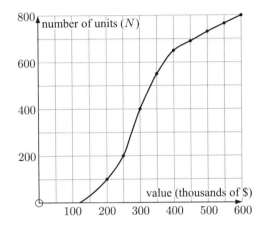

   a How many units sold for less than \$200 000?

   b Write down the median selling price.

   c Find the interquartile range of the selling prices.

   d One of the units is chosen at random. Determine the probability that its selling price was more than \$330 000.

5 The number of new potatoes and their median weight, in a sample of 2.5 kg bags, is given below.
$\overline{x} = 120$ and $\overline{y} = 22$.

Median weight (x g)	88	97	105	110	125	140	145	150
Number in bag (y)	28	26	25	23	21	19	18	16

   a Determine the equation of linear regression for this data by eye.

   b Use your equation to estimate the number of potatoes in a bag if the median weight is:

     i 100 grams
     ii 200 grams.

   c Which of the answers in **b** is likely to be more reliable? Give a reason for your answer.

6 A boxplot has been drawn to show the heights of some petunia seedlings, in centimetres.

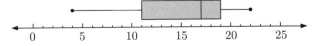

Mathematics SL – Exam Preparation & Practice Guide (3rd edition)

a Write down the:
  i tallest height   **ii** smallest height
  iii 75th percentile   **iv** median height.

b Write down the:
  i range   **ii** interquartile range.

c What percentage of seedlings were taller than 11 cm?

d Was the distribution of seedlings symmetrical?

7 Two unbiased dice are rolled, and the difference between the scores is noted.

  a Display the possible results in a table of outcomes.

  b Hence find the probability that the difference between the scores is 3.

8 This Venn diagram illustrates the number of students in a particular class who play hockey (H) and tennis (T).

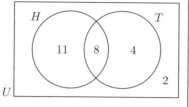

A student from the class is picked at random. Find the probability that he or she:

a plays hockey   **b** does not play tennis

c plays at least one of the two sports

d plays tennis given that he or she plays hockey.

9 $f(x)$ is the probability density function of a continuous random variable X.

  a What two properties must $f(x)$ have?

  b How is $P(x_1 \leqslant X \leqslant x_2)$ found?

10 A random variable X has the following distribution table:

x	-2	0	3	5
$P(X = x)$	$\frac{1}{3}$	$\frac{1}{6}$	k	$\frac{1}{12}$

  a Is the random variable discrete or continuous?

  b Find k.   **c** Find $E(X)$.

11 In the town of Expiet, 71% of the population are right-handed, 44% are either right-handed or have blonde hair but not both, and 21% do not have blonde hair.
Let R be the event that a person is right-handed and B be the event that a person has blonde hair.

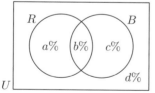

  a Find the values of a, b, c, and d.

  b A member of this population is selected at random. Find the probability that the person is:

    i right-handed but not blonde

    ii right-handed *and* has blonde hair

    iii right-handed *or* has blonde hair.

12 **a** Illustrate on a 2-dimensional grid, the possible results when two dice are rolled.

  b Hence find the probability that the sum of the two results is:

    i more than 8   **ii** more than 3 but less than 8
    iii exactly 6.

13 Suppose you toss a coin and roll a die simultaneously.
Let T represent a tail with the coin.
Let E represent a 2 or a 5 with the die.

  a Copy and complete the tree diagram showing the probabilities of the different outcomes.

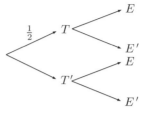

  b Find: **i** $P(T \cap E')$ **ii** $P(T \cup E')$

14 Assume that for each child, $P(\text{boy}) = P(\text{girl}) = \frac{1}{2}$.
With the aid of a tree diagram, find the probability of getting at least one child of each sex if you have 3 children.

15 The scatter diagram shows the age and annual income for 10 randomly chosen individuals. The mean age is 27 and the mean income is \$20 000.

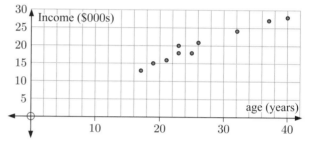

  a Describe the relationship between the age and annual income for these individuals.

  b Determine the equation of a line of best fit by eye, for age and income.

  c Hence estimate the annual income for someone who is:

    i 30 years old   **ii** 60 years old.

  d Comment on the reliability of your answers in **c**.

16 Twins Tom and Jerry are keen archers. The probability that Tom successfully hits a target is 0.7. The probability that Jerry successfully hits a target is 0.6. Suppose they both shoot at a target. Find the probability that:

  a only one of them is successful

  b at least one of them is successful.

17 A box of chocolates contains 6 dark brown, 4 light brown, and 2 white truffles.

  a Copy and complete the following tree diagram displaying the probabilities if two truffles are selected from the box without replacement.

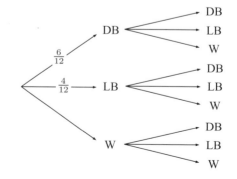

b Suppose you chose 2 truffles from the box at random, without replacement. Find the probability that you would get:

  i 2 white truffles

  ii different coloured truffles.

18 In a class of 30 students, 17 have brown hair, 12 have blue eyes, and 4 have neither brown hair nor blue eyes.

  a How many of the students have both brown hair and blue eyes?

  b A student is randomly selected. Find the probability that the student:

    i has blue eyes but not brown hair

    ii has brown hair if it is known that he or she has blue eyes.

SKILL BUILDER QUESTIONS (CALCULATORS)

1 This table shows the distribution of marks for a spelling test.

Mark	4	5	6	7	8	9	10
Frequency	2	3	1	4	8	3	4

Calculate the: **a** mean   **b** mode   **c** median.

2

x	0	1	2	3	4
Frequency	6	4	3	a	2

  a Find the value of a if $\overline{x} = 1.65$.

  b Hence find the standard deviation of the scores.

3 Calculate the mean and standard deviation of the following sets of data:

  a Birth weights of babies (in kg)

    4.0 3.8 2.8 3.7 2.8 3.1 4.5 3.9
    3.2 3.8 4.3 3.3 3.6 3.2 2.9 4.0

  b Times to swim 50 metres backstroke

Time (secs)	Frequency
$40 \leqslant t < 50$	3
$50 \leqslant t < 60$	8
$60 \leqslant t < 70$	13
$70 \leqslant t < 80$	12
$80 \leqslant t < 90$	4
$90 \leqslant t < 100$	2

4 The mean of the following set of numbers is 97.

    90, 100, 93, 96, p, 107, 98, 98, 92

  a Calculate the value of p.   **b** Find the median value.

5 A sample of the distances of drives hit by a golfer was recorded in the table alongside.

Distance (m)	Frequency (f)
$225 \leqslant d < 230$	1
$230 \leqslant d < 235$	3
$235 \leqslant d < 240$	5
$240 \leqslant d < 245$	7
$245 \leqslant d < 250$	3
$250 \leqslant d < 255$	6
$255 \leqslant d < 260$	4
$260 \leqslant d < 265$	1

  a How many drives were chosen in the sample?

  b Construct a frequency histogram of the data.

  c Estimate the mean and median, and find the modal class of the sample. Use these answers to comment on the symmetry of the data.

  d Construct a cumulative frequency table of the data.

e What percentage of the drives sampled travelled less than 250 metres?

f If the golfer hit 100 drives, how many would you expect to travel more than 235 metres?

6 The mean average rainfall in Adelaide for October is 58 mm with a standard deviation of 4 mm. Over a 100 year period, assuming the rainfall distribution is normal, how many times would you expect there to be:

  a more than 60 mm   **b** between 50 mm and 60 mm

of rainfall in Adelaide during October?

7 38% of the students in a Year 12 IB Mathematics class are female. Of the female students, 13% are left-handed. 24% of the male students are left-handed.

Find the probability that a randomly chosen student from the class:

  a is left-handed

  b is female, given that the student is left-handed.

8 The following table lists the ages of contestants in a game, and the times they take to complete the task.

Age (x years)	28	40	21	38	30	26
Time (y min)	20	32	15	40	26	25

Age (x years)	18	32	25	29	20	24
Time (y min)	19	28	21	25	16	22

  a Find the value of the correlation coefficient r, and explain what this value means.

  b **i** Write down the equation of the linear regression line in the form $y = mx + c$.

    ii Explain the meaning of the coefficient m in this equation.

9 To test the effects of adrenaline on mice, subjects were timed through an obstacle course with and without adrenaline injections. The results in seconds are shown below:

Subject	With adrenaline (x)	Without adrenaline (y)
A	35	38
B	42	44
C	31	32
D	50	38
E	62	70
F	28	31
G	57	68
H	39	49

  a Using your graphics calculator, determine the equation of the regression line of y against x.

  b State Pearson's correlation coefficient.

  c Comment on the strength of the correlation.

  d Which data point is an outlier?

  e Estimate the benefit of an adrenaline injection to a mouse that would otherwise take 48 seconds to complete the obstacle course.

10 Consider the following data on farm production.

Monthly rainfall (mm)	5	10	15	20	25	30
Yield (tonnes)	12	16	18	22	25	27

  a Determine the coefficient of correlation r.

b What does the value of r suggest about the nature and strength of the relationship between monthly rainfall and crop yield?

c Find the equation of the least squares regression line connecting the variables.

d Use your regression line to estimate the yield if the monthly rainfall is:

    i 0 mm   **ii** 12 mm.

e Which of the estimates in **d** would you expect to be more reliable? Explain your answer.

11 Events A and B are independent.

Given that $P(A \cup B) = 0.63$ and $P(B) = 0.36$, find $P(A)$.

12 Given that $P(A) = 0.46$, $P(B) = \frac{5}{7}$, and $P((A \cup B)') = \frac{1}{12}$, find $P(A \cap B)$.

13 A bag contains seven purple tickets and three red tickets. Michelle draws two tickets from the bag without replacement.

a Illustrate on a tree diagram the possible outcomes and the probabilities for each draw.

b Find the probability that Michelle will select:

    i at least one red ticket

    ii one ticket of each colour

    iii a purple ticket second.

14 The cumulative frequency curve below represents the finishing time, in minutes, of 30 competitors in a recent orienteering contest.

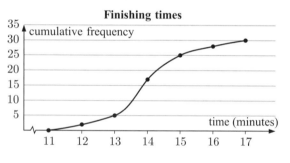

Finishing times

a Find the median finishing time, giving your answer to 1 decimal place.

b Find the time required for a runner to finish in the 1st quartile.

c How many runners finished in a time between 12 and 15 minutes?

d Find the probability that a randomly selected runner finished quicker than 13 minutes.

15 The mean contents of a certain brand of soft drink bottle is 310 mL with a standard deviation of 5 mL. Assuming the contents are normally distributed, find:

a the percentage of bottles which contain between 300 mL and 310 mL

b the percentage of bottles which contain at least 304 mL

c the probability that a randomly selected bottle contains less than 300 mL.

16 Ashleigh's exam results for English and History are summarised in the table:

	English	History
Ashleigh	80	72
Class average	75	60
Class standard deviation	8	15

The results for each exam are normally distributed.

a Estimate the percentage of students who scored higher marks than Ashleigh in:

    i English   **ii** History.

b In which subject did Ashleigh perform better relative to her class?

17 The marks obtained by students in a mathematics test had mean μ and standard deviation σ. 12% of the students gained a mark greater than 90, but 20% of the students scored a mark less than 60. Assuming the marks were normally distributed, estimate μ and σ correct to 1 decimal place.

18 Four fifths of the residents in a particular suburb oppose the construction of traffic lights at one of the suburb's intersections. One of the residents decides to conduct a survey, and randomly samples 20 people who live in the suburb. Find the probability that:

a exactly 16 residents   **b** 16 or more residents

oppose the construction of the lights.

19

X	30	50	80	60	50	90	40	50
Y	65	12	28	42	46	26	54	48

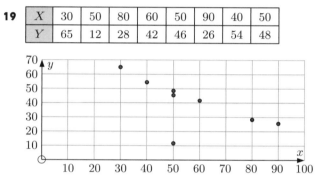

a For the given data, find:

    i the correlation coefficient r

    ii the equation of the least squares regression line.

b Identify and remove the outlier from the data. For the data which remains, find:

    i the correlation coefficient r

    ii the equation of the least squares regression line.

c Comment on the effect that removing the outlier had on:

    i the gradient of the regression line

    ii the strength of correlation of the data.

20 9 students sat a mathematics examination. The results they obtained and the number of hours that each of them studied are shown in the table.

Study time (h)	7	6	3	16	15	11	18	32	20
Result (%)	56	42	25	80	65	60	85	96	90

a Write down the equation of the least squares regression line.

b Tony's score in the examination was 70%. Using the line of best fit, estimate how long he studied for.

c In terms of the marks obtained in the examination, interpret the y-intercept and the gradient of the equation of the line of best fit.

21 Robert takes a multiple choice test. There are 15 questions and each question has four alternative answers. The pass mark is 8, and Robert must score 10 or better in order to achieve a C in the subject.

Robert is confident that he knows the answer to 5 of the questions, but he has to guess the remainder of the answers.

Assuming that Robert does correctly answer the 5 questions that he is confident about, determine the probability that he will:

   a fail the test

   b answer exactly 8 out of 15 correctly

   c achieve a C or better for the subject.

22 A radar speed detection device is used to measure the speed of approaching vehicles. It is found to produce normally distributed errors with mean zero and standard deviation 1 km h^{-1}.

   a Find the probability that a speed registered is no more than 1 km h^{-1} higher than the actual speed.

   b Find the probability that a speed registered is within 0.5 km h^{-1} of the actual speed.

   c If this device measures 850 speeds on a certain day, how many would you expect to exceed the actual speeds by more than 2 km h^{-1}?

23 The lengths in centimetres of adult fish of a certain species are described by the variable $X \sim N(40, 5^2)$. The mean is 40 cm and the standard deviation is 5 cm.

   a Find the probability that a randomly chosen adult fish of this species is:

     i longer than 45 cm

     ii between 35 and 50 cm long.

   b Determine the minimum length of the longest 10% of this species of fish.

24 A machine fills bottles with tomato sauce. Each bottle is filled independently of all other bottles. The volume of sauce in each bottle is normally distributed with mean 500 mL and standard deviation 2.5 mL. Bottles are deemed to require extra sauce if the machine delivers less than 495 mL.

   a Calculate the probability that a randomly selected bottle requires extra sauce.

   b For a day in which 10 000 bottles are produced, calculate the expected number of bottles that require extra sauce.

25 During sleep, the reduction of a person's oxygen consumption has a normal distribution with mean 38.4 mL min^{-1} and standard deviation 4.6 mL min^{-1}.

   a Determine the probability that during sleep a person's oxygen consumption will be reduced by:

     i more than 43.5 mL min^{-1}

     ii at most 36.4 mL min^{-1}

     iii anywhere from 30 to 40 mL min^{-1}.

   b If 90% of people reduce their oxygen consumption by more than $k \text{ mL min}^{-1}$, determine k.

26 The continuous random variable X is normally distributed with $P(X < 56) = 0.8$.

   a How many standard deviations from the mean is a score of 56?

   b If the standard deviation of X is 4, find the mean of the distribution. Give your answer correct to one decimal place.

27 Containers of a particular brand of ice cream have a capacity of 1050 mL. They are advertised as containing 1 litre of ice cream. The quantity of ice cream added to each container is normally distributed with mean 1020 mL and standard deviation 15 mL.

   a Find the probability that the container has less than the advertised capacity.

   b Find the percentage of containers that overflow.

   c Find the number of containers from a sample of 1500 that you would expect to contain between 1 litre and 1.03 litres.

28 For a student to pass a particular course they must pass at least 8 of 10 tests. For each test the probability of the student passing is 0.88. Determine the probability that the student:

   a passes exactly 8 of the 10 tests

   b passes the course.

29 5% of all items coming off a production line are defective. The manufacturer packages his items in boxes of six, and guarantees "double your money back" if more than two items in a box are defective. On what percentage of the boxes will the manufacturer have to pay double money back?

30 A tinned food company examined a sample of its corn and pineapple tins for defects. The results are summarised in the table below.

	Defective	Not defective
Corn	37	581
Pineapple	24	617

   a How many tins were included in the sample?

   b Estimate the probability that the next randomly selected tin:

     i is defective   **ii** is a corn tin given it is defective

     iii is defective given it is a corn tin.

31 A hospital recorded the age and gender of its melanoma patients over one year. The data is shown alongside.

	< 50	$\geqslant 50$
Male	136	469
Female	155	310

   a How many melanoma patients were treated at the hospital that year?

   b Find the probability that a randomly selected melanoma patient was:

     i male   **ii** younger than 50

     iii male, given they were 50 years or older

     iv 50 years or older, given they were female.

32 A penicillin injection causes an allergic reaction in one out of ten people. Estimate the probability that fewer than 470 reactions will occur among 5000 people injected with penicillin.

33 The lengths of wooden chopsticks produced by a machine are normally distributed with standard deviation 0.5 cm. It is found that 1% of all these chopsticks are less than 24 cm long. Find the mean length of the chopsticks produced by the machine.

34 The lengths of steel rods cut by a machine are normally distributed with mean 13.8 cm. It is found that 1.5% of all rods are less than 13.2 cm long. Find the standard deviation of rod lengths produced by this machine.

35 Consider the probability distribution function defined by
$$P(x) = P(X = x) = \tfrac{1}{24}(x + 6) \quad \text{for} \quad x \in \{1, 2, 3\}.$$

   a Find $P(x)$ for $x = 1, 2,$ and 3.

   b Find the mean value of X.

36 Josephine's number of safe hits at each softball match has the probability distribution opposite. Find:

x	0	1	2	3
$P(x)$	0.05	k	0.5	0.3

   a the value of k

   b Josephine's expected average number of safe hits per game.

37 The table alongside shows the probability distribution for X.

x	0	1	2	3
$P(X=x)$	0.3	0.2	m	n

If $E(X) = 1.55$, find the value of m.

38 An investigation into the weight of packed vegetables found the following:

Number of tomatoes in a 1.5 kg bag	Median weight of tomatoes in bag (g)
15	90
11	125
14	110
12	125
14	136
17	82
12	115
10	150

a Find the correlation coefficient r.

b Describe the relationship between the variables.

c Write down the equation of the least squares regression line.

d Hence estimate the median weight of the tomatoes if there are:
  i 13   **ii** 20 in the bag.

e Comment on the reliability of your estimates in **d**.

39 Given $X \sim N(13, \sigma^2)$ and $P(X \leqslant 15) = 0.613$, find σ.

40 Suppose X is normally distributed with $P(X \leqslant 24) = 0.035$ and $P(X \geqslant 33) = 0.262$. Find the mean and standard deviation of X correct to 3 significant figures.

TOPIC 6:   CALCULUS

LIMITS

If $f(x)$ can be made as close as we like to some real number A by making x sufficiently close to a, we say that $f(x)$ approaches a **limit** as x approaches a, and we write $\lim\limits_{x \to a} f(x) = A$.

We say that as x approaches a, $f(x)$ **converges** to A.

We can use the idea of limits as $x \to \pm\infty$ and as $f(x) \to \pm\infty$ to find asymptotes.

A graph will never cross its vertical asymptotes, but may cross its horizontal asymptotes.

RATES OF CHANGE

The **instantaneous rate of change** of a variable at a particular instant is given by the **gradient of the tangent** to the graph at that point.

$\dfrac{dy}{dx}$ gives the rate of change in y with respect to x.

If $\dfrac{dy}{dx}$ is positive, then as x increases, y also increases.

If $\dfrac{dy}{dx}$ is negative, then as x increases, y decreases.

DIFFERENTIATION

The **derivative function** $f'(x) = \lim\limits_{h \to 0} \dfrac{f(x+h) - f(x)}{h}$ provides:

- the rate of change of f with respect to x
- the gradient of the tangent to $y = f(x)$ for any value of x.

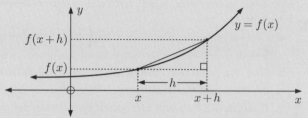

When we use the limit definition to find a derivative, we call this the **method of first principles**.

$f(x)$	$f'(x)$	Name of rule
c	0	
x^n	nx^{n-1}	
$cu(x)$	$cu'(x)$	
$u(x) + v(x)$	$u'(x) + v'(x)$	addition rule
$u(x)v(x)$	$u'(x)v(x) + u(x)v'(x)$	product rule
$\dfrac{u(x)}{v(x)}$	$\dfrac{u'(x)v(x) - u(x)v'(x)}{[v(x)]^2}$	quotient rule
$e^{f(x)}$	$e^{f(x)}f'(x)$	exponentials
$\ln f(x)$	$\dfrac{f'(x)}{f(x)}$	logarithms
$\sin x$	$\cos x$	
$\cos x$	$-\sin x$	trigonometric functions
$\tan x$	$\dfrac{1}{\cos^2 x}$	

Chain rule

If $y = g(u)$ where $u = f(x)$ then $\dfrac{dy}{dx} = \dfrac{dy}{du}\dfrac{du}{dx}$.

Higher derivatives

The second derivative of the function $f(x)$ is the derivative of $f'(x)$.

$$f''(x) = \frac{d}{dx}(f'(x))$$

The nth derivative of the function $f(x)$ is

$$f^{(n)}(x) = \frac{d^n}{dx^n} f(x)$$

PROPERTIES OF CURVES

Tangents and normals

For the curve $y = f(x)$, the gradient of the **tangent** at $x = a$ is $m_T = f'(a)$.

The equation of the tangent to the curve at the point $A(a, b)$ is $\dfrac{y - b}{x - a} = f'(a)$.

The gradient of the **normal** at $x = a$ is $m_N = -\dfrac{1}{f'(a)}$.

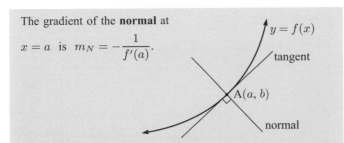

Increasing and decreasing functions

$f(x)$ is **increasing** on an interval $S \Leftrightarrow f(a) \leqslant f(b)$ for all $a, b \in S$ such that $a < b$.

$f(x)$ is increasing on $S \Leftrightarrow f'(x) \geqslant 0$ for all x in S.

$f(x)$ is **decreasing** on $S \Leftrightarrow f(a) \geqslant f(b)$ for all $a, b \in S$ such that $a < b$.

$f(x)$ is decreasing on $S \Leftrightarrow f'(x) \leqslant 0$ for all x in S.

Functions which have the same behaviour for all $x \in \mathbb{R}$ are called **monotone increasing** or **monotone decreasing**.

Stationary points

A **stationary point** of a function is a point such that $f'(x) = 0$.

You should be able to identify and explain the significance of local and global maxima and minima, and inflections both stationary and non-stationary.

Stationary point	Sign diagram of $f'(x)$ near $x = a$	Shape of curve near $x = a$
local maximum	$\xleftarrow{\quad + \quad|\quad - \quad}_{a} x$	curve peak at $x = a$
local minimum	$\xleftarrow{\quad - \quad|\quad + \quad}_{a} x$	curve valley at $x = a$
stationary inflection	$\xleftarrow{\; + \;|\; + \;}_{a} x$ _or_ $\xleftarrow{\; - \;|\; - \;}_{a} x$	_or_ at $x = a$ $\quad$ $x = a$

There is a **point of inflection** at $x = a$ if $f''(a) = 0$ **and** the sign of $f''(x)$ changes on either side of $x = a$. It corresponds to a change in *shape* of the curve.

If the tangent at a point of inflection is horizontal, we say we have a **stationary inflection point**.

gradient $= 0$

If the tangent at a point of inflection is *not* horizontal, we say we have a **non-stationary inflection point**.

If $f''(x) \leqslant 0$ for all $x \in S$, the curve is **concave downwards** on the interval S.

If $f''(x) \geqslant 0$ for all $x \in S$, the curve is **concave upwards** on the interval S.

KINEMATIC PROBLEMS

An object moves along a straight line. Its position from the origin at time t is given by a displacement function $s(t)$.

Its instantaneous velocity is given by $v = \dfrac{ds}{dt}$,

and its instantaneous acceleration by $a = \dfrac{d^2 s}{dt^2}$ or $a = v\dfrac{dv}{ds}$.

You should understand the difference between *instantaneous* velocity or acceleration, and *average* velocity or acceleration over a time period.

You should also understand the physical meaning of the different combinations of signs of velocity and acceleration.

Signs of $s(t)$:

$s(t)$	Interpretation
$= 0$	P is at O
> 0	P is located to the right of O
< 0	P is located to the left of O

Signs of $v(t)$:

$v(t)$	Interpretation
$= 0$	P is instantaneously at rest
> 0	P is moving to the right
< 0	P is moving to the left

Signs of $a(t)$:

$a(t)$	Interpretation
> 0	velocity is increasing
< 0	velocity is decreasing
$= 0$	velocity may be a max. or min.

The **speed** at any instant is the magnitude of the object's velocity. If $S(t)$ represents the speed then $S = |v|$.

If the signs of $v(t)$ and $a(t)$ are the same then the speed of the object is increasing.

If the signs of $v(t)$ and $a(t)$ are different then the speed of the object is decreasing.

OPTIMISATION PROBLEMS

It is important to remember that a local minimum or maximum does not always give the minimum or maximum value of the function in a particular domain. You must check for other turning points in the domain and whether the end values of the domain give higher or lower values.

Optimisation problem solving method

1 Draw a large, clear diagram of the situation.

2 Construct an equation with the variable to be optimised as the subject. It should be written in terms of **one** other variable such as x.
Write down any restrictions on the value of x.

3 Find the first derivative of the formula, and the values of x which make it zero.

4 Show, using a sign diagram or second derivative test, that you have a maximum or minimum stationary point. Test the stationary points and end points of the domain to find the optimal solution.

Mathematics SL – Exam Preparation & Practice Guide (3rd edition)

Consider the graph:

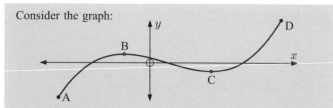

A is a **global minimum** as it is the minimum value of y anywhere on the domain.

B is a **local maximum** as $f'(x) = 0$ and the curve is concave downwards at that point.

C is a **local minimum** as $f'(x) = 0$ and the curve is concave upwards at that point.

D is a **global maximum** as it is the maximum value of y anywhere on the domain.

INTEGRATION

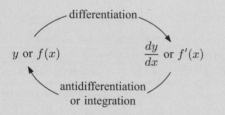

If $F(x)$ is a function where $F'(x) = f(x)$, then $F(x)$ is the **antiderivative** of $f(x)$.

Fundamental theorem of calculus

For a continuous function $f(x)$ with antiderivative $F(x)$, $\int_a^b f(x)\, dx = F(b) - F(a)$.

Area under a curve

If $f(x)$ is a continuous *positive* function on the interval $a \leqslant x \leqslant b$, then the area under the curve between $x = a$ and $x = b$ is $\int_a^b f(x)\, dx$.

To find the total area enclosed by $y = f(x)$ and the x-axis between $x = a$ and $x = b$, we need to be careful about where $f(x) < 0$.

On an interval $c \leqslant x \leqslant d$ where $f(x) < 0$, the area is $-\int_c^d f(x)\, dx$.

For example:

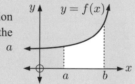

The total shaded area
$$= \int_a^b f(x)\, dx - \int_b^c f(x)\, dx$$
$$\neq \int_a^c f(x)\, dx.$$

The area *between* two functions is given by
$$A = \int_a^b (y_U - y_L)\, dx$$
where $y_U \geqslant y_L$ on the domain $a \leqslant x \leqslant b$.

Indefinite integrals

When performing an indefinite integral, we use the rules for differentiation in reverse. Do not forget to include the **constant of integration**.

If $F'(x) = f(x)$ then $\int f(x)\, dx = F(x) + c$.

$\int f(x)\, dx$ is the **indefinite integral** of $f(x)$ with respect to x.

$\int k\, f(x)\, dx = k \int f(x)\, dx$, $\quad k$ a constant

$\int [f(x) + g(x)]\, dx = \int f(x)\, dx + \int g(x)\, dx$

Function	Integral
k	$kx + c$
x^n	$\dfrac{x^{n+1}}{n+1} + c$, $\ n \neq -1$
e^x	$e^x + c$
$\dfrac{1}{x}$	$\ln|x| + c$
e^{ax+b}	$\dfrac{1}{a} e^{ax+b} + c$, $\ a \neq 0$
$(ax+b)^n$	$\dfrac{(ax+b)^{n+1}}{a(n+1)} + c$, $\ n \neq -1$
$\dfrac{1}{ax+b}$	$\dfrac{1}{a} \ln|ax+b|$, $\ a \neq 0$
$\cos(ax+b)$	$\dfrac{1}{a} \sin(ax+b) + c$, $\ a \neq 0$
$\sin(ax+b)$	$-\dfrac{1}{a} \cos(ax+b) + c$, $\ a \neq 0$

Integration by substitution

$\int f(u) \dfrac{du}{dx}\, dx = \int f(u)\, du$

Definite integrals

- $\int_a^a f(x)\, dx = 0$

- $\int_b^a f(x)\, dx = -\int_a^b f(x)\, dx$

- $\int_a^b f(x)\, dx + \int_b^c f(x)\, dx = \int_a^c f(x)\, dx$

- $\int_a^b c f(x)\, dx = c \int_a^b f(x)\, dx$

- $\int_a^b [f(x) \pm g(x)]\, dx = \int_a^b f(x)\, dx \pm \int_a^b g(x)\, dx$

Kinematics

The displacement function is determined by the integral $s(t) = \int v(t)\, dt$.

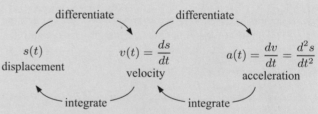

For the time interval $t_1 \leqslant t \leqslant t_2$:

- displacement $= s(t_2) - s(t_1) = \int_{t_1}^{t_2} v(t)\, dt$

- total distance travelled $= \int_{t_1}^{t_2} |v(t)|\, dt$.

To find the total distance travelled given $v(t) = s'(t)$ on $a \leqslant t \leqslant b$, we:

- draw a sign diagram for $v(t)$ so we can determine when any changes in direction occur
- determine $s(t)$ by integration
- find $s(a)$, $s(b)$, and $s(t)$ at each time the direction changes
- draw a motion diagram
- determine the total distance travelled from the motion diagram.

SOLIDS OF REVOLUTION

When the region enclosed by $y = f(x)$, the x-axis, and the vertical lines $x = a$, $x = b$ is rotated about the x-axis to generate a solid, the volume of the solid is given by

$V = \pi \int_a^b y^2 dx$

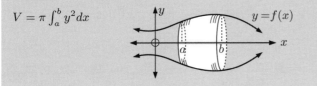

SKILL BUILDER QUESTIONS (NO CALCULATORS)

1 The derivative of $f(x)$ is defined by
$$f'(x) = \lim_{h \to 0} \frac{f(x+h) - f(x)}{h}.$$
  a Use this definition to differentiate $f(x) = 7x - x^2$.
  b Find the equation of the tangent to $y = f(x)$ at the point where $x = 1$.

2 Consider the curve $y = -2x^2 + 3$.
  a Differentiate the function from first principles.
  b Find the gradient of the *tangent* to the curve at the point where $x = -1$.
  c Find the equation of the *normal* to the curve at the point where $x = -1$.
  d At what point does the normal in **c** meet the curve again?

3 Find $\frac{dy}{dx}$ for:
  a $y = \frac{3x+1}{\sqrt{x}}$ **b** $y = \frac{1}{x^4+9}$
  c $y = x^2\sqrt{1-x^2}$ **d** $(2x+3)^5$

4 Let $g(x) = -x\cos x$.
  a Find $g'(x)$.
  b Find the gradient of the tangent to the graph $y = g(x)$ at the point where $x = \frac{\pi}{3}$.

5 Consider the function $f(x) = x^3 - 2x^2$ on the domain $-1 \leqslant x \leqslant 1$.
  a Find $f'(x)$.
  b Find the greatest and least values of the function, giving reasons for your answers.

6 Let $y = (2+x)\sqrt{3-x}$.
  a State the domain of the function.
  b Find $\frac{dy}{dx}$.
  c Find the coordinates of the local maximum.

7 Consider the curves $y = \sqrt{3x+1}$ and $y = \sqrt{5x - x^2}$.
  a Find the point at which these curves meet.
  b Show that the curves have the same gradient at this intersection point.
  c Find the equation of the common tangent.

8 A man standing on a cliff above the ocean throws a ball high in the air. The height of the ball above the water t seconds after release is given by $h(t) = 100 + 32t - 4t^2$ m.
  a Find $h'(t)$.
  b How high above the water will the ball reach?

9 Find $\frac{dy}{dx}$ for: **a** $y = \frac{1-2x}{\sqrt[3]{x}}$ **b** $y = 2x(1+2x)^4$

10 Find $\frac{d^2y}{dx^2}$ for: **a** $y = \frac{3}{x^2}$ **b** $y = x^2\sin 3x$

11 Let $f(x) = \frac{x-4}{x+2}$.
  a Find the equations of the asymptotes of the function.
  b Find $f'(x)$.
  c Find the equation of the tangent to $y = f(x)$ at the point where $x = 3$.

12 Consider the curve $y = \left(x + \frac{1}{x}\right)^4$.
  a Find the asymptote of the function.
  b Find $\frac{dy}{dx}$.
  c Given that $\frac{d^2y}{dx^2} > 0$ for all $x \neq 0$, discuss the *shape* of the curve.
  d Find the point for $x > 0$ at which the function has its minimum value.

13 For the first 6 seconds of its motion, a particle moving in a straight line has velocity given by $v = t^3 - 9t^2 + 24t$ m s^{-1}, where t is the time in seconds.
  a Find the acceleration function for the particle.
  b Find the greatest velocity of the particle in the first 6 seconds.

14 **a** Find the equation of the tangent to $y = x^3 + 2x + 1$ at the point where $x = -1$.
  b Show that $(x+1)^2(x-2) = x^3 - 3x - 2$.
  c At which point does this tangent meet the curve again?

15 A particle moves in a straight line with displacement function $s(t) = 12t - 3t^3 + 1$ cm where $t \geqslant 0$ is in seconds.
  a Find the velocity and acceleration functions for the particle's movement.
  b When is the particle's:
    i speed decreasing   **ii** velocity decreasing?

16 Let $g(x) = x^2 e^{-(x+2)}$.
  a Find: **i** $g'(x)$ **ii** $g''(x)$.
  b Find intervals where $y = g(x)$ is:
    i increasing   **ii** concave up.

17 Let $y = x(x^2 - 12x + 45)$.
  a Find $\frac{dy}{dx}$ and $\frac{d^2y}{dx^2}$.
  b Find the turning points of the function.
  c Find the point of inflection of the function.
  d Sketch the graph of $y = x(x^2 - 12x + 45)$.
  e For what range of values of a does the equation $x^3 - 12x^2 + 45x - a = 0$ have three distinct real roots?

18 Find the equation of the normal to the curve $y = \frac{8}{x^2}$ at the point where $x = 2$.

19 **a** Find the derivatives with respect to x of:
    i $\frac{x}{e^x}$ **ii** $\frac{e^{2x}+1}{e^{2x}-1}$

b Without simplifying, find $\int (x^2 + e^{2x+1})\, dx$.

20 Consider the polynomial $p(x) = x^3 + ax^2 + b$.

   a Show that $p(x)$ has a stationary point at $x = 0$.

   b Suppose $p(x)$ also has a stationary point at $(-2,\ 6)$. Find:

   i the values of a and b

   ii the nature of both stationary points.

   c Suppose instead that the second stationary point of $p(x)$ is at $(h,\ k)$ with $h \neq 0$. Show that $a = -\frac{3}{2}h$ and $b = k + \frac{1}{2}h^3$.

21 The area of the figure shown is given by $A = xy + (0.6)x^2$. Its perimeter is 48 m.

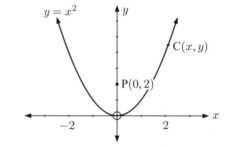

   a Express y in terms of x.

   b Hence find the maximum possible area of the figure.

22 Find $\dfrac{dy}{dx}$ for:

   a $y = x \ln(x+1),\ x > -1$ **b** $y = x \ln x^2,\ x > 0$

   c $y = \dfrac{e^{2x}}{2x+1},\ x \neq -\frac{1}{2}$ **d** $y = \ln\left(\dfrac{x-4}{x^2+4}\right),\ x > 4$

23 **a** Show that if $f(x) = \ln\left(\dfrac{1-2x}{x^2+2}\right)$, then

$$f'(x) = \dfrac{2x^2 - 2x - 4}{(1-2x)(x^2+2)}.$$

   b On what intervals is $f(x)$ decreasing?

24 The diagram below shows an *open* trough for which the cross-section is an isosceles right-angled triangle. The total outside surface area is fixed at 27 square metres.

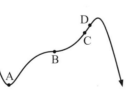

   a By considering the total outside surface area of the trough, show that $x^2 + 2xy = 27$.

   b Find an expression for the volume V of the trough in terms of x only.

   c Hence show that the dimensions of the trough which yield the maximum volume are $x = y = 3$ metres.

25 On the graph of $y = f(x)$ shown, A and B are stationary points, and C is a point of inflection.

Copy and complete the following using $+$, 0, or $-$:

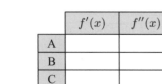

	$f'(x)$	$f''(x)$
A		
B		
C		
D		

26 Consider $f(x) = x + 5 + \dfrac{4}{x}$.

   a State the asymptote of $y = f(x)$.

---

b Find the zeros of $f(x)$.

c Find the stationary points of $y = f(x)$ and their nature.

d Sketch the graph of $y = f(x)$, clearly labelling the information in **a**, **b**, and **c** above.

27 **a** For the graph of $y = 4x^3 - 3x^4$ find:

   i the intercepts on the axes

   ii the coordinates and nature of the stationary points

   iii the coordinates of the non-stationary point of inflection.

   b Sketch the graph of $y = 4x^3 - 3x^4$, showing the information found in **a**.

   c Find values of k for which the equation $4x^3 - 3x^4 = k$ has exactly two distinct positive solutions.

28 Consider $f(x) = 1 - \dfrac{4x}{x^2+4}$.

   a Find the axes intercepts.

   b Find the position and nature of the stationary points of the graph of $f(x)$.

   c Sketch the graph of $y = f(x)$. Clearly show the information found above.

29 Find $f'(x)$ for these functions:

   a $f(x) = 3\sin(x-4)$ **b** $f(x) = 12x - 2\cos(\frac{x}{3})$

   c $f(x) = \dfrac{\sin 2x}{1+2x}$ **d** $f(x) = \sqrt{\sin(2x+1)}$

   e $f(x) = e^{2\sin x}$ **f** $f(x) = \tan(3x-4)$

30 Let $f(x) = \dfrac{x+2}{\sqrt{x-1}}$.

   a State the values of x for which $f(x)$ is defined.

   b Find the equation of the normal to the curve $y = f(x)$ at $x = 10$.

31

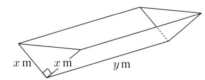

A comet travels in an orbit which can be described by the equation $y = x^2$ as shown in the diagram.

   a Show that the distance of the comet at $C(x,\ y)$ from an observer at the point $P(0,\ 2)$ is given by $s(x) = \sqrt{x^4 - 3x^2 + 4}$.

   b Find the least and the greatest distance between the comet and the observer for $-2 \leqslant x \leqslant 2$.

32 Terry wants to fence off a rectangular garden plot of area 48 m^2. Three sides will be fenced with strong wire mesh costing \$18 per metre, and the remaining side will be fenced with corrugated iron costing \$30 per metre.

   a By letting x be the length in metres of the side fenced with corrugated iron, show that the cost of fencing is

$$C = 48\left(\dfrac{36}{x} + x\right) \text{ dollars}.$$

   b Find the dimensions of the garden plot which will minimise the cost of fencing.

33 An offshore oil rig is at point R, 8 km from a straight shore. The point P is on the shore directly opposite the rig. A refinery is on the shore at S which is 11 km from P.

A pipeline is to be constructed under the sea from R to reach the shore at the point Q. From Q a pipeline is to be taken overland to S. The cost of the pipeline is $5 million per km under the sea and $3 million per km overland.

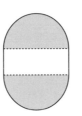

  a If Q is x km from P, show that the cost to construct the pipeline from R to S is
  $$C(x) = 5\sqrt{x^2 + 64} + 33 - 3x \text{ million dollars.}$$

  b What is the minimum cost of the pipeline?

34 An ornamental pond of area A is to be built with straight sides and semi-circular ends as shown. The cost of tiling per unit length is 25% more along the rounded ends than along the straight walls. Show that the total cost of tiling the walls is least when the shaded area is $\frac{2}{3}A$.

35 For the function shown, find:

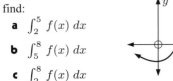

  a $\int_2^5 f(x)\,dx$

  b $\int_5^8 f(x)\,dx$

  c $\int_2^8 f(x)\,dx$

36 Given that
$$\int_0^a f(x)\,dx = 4,$$
find a.

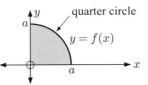

37 Find the integrals:

  a $\int (2x^2 + x - 3)\,dx$
  b $\int_0^1 \sqrt{5x + 4}\,dx$

  c $\int \left(x + \frac{1}{x}\right)^2 dx$
  d $\int_0^1 \frac{1}{2x + 1}\,dx$

  e $\int (e^x - 1)^2\,dx$
  f $\int_0^4 \frac{1}{\sqrt{x + 4}}\,dx$

38 Suppose $g'(x) = 2\cos 3x$ and that $g(\frac{\pi}{2}) = 4$. Find $g(x)$.

39 Suppose $f'(x) = (x^2 + 2)^2$ and that $f(1) = \frac{8}{15}$. Find $f(x)$.

40 Suppose $f'(x) = \sqrt{4x + 5}$ and that $f(0) = -\frac{\sqrt{5}}{6}$.

  a For what values of x is $f'(x)$ defined?

  b Find $f(x)$.

41 If $f(x) = x(3 - 2x)^{\frac{1}{2}}$, find $f'(x)$, and write your answer in the form $\frac{k(1 - x)}{(3 - 2x)^{\frac{1}{2}}}$. Hence, find $\int \frac{x - 1}{(3 - 2x)^{\frac{1}{2}}}\,dx$.

42 Find:

  a $\int \frac{2x^2 - x - 3}{x^2}\,dx$
  b $\int_1^5 \frac{2x^3 + 1}{x^2}\,dx$

43 Use the identity $\sin^2\theta = \frac{1}{2} - \frac{1}{2}\cos 2\theta$ to find $\int \sin^2 3x\,dx$.

44 Find the area of the region lying below the parabola $y = 1 - x^2$ and above the line $y = -3$.

45 If $y = x\sqrt{4 - x}$, find $\frac{dy}{dx}$ and simplify your answer.

Hence, evaluate $\int_0^2 \frac{8 - 3x}{\sqrt{4 - x}}\,dx$.

46 Consider the graph of $f(x) = x^3 - x^2 - 4x + 4$.

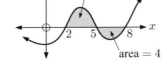

  a Find $\int_{-2}^2 f(x)\,dx$.

  b Does the value obtained in **a** represent the shaded area? Explain your answer.

47 A particle undergoing straight line motion has velocity
$$v = \frac{10}{\sqrt{5t + 4}} \text{ m s}^{-1} \text{ at time } t \text{ seconds, } t \geqslant 0.$$

  a If its position at time $t = 0$ is $s = 0$, find its position at time t.

  b What is the acceleration at time t?

48 Find:

  a $\int_0^\pi \sin x\,dx$
  b $\int_{-\frac{\pi}{4}}^{\frac{\pi}{4}} \cos 2x\,dx$

49 By considering $\frac{d}{dx}(x^2 \ln x)$, find $\int x \ln x\,dx$.

50 If $y = x^2 e^{-x^2}$, show that $\frac{dy}{dx} = 2x(1 - x^2)e^{-x^2}$.

Hence find $\int x(1 - x^2)e^{-x^2}\,dx$.

51 **a** Find the points of intersection of the graphs of $y = x^2 + 2x - 3$ and $y = x - 1$.

  b Hence find the area bounded by the graphs.

52 **a** Find the points of intersection of the graphs of $y = 4 - x^2$ and $y = -2x - 4$.

  b Hence find the area bounded by the graphs.

53 A particle moves on a straight line with acceleration given by $2 - 3t$ m s^{-2}. Initially when $t = 0$ s, the particle has displacement 3 m. When $t = 1$ s, the particle is momentarily at rest.

  a Find the velocity function of the particle.

  b At what other time is the particle momentarily at rest?

  c Find the displacement function of the particle.

54 At time t seconds, the velocity of a particle moving in a straight line is given by $v = 2t - 3t^2$ m s^{-1}.

  a Find the change in *displacement* of the particle from $t = 0$ to $t = 1$.

  b Find the *total distance* moved by the particle in the interval from $t = 0$ to $t = 1$.

55 The line $y = x - 2$ is a tangent to the curve $y = x^3 - 2x$.

  a Show that $(x - 1)^2(x + 2) = x^3 - 3x + 2$.

  b Explain why the point of contact T occurs when $x = 1$. Find the coordinates of T, and the other point of intersection P of the line and the curve.

  c Find the axes intercepts of $y = x^3 - 2x$.

d Use the results of **b** and **c** to sketch $y = x - 2$ and $y = x^3 - 2x$ on the same set of axes.

e Find the area of the region bounded by the curve and the segment [PT] of the given straight line.

56

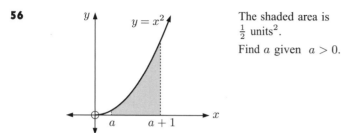

The shaded area is $\frac{1}{2}$ units^2.

Find a given $a > 0$.

57 Let $f(\theta) = \dfrac{2 - \cos\theta}{\sin\theta}, \quad 0 < \theta \leqslant \frac{\pi}{2}$.

  a Show that $f'(\theta) = \dfrac{1 - 2\cos\theta}{\sin^2\theta}$.

  b Find the minimum value of $f(\theta)$.

58 Let $f(\theta) = \cos\theta\sin^2\theta, \quad 0 < \theta \leqslant \frac{\pi}{2}$.

  a Show that $f'(\theta) = \sin\theta(3\cos^2\theta - 1)$.

  b Find the maximum value of $f(\theta)$.

59 $f(x)$ is said to be *odd* if $f(-x) = -f(x)$ for all x.

  a Sketch the graph of one odd function.

  b Evaluate $\int_{-1}^{1} f(x)\,dx$ for any odd function $f(x)$.

  c Show that $f(x) = x^3\cos 2x$ is an odd function.

  d Hence evaluate $\int_{-1}^{1} \left(e^{-2x} + x^3\cos 2x\right) dx$.

60 The position of a point moving on a straight line is given by $x = \sin t + \frac{1}{2}\sin 2t$ cm at any time $t \geqslant 0$ s.

  a Determine:

    i the position and velocity of the point at $t = 0$ s and $t = 2\pi$ s

    ii the times when the point comes to rest for $0 \leqslant t \leqslant 2\pi$, and the acceleration at each of these instants.

  b Hence describe the motion of the point during the time interval $0 \leqslant t \leqslant 2\pi$.

61 **a** Sketch the graph of $f(x) = \sin\left(x + \frac{\pi}{6}\right)$ for $-2\pi \leqslant x \leqslant 2\pi$.

  b Find the area that lies above the line $y = \frac{1}{2}$ and below the graph of $y = f(x)$ for $-2\pi \leqslant x \leqslant 2\pi$.

62 Find $\displaystyle\int_{0}^{\frac{\pi}{2}} (\sin 3x + 5\cos x)\,dx$.

63 **a** If $y = \ln(\tan x), \quad 0 < x < \frac{\pi}{2}$, find the constant k for which $\dfrac{dy}{dx} = \dfrac{k}{\sin 2x}$.

  b Alongside is a graph of $y = \dfrac{1}{\sin 2x}$.

Show that the shaded area enclosed by the curve, the x-axis, and the lines $x = \frac{\pi}{6}$ and $x = \frac{\pi}{3}$, is $\frac{1}{2}\ln 3$ units^2.

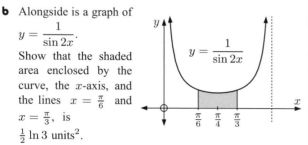

64 Find the volume of revolution when the shaded region is revolved through $360°$ about the x-axis.

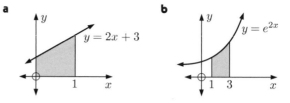

65 A parabola passes through the points $(-\pi, 0)$, $(\pi, 0)$, and $(0, \alpha)$. The area between the parabola and the x-axis is 4 units^2. Calculate the possible values of α.

66 Find the volume of the solid formed when the region enclosed by the graph of $y = x^2 - 2x$ and the x-axis is rotated through 2π about the x-axis.

67 **a** Write down the derivative with respect to x of:

    i $f(x) = \ln x$ **ii** $F(x) = x\ln x - x$.

  b What is the relationship between $f(x)$ and $F(x)$?

  c Sketch the graph of the curve C whose equation is $y = \ln x$.

  d Let O be the origin, and let P be a point on C with x-coordinate t, $1 < t \leqslant e$.

    i Show that the area bounded by [OP], the curve C, and the x-axis, is $t - \frac{1}{2}t\ln t - 1$ units^2. For what value of t will this area be maximised?

    ii Write down the equation of the tangent to the curve C at the point $P(t, \ln t)$. Find the condition on t for this tangent to pass through the origin.

68 **a** On the same set of axes, sketch the two functions $f(x) = \sin x$ and $g(x) = \sin 2x$ for $0 \leqslant x \leqslant \pi$.

  b Show the zeros and turning points of both f and g.

  c Find the area of each of the two regions bounded by the graphs.

69 A piece of wire 40 cm long is bent to form the boundary OPQ of a sector of a circle with centre O and radius x cm.

The angle of the sector is θ radians and the length of the arc is s cm.

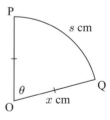

  a Show that $s = 40 - 2x$.

  b Given that $s = \theta x$ and the area of the sector is given by $A = \frac{1}{2}\theta x^2$, show that $A = 20x - x^2$ cm^2.

  c Find the value of x for which the area A is a maximum.

  d Hence find θ when the area is a maximum.

70 A particle undergoing straight line motion has velocity $v(t) = e^{2t} - 3e^t$ metres per second at time t seconds, $t \geqslant 0$.

  a Find the initial velocity.

  b Show that the particle is stationary when $t = \ln 3$ seconds.

  c If the initial position of the particle is 1 metre to the right of the origin, show that its position at $t = \ln 5$ seconds is also 1 metre to the right of the origin.

71 Suppose $f(x) = \dfrac{3x}{e^x}, \quad 0 \leqslant x \leqslant 4$.

  a Find $f''(x)$.

b Show that the graph $y = f(x)$ has:

   i a maximum turning point at $\left(1, \dfrac{3}{e}\right)$

   ii a non-stationary inflection point at $\left(2, \dfrac{6}{e^2}\right)$.

c Sketch the graph $y = f(x)$, showing the information found above.

d Show that $F(x) = -\dfrac{3(x+1)}{e^x}$ is the antiderivative of $f(x)$.

e Show that the area bounded by $y = f(x)$, the x-axis, and the line $x = 4$, is $3 - \dfrac{15}{e^4}$ units^2.

72 Let $f(x) = -(x-2)^2 + 4$. The point $P(a, f(a))$, $0 < a < 4$, lies on the graph of $y = f(x)$ such that the normal L to the graph at P passes through the origin.

a Sketch $y = f(x)$, showing the vertex and axes intercepts.

b Show that the gradient of the normal at point P is $\dfrac{1}{2a-4}$.

c Find the equation of the line L in terms of a.

d Show that $a = 3 \pm \frac{1}{\sqrt{2}}$.

e For the case $a = 3 + \frac{1}{\sqrt{2}}$, explain why the area of the region enclosed by L and $y = f(x)$ is given by
$$\int_0^{3+\frac{1}{\sqrt{2}}} \left(-x^2 + \left(4 - \frac{1}{2+\sqrt{2}}\right)x\right)\, dx.$$

73 The diagram shows a line $y = \sqrt{3}x$ and an arc of the circle $x^2 + y^2 = r^2$, $r > 0$.

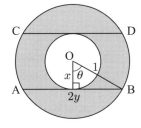

a Show that $\alpha = \frac{\pi}{6}$.
Hence state the arc length l and area A of the sector shown.

b By considering A as the area between the two curves $x^2 + y^2 = r^2$ and $y = \sqrt{3}x$, show that
$$A = \int_0^{\frac{r}{2}} \sqrt{r^2 - x^2}\, dx - \frac{\sqrt{3}r^2}{8}.$$

c Using parts **a** and **b** above, show that
$$\int_0^{\frac{r}{2}} \sqrt{r^2 - x^2}\, dx = \frac{\pi r^2}{12} + \frac{\sqrt{3}r^2}{8}.$$

d Hence show that $\int_0^1 \sqrt{36 - 9x^2}\, dx = \pi + \frac{3\sqrt{3}}{2}$.

74 In the diagram alongside, O is the centre of two concentric circles. The larger circle has radius 1, and the smaller circle has radius x. [AB] and [CD] are parallel chords of the larger circle and tangents to the smaller circle. The length of [AB] is $2y$, and $\widehat{AOB} = 2\theta$.

a Let S be the area of the shaded region. Show that $S = \pi y^2 = \pi \sin^2 \theta$.

b Find the area of the shaded region that is *below* [AB].

c Hence show that the shaded area that is *between* [AB] and [CD] is given by $f(\theta) = \pi \sin^2 \theta + \sin 2\theta - 2\theta$.

d Let $g(\theta) = \pi \sin 2\theta + 2 \cos 2\theta$. Show that $f'(\theta) = g(\theta) - 2$.

e The diagram below shows the graph of $g(\theta)$.

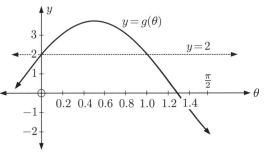

   i Read the solution of $f'(\theta) = 0$ from this graph for $0 < \theta < \frac{\pi}{2}$.

   ii Show that this value of θ maximises $f(\theta)$.

SKILL BUILDER QUESTIONS (CALCULATORS)

1 Let $f(x) = -x^2 + 4x$.

a Find $\displaystyle\lim_{h\to 0} \frac{f(x+h) - f(x)}{h}$ and explain what this value represents.

b Find the equation of the tangent to $y = f(x)$ at the point where $x = k$.

c Suppose this tangent has positive gradient and passes through $(4, 9)$. Find the value of k.

2

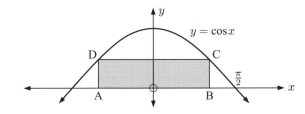

Rectangle ABCD is inscribed under one arch of $y = \cos x$. Suppose the point C has x-coordinate x.

a Write an expression for A, the area of rectangle ABCD, in terms of x.

b Find the coordinates of C such that ABCD has maximum area.

3 The function f is defined by $f(x) = x - \dfrac{1}{\sqrt{x}}$.

a For what values of x is the function defined?

b Find $f'(x)$ and explain why the function is increasing over its whole domain.

c Find any axes intercepts.

d Write the equations of any asymptotes.

e Sketch the graph of $y = f(x)$.

f Find the area enclosed by the function, the x-axis, and the line $x = 4$.

4 The weight of a radioactive substance is given by the function $W(t) = 100 \times e^{-\frac{t}{20}}$ grams where t is the time in days, $t \geqslant 0$.

a Find the initial amount of radioactive substance present.

b Find the time necessary for half of the mass to decay.

c Find $\dfrac{dW}{dt}$ and interpret its sign.

d Discuss W as t increases.

e Sketch the graph of W against t showing the information obtained above.

5 Let $f(x) = xe^{-2x^2}$ on the interval $0 \leqslant x \leqslant 2$.

a Find the stationary point of $f(x)$ on this interval.

b *Hence* determine the maximum and minimum values of $f(x)$ on this interval.

c The area between $y = f(x)$ and the x-axis, from $x = 0$ to $x = 2$, is revolved through $360°$ about the x-axis.

    i Write an integral which gives the volume of the resulting solid.

    ii Evaluate the integral to find the volume.

6 An open cylindrical bin is to be made from PVC plastic and is to have a capacity of 500 litres. Suppose the bin has radius r m.

a Show that the surface area of the bin is given by
$$A(r) = \frac{1}{r} + \pi r^2 \text{ m}^2.$$

b Find the dimensions of the bin which minimise the plastic required.

7 Consider the graph of $y = f(x)$, where $f(x) = 3x^3 + 3x^2 - 3x - 1$.

a Find the y-intercept.

b Find the stationary points and their nature.

c Find the location and nature of the inflection point.

d Sketch the graph of $y = f(x)$, $-2 \leqslant x \leqslant 1$, clearly labelling the information in **a**, **b**, and **c** above.

e Use technology to find the x-intercepts.

8 A psychologist proposes that the ability of a child to memorise during the first two years can be modelled by the continuous function $f(x) = x \ln x + 1$, where x is the age in years, $0 < x \leqslant 2$.

a During which month is the ability at a minimum in the first two years?

b When is it a maximum during this period?

9 The population of insects in a colony at time t may be described by the function $f(t) = \dfrac{N}{1 + 2e^{-\frac{t}{2}}}$ where N is a positive constant.

a Find $f'(t)$ and show that $f'(t) > 0$ for all values of t.

b Find $f''(t)$ and show that the maximum rate of growth of the population occurs when $t = \ln 4$. Find the size of the population at this time.

c Sketch the graph of $f(t)$ for $t \geqslant 0$, showing its asymptotes and axes intercepts.

10 Let $g(x) = \dfrac{\ln x}{x}$ for $0 < x \leqslant 5$.

a Find the point where the graph of $g(x)$ cuts the x-axis.

b Find $g'(x)$ and $g''(x)$, and hence show that the graph of $g(x)$ has one stationary point and one point of inflection. Find the coordinates of these points, and find the gradient of the graph at the point of inflection.

c Describe the behaviour of $g(x)$ for x close to 0.

d Sketch the graph of $g(x)$, showing all the above information.

e By using your graph, or otherwise, explain why
$$\ln x \leqslant \frac{x}{e} \quad \text{for } x > 0.$$

11 Let $f(x) = \ln(x\sqrt{1 - 2x})$.

a State the domain of the function.

b Show that $f'(x) = \dfrac{1 - 3x}{x(1 - 2x)}$.

c At what point(s) on the graph of $y = f(x)$ does the normal have gradient $-\frac{6}{5}$?

12 Consider the function $f(x) = \left(2 - \dfrac{1}{x}\right)e^{-x}$, $x > 0$.

a Find the zero of $f(x)$.

b Discuss the behaviour of $f(x)$ near $x = 0$ and as $x \to \infty$.

c Find the position and nature of the stationary point.

d Sketch the graph of $y = f(x)$, showing all the above information.

e Find the area enclosed by $y = f(x)$ and the line $y = x - 1$.

13 Let $f(x) = 1 + \dfrac{1}{2x - 1}$.

a Find $f'(x)$, and show that the graph of $f(x)$ has no turning points.

b Draw the graphs of $f(x)$ and $g(x) = e^x$ on the same set of axes.
Hence determine the *number* of real roots of the equation $(2x - 1)e^x - 2x = 0$.

c Solve the equation in **b**.

14 A particle moves from rest along a straight line. Its velocity is given by $v = 2\sqrt{t} - t$ m s^{-1}, where $t \geqslant 0$ is the time in seconds.

a Find the acceleration function of the particle.

b Show that the direction of motion changes at $t = 4$ seconds.

c Find the total distance travelled in the first nine seconds of motion.

d If the particle starts at the origin, find its displacement function.

15 **a** Determine algebraically, the area of the region bounded by the curve $y = \dfrac{1}{\sqrt{x}}$, the x-axis, and the lines $x = 1$ and $x = 9$.

b If the area in **a** is rotated $360°$ about the x-axis, what is the volume of the resulting solid?

16 Let f be the function defined by $f(x) = \dfrac{1}{x} - \dfrac{4}{x - 2}$.

a Find the value of x for which $f(x) = 0$.

b Find the coordinates and the nature of the stationary points of f.

c Show that if $f''(x) = 0$ then $(x - 2)^3 = 4x^3$.
Hence find the coordinates of the point on the graph for which $f''(x) = 0$. Give your answer accurate to two decimal places.

d Draw the graph of f, showing all the above information.

e Find algebraically, the area enclosed by the graph, the x-axis, and the lines $x = \frac{1}{2}$ and $x = 1\frac{1}{2}$.

17 a The tangent to $y = x^2 - 3x$ at the point where $x = a$, has gradient 1.

    i Find the value of a.

    ii Find the equation of the normal to the curve at this point.

b Find the exact area of the region enclosed by the graphs of $y = x^2 - 3x$ and the line $y = x$.

18

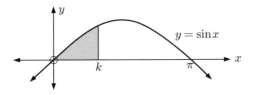

The shaded region has area 0.42 units^2. Find k.

19 a Sketch the curve $y = 3x^2 + 1$ for $0 \leqslant x \leqslant 3$.

b Find the area between the curve and the x-axis for $0 \leqslant x \leqslant 3$.

c Find a constant k such that the area between the curve and the x-axis for $0 \leqslant x \leqslant k$ is 10 units^2.

20 O is a point on a straight line. A particle moving on the straight line has a velocity of 27 cm s^{-1} as it starts from O. Its acceleration t seconds later is $(6t - 30)$ cm s^{-2}.

a Find the velocity function for the particle.

b Find the displacement function for the particle.

c Find the *total* distance that the particle has travelled when it comes momentarily to rest for the *second* time.

21 a Find the indefinite integral $\int (x^3 + 2)^2 \, dx$.

b Find exactly the solution of $x^3 + 2 = 0$.

c Hence find the volume of the solid obtained when the curve $y = x^3 + 2$, from its x-intercept to the y-axis, is revolved through 2π about the x-axis.

22 A particle moves along the x-axis with velocity $v(t) = e^{-2t}$ metres per second.

a Find the value of t for which the acceleration of the particle is $-\frac{1}{4}$ metres per second per second. Give your answer to 3 significant figures.

b At time $t = 0$, the particle is 2 metres to the right of the origin. Find:

    i the displacement function for the particle

    ii the position of the particle at time $t = 1$ second.

23 The velocity of a boat travelling in a straight line is given by $v(t) = 30 - 20e^{-0.2t}$ m s^{-1}, $t \geqslant 0$.

a What is the boat's initial velocity?

b What is the velocity after 2 seconds? Give your answer correct to two decimal places.

c How long does it take for the boat's velocity to reach 20 m s^{-1}? Give your answer correct to two decimal places.

d What happens to $v(t)$ as $t \to \infty$?

e Calculate $v'(t)$ and show that the acceleration is always positive.

f Graph $v(t)$ against t, showing the information from **a** to **d**.

g Find the formula for the boat's displacement $s(t)$ if its initial position is 10 m in the positive direction.

24 a Find a given that $\int_a^{2a} \sqrt{x} \, dx = 2$.

b Find the equation of the normal to the curve $y = \sqrt{x}$ at the point where $x = a$.

25 Two industrial plants, Cinder and Puff-Out, are situated 2 km apart on a straight road. Each plant emits pollutants into the atmosphere.

At a point x km from Cinder, on the road towards Puff-Out, the total concentration of pollutants is given by

$$C(x) = \frac{8}{x^2} + \frac{1}{(2-x)^2} \text{ units}, \quad 0 < x < 2.$$

a Find $C'(x)$.

b Show that $C'(x) = 0$ when $\left(\dfrac{x}{2-x}\right)^3 = 8$.

c Find the value of x for which the total concentration of pollutants is minimised.

26 The number of bacteria found in a sample of human tissue t hours after infection occurred, is modelled by the function $N = (8 - t)e^{t-6}$ millions, $0 \leqslant t \leqslant 8$.

The graph of this function is shown alongside, and takes into account the effect of the body's immune system, which eventually kills the bacteria.

a Show that $\dfrac{dN}{dt} = (7 - t)e^{t-6}$.

b Find the coordinates of the:

    i turning point   **ii** point of inflection

    iii t-intercept.

c Use these coordinates to state:

    i the time when all the bacteria are dead

    ii the maximum number of bacteria reached in the sample

    iii the time at which the rate of increase of the bacteria is a maximum.

d Copy the graph and indicate clearly which points on the graph represent your answers to **c**.

27

a The function f has the form $f(x) = a \cos bx$, $-\pi \leqslant x \leqslant \pi$.

State the values of a and b.

b **i** Find the equation of the *normal* to $y = f(x)$ at the point where $x = c$.

    ii Find the values of c such that the normal passes through the origin.

c Sketch $y = f(x)$ and the normals found in **b ii** on the same set of axes.

28 Find the volume of revolution when the region between $y = \sin x$, the x-axis, and the lines $x = \frac{\pi}{4}$ and $x = \frac{5\pi}{6}$, is rotated through 2π about the x-axis.

29 Consider $f(x) = x + \sin x$, $x \geqslant 0$.

    a Sketch $y = f(x)$ for $0 \leqslant x \leqslant 2\pi$.

    b Find the area enclosed by the curve, the x-axis, and $x = \frac{\pi}{2}$.

    c Suppose $f(x) = x + \sin x$ and $g(x) = x^2$ meet at $x = a$, $a > 0$. Find a correct to 3 decimal places.

    d Find the area enclosed by $y = x + \sin x$ and $y = x^2$.

30 Consider $f(t) = \sin^2 t - \sin t$ where $0 \leqslant t \leqslant 2$.

    a Sketch the graph of $y = f(t)$ over the given domain.

    b Find the area enclosed by the curve, the t-axis, and $t = 2$.

31 The shaded area is 24 units^2. Find k.

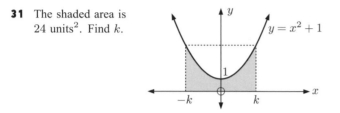

32 At time t seconds a particle is moving in a straight line with acceleration $4 \cos t$ m s^{-2}. At $t = 0$ its velocity is 2 m s^{-1}.

    a Find the velocity at $t = 4$ seconds.

    b Find the total distance travelled in the interval $t = 0$ to $t = 5$ seconds. Give your answer to two decimal places.

33 Let $f(x) = 2\cos x - \sin x + 2x\sin x$, $0 \leqslant x \leqslant 2$.

    a Show that $f'(x) = (2x - 1)\cos x$.

    b Find the minimum value of $f(x)$ for $0 \leqslant x \leqslant 2$.

34 Find a given that $0 < a < 2\pi$ and $\int_a^{a+2} \sin x\, dx = 0.3$.

TRIAL EXAMINATION 1

Paper 1 - No calculators   (1 hour 30 minutes)

Section A

1 The first three terms of an infinite geometric sequence are 24, x, and 6, where $x > 0$.

    a Write down x.   **b** Find the common ratio r.

    c Find u_5.   **d** Find the sum to infinity of the sequence.

    (7 marks)

2 Let $h(x) = e^{-x}\cos x$.

    a Find $h'(x)$.   **b** Find $h'(\frac{\pi}{2})$.

    c Find the equation of the tangent to the curve at the point where $x = \frac{\pi}{2}$.   (8 marks)

3 Adrian and Bevan are competing in an archery competition. Let A be the event of Adrian hitting the target, and B be the event of Bevan hitting the target. The tree diagram below shows the probabilities for the events A and B.

    a Write down the values of x, y, and z.

    b Find the probability that Bevan hits the target.

    c Find $P(A' \mid B)$.

    (7 marks)

4   **a** If $\sin 2\theta = \tan \theta$, show that either $\sin \theta = 0$ or $\cos \theta = \pm\frac{1}{\sqrt{2}}$.

    b Hence, find θ such that $\sin 2\theta = \tan \theta$ for $-\pi \leqslant \theta \leqslant \pi$.   (6 marks)

5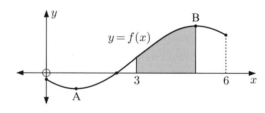

$f(x)$ is a quadratic function with vertex $(3, 7)$ and y-intercept 2.5. $f(x)$ can be written in the form $a(x - h)^2 + k$.

    a Find h and k.   **b** Find a.

    c Find the coordinates of A.   (7 marks)

6 Let $f'(x) = 2x - \dfrac{3}{\sqrt{x}}$ and $f(4) = 3$. Find $f(x)$.

    (4 marks)

7 Random variable X has the following probability distribution:

x	1	2	3	4
$P(X = x)$	m	0.15	$2m$	n

    a Find the value of $3m + n$.

    b Write $E(X)$ in terms of m only.

    c Find m if $E(X) = 2.7$.   (6 marks)

Section B

8 Points $A(2, -1, 3)$ and $B(1, 2, -4)$ lie on line L_1.

A second line L_2 is parallel to $\begin{pmatrix} 4 \\ 2m \\ m \end{pmatrix}$ and is perpendicular to L_1.

    a Find $\overrightarrow{BA}$.

    b Find a vector equation for L_1 in the form $\mathbf{r} = \mathbf{p} + t\mathbf{q}$.

    c Find m.

    d If L_2 passes through the point $C(2, 3, k)$, find a vector equation for L_2.

    e If L_1 and L_2 intersect, find the value of k.   (16 marks)

9

The graph shows the function $f(x) = -4\cos\left(\frac{\pi}{4}(x - 1)\right) + 2$, $0 \leqslant x \leqslant 6$. A and B are turning points of the function.

    a Find the y-intercept.   **b** Find the x-intercept.

    c Show that $f'(x) = \pi \sin\left(\frac{\pi}{4}(x - 1)\right)$.

    d By considering $f'(x) = 0$, find the x-coordinates of A and B.

    e Find the area of the shaded region in terms of π.

    (15 marks)

10 $f(x) = 2x - 1$ and $g(x) = 3x^2 - 1$.

    a Find $(g \circ f)(x)$.

    b $g \circ f$ is translated through $\begin{pmatrix} -1 \\ 4 \end{pmatrix}$ to produce the function $h(x)$. Find $h(x)$.

    c Write $h(x)$ in the form $a(x - h)^2 + k$.

    d State the coordinates of the vertex of:

        i $g(x)$ **ii** $h(x)$.

    e Find c given that $y = 2x + c$ is a tangent to $h(x)$.   (14 marks)

Paper 2 - Calculators (1 hour 30 minutes)

Section A

1 In the diagram, $\widehat{AOB}$ measures θ, and arc length AXB is 14.3 m.

   a Find θ, in radians.

   b Find the shaded area.

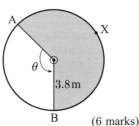

(6 marks)

2 Consider the binomial expansion of $(2x^2 - 1)^{12}$.

   a Find an expression for the $(r+1)$th term.

   b Find the coefficient of the x^{10} term. (6 marks)

3 The number of children in the families of students in a class is shown in the following table:

Number of children	1	2	3	4	5	8
Frequency	4	11	7	8	2	1

   a Find the mean and median of the data.

   b What is the standard deviation?

   c What is the interquartile range? (6 marks)

4 $u_n = 19 - 2n$ is the nth term of a sequence.

   a Explain why the sequence is arithmetic.

   b Write down the common difference.

   c Is -55 a term of the sequence?

   d Find the sum of the first n terms of the sequence. (8 marks)

5 The angle between $\mathbf{a} = \begin{pmatrix} 1 \\ -1 \\ 2 \end{pmatrix}$ and $\mathbf{b} = \begin{pmatrix} 3 \\ 1 \\ t \end{pmatrix}$ is $60°$.

Find t, correct to 3 decimal places, given $t > 0$. (5 marks)

6 The graph of $f(x) = 2x^3 + bx^2 + cx$ is shown alongside, but is not drawn to scale.

   a Use points A and C to find the values of b and c.

   b Find the x-coordinate of B, that is, k, given that $k > 1$.

   (6 marks)

7 Two variables x and y have the experimental values shown:

x	2	3	4	5	6	8
y	4.5	6.7	8.9	10.9	13.2	17.2

   a Explain why x and y have a positive correlation.

   b Find the equation of the linear regression line.

   c Describe the correlation between x and y.

   d Use the equation of the linear regression line to predict the value of y when $x = 7$.

   e Is it reliable to use the regression line to find y when $x = 12$? (8 marks)

Section B

8 The graph of $f(x) = x^2 \ln(9 - x^2)$, $-3 < x < 3$ is shown. It cuts the x-axis at a and b and has a maximum turning point at $x = c$.

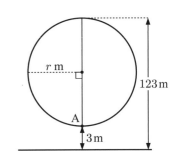

   a Find the values of a and b correct to 3 decimal places.

   b Find the value of c.

   c Find the equations of the asymptotes of the graph. Explain your answers.

   d Find the area of the shaded region.

   e If the region shaded is rotated $360°$ about the x-axis, what is the volume of the solid generated? (13 marks)

9 The height of a Ferris wheel seat above ground level is given by $H(t) = a \sin(b(t - c)) + d$, where a, b, c, and d are constants.

The Ferris wheel starts moving clockwise when the seat is at A, 3 m above ground level.

In 20 minutes the seat is returned to A.

   a Find the radius of the wheel.

   b Find the values of a and d.

   c Explain why $b = \frac{\pi}{10}$.

   d Determine the value of c.

   e How high is the seat above the ground after 8 minutes of motion?

   f After how long is the seat 100 m above ground level? (18 marks)

10

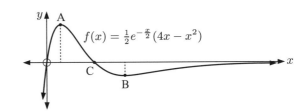

Consider the graph of the function $f(x) = \frac{1}{2}e^{-\frac{x}{2}}(4x - x^2)$.

   a From the graph, state the equation of any asymptote.

   b State the x-intercept(s) of the graph of f.

   c Without finding $f'(x)$, find the coordinates of the turning points at A and B, correct to 3 significant figures.

   d If $y = x^2 e^{-\frac{x}{2}}$, show that $\frac{dy}{dx} = \frac{1}{2}e^{-\frac{x}{2}}(4x - x^2)$.

   e Hence, find $\int e^{-\frac{x}{2}}(4x - x^2)\,dx$. (14 marks)

Paper 1 - No calculators   (1 hour 30 minutes)

Section A

1 A bag contains 3 blue, 2 green, and 1 yellow ball. Two balls are drawn at random from the bag without replacement.

   a Copy and complete the tree diagram, displaying the probabilities on the branches.

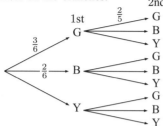

   b Find the probability that the second ball drawn is green.

   c Find the probability that the first ball was blue given that the second was green.   (7 marks)

2 Suppose $f(x) = 3^x$ and $g(x) = x + 1$.

   a Find $(f \circ g)(x)$.   **b** Find $(g^{-1} \circ f)(x)$.

   c Find x such that $(g^{-1} \circ f)(x) = 8$.   (7 marks)

3 **a** Use the substitution $u = x^2$ to find $\int x e^{-x^2} \, dx$.

   b Find $m > 0$ such that $\int_0^m x e^{-x^2} \, dx = \dfrac{e-1}{2e}$.

              (6 marks)

4 **a** Solve for $\frac{\pi}{2} < x < \pi$: $4\cos^2 x = 3$.

   b Hence find: **i** $\tan x$ **ii** $\sin 2x$.   (6 marks)

5 $12, a, 3, \ldots$ is a geometric sequence in which $a > 0$.

   a Find:

       i a **ii** the common ratio r **iii** the 12th term, u_{12}.

   b Find the sum to infinity of the sequence.   (7 marks)

6 $A(1, 2, -1)$ lies on a line L which is parallel to $\mathbf{v} = \begin{pmatrix} 2 \\ 0 \\ -2 \end{pmatrix}$. Point B is $(3, -2, 1)$.

   a Write a vector equation for line L.

   b Show that $\overrightarrow{AB}$ is perpendicular to L.

   c Hence find the shortest distance from B to line L.

              (7 marks)

7 In triangle ABC, $\hat{BAC} = 60°$, $AB = 4$ cm, $BC = 5$ cm, and $AC = x$ cm.

   a Show that x satisfies the equation $x^2 - 4x - 9 = 0$.

   b Find x in simplest radical form.

              (5 marks)

Section B

8 Consider $f(x) = 1 - \dfrac{2}{1+x^2}$.

   a Find the x and y-intercepts of the graph $y = f(x)$.

   b Discuss $f(x)$ as $x \to \pm\infty$.

   c Find the position and nature of the stationary point of f.

   d Show that $y = f(x)$ has points of inflection at $x = \pm\frac{1}{\sqrt{3}}$.

   e Use **a** to **d** above to sketch the graph of $y = f(x)$.

              (13 marks)

9 Suppose $\mathbf{v} = \mathbf{i} + 2\mathbf{j} - \mathbf{k}$ and $\mathbf{w} = 3\mathbf{i} - \mathbf{j} - 2\mathbf{k}$.

   a Find $\mathbf{w} - 2\mathbf{v}$ and a vector of length 2 in the direction of $\mathbf{w} - 2\mathbf{v}$.

   b Line L_1 passes through $(4, -11, 5)$ and has direction vector $\mathbf{v}$.

       Line L_2 passes through $(10, k, -2)$ and has direction vector $\mathbf{w}$.

       i Find vector equations for lines L_1 and L_2.

       ii L_1 and L_2 meet at a point where $x = 13$. Find the coordinates of this point, and the value of k.

       iii Find the cosine of the acute angle between L_1 and L_2.   (15 marks)

10 **a** **i** Write $\cos\left(\frac{\pi}{4}\right)$ in terms of $\sin\left(\frac{\pi}{8}\right)$.

       ii Hence show that $\sin(\frac{\pi}{8}) = \sqrt{\dfrac{\sqrt{2}-1}{2\sqrt{2}}}$.

   b A circle of radius r encloses a regular octagon as shown.

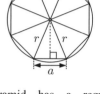

       i Show that a and r are related by $a = 2r\sin\left(\frac{\pi}{8}\right)$.

       ii Show that the area of the octagon is $A = 2\sqrt{2}r^2$.

   c 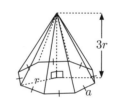 A pyramid has a regular octagonal base and the dimensions shown. The volume of the pyramid is given by $V = \frac{1}{3} \times$ area of base $\times$ height.

       i Write a formula for V in terms of r.

       ii Find $\dfrac{dV}{dr}$.

       iii Determine the relationship between $\dfrac{dV}{dr}$ and the base area of the pyramid.   (17 marks)

Paper 2 - Calculators   (1 hour 30 minutes)

Section A

1 Find:

   a a

   b the area of $\triangle$ABC.

              (5 marks)

A   35.6 cm   18°   C a cm   43°   B

2 Find the coefficient of the x^6 term in the expansion of $(2x + 5)^{10}$.   (4 marks)

3 Consider $f(x) = \dfrac{1}{x^2 - 4}$, $-3 \leqslant x \leqslant 3$.

   a Write down the equation of each vertical asymptote.

   b Sketch a graph of $y = f(x)$.

   c State the range of $f(x)$ on the given domain.

   d Write down the equation of the function $g(x)$ which is a reflection of $f(x)$ in the x-axis followed by a horizontal stretch with scale factor 2.   (9 marks)

4 The diagram shows a rectangular prism in which M is the midpoint of [BC].
Suppose A is $(0, 0, 0)$ and B is $(5, 0, 0)$.

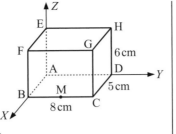

  a State the coordinates of E, M, and G.

  b Find: **i** $\overrightarrow{ME}$ **ii** $\overrightarrow{MG}$

  c Use a vector method to find the measure of $\widehat{EMG}$.

                      (8 marks)

5 **a** Show that $\frac{9}{2} + \frac{3}{2}\cos 2\theta = 3\cos^2\theta + 3$.

  b *Hence* solve the equation $\frac{3}{2}\cos 2\theta - 10\cos\theta + \frac{9}{2} = 0$ for $0 \leqslant \theta \leqslant \pi$.   (7 marks)

6 The times taken by 200 students to complete a 400 metre run were recorded. The cumulative frequency graph for the times is given below.

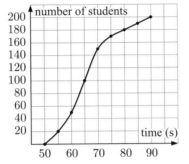

  a How many students took less than 60 seconds to complete the 400 metre run?

  b Find the median and interquartile range for the times taken by the 200 students.

  c Find the probability that a randomly selected student took more than 75 seconds to complete the run.   (7 marks)

7 A train is stopped at a station. As it moves away, its acceleration is given by $a(t) = \dfrac{2}{\sqrt{t+1}}$ m s^{-2}, $0 \leqslant t \leqslant 10$ s.

  a Find the velocity function $v(t)$.

  b How far does the train travel in the first 10 seconds?

                      (5 marks)

Section B

8 **a** If $f(x) = e^{3x}\sin 2x$, show that $f'(x) = 0$ when $\tan 2x = -\frac{2}{3}$.

  b The graph of $f(x) = e^{3x}\sin 2x$, $x \geqslant 0$ is shown below.

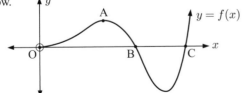

    The graph intersects the x-axis at the points B and C. The point A is a local maximum.

    i Find the x-coordinates of B and C.

    ii Find the x-coordinate of A.

  c **i** If $g(x) = \frac{1}{13}(3e^{3x}\sin 2x - 2e^{3x}\cos 2x)$, show that $g'(x) = e^{3x}\sin 2x$.

    ii Explain the relationship between $f(x)$ and $g(x)$.

  d Find the area between the graph of $f(x) = e^{3x}\sin 2x$ and the x-axis from O to B.   (17 marks)

9 **a** The normal distribution graph below describes the weights of mice.

    i Complete the X-scale, and add a Z-scale to the graph.

    ii The shaded region A corresponds to 12% of the population. What is the greatest weight of any mouse in the lightest 12% of the population?

    iii The shaded region B corresponds to 8% of the population. Find the lowest weight of a mouse in the heaviest 8% of the population.

  b A random variable X is normally distributed so that $X \sim \mathrm{N}(\mu, \sigma^2)$. 20% of the values are below 6, and the mean $\mu = 9$. Find σ.

  c Whenever Pelé takes a penalty shot for goal he has an 80% chance of being successful. Suppose he takes twenty penalty shots at goal. Find:

    i the expected number of successes

    ii the probability that he scores with all but two shots

    iii the probability that he scores with at least 18 shots.   (16 marks)

10 The following table shows the number of people using a public swimming pool over a 10 day period.

Max. Temp. T ($^\circ$C)	23.8	27.6	32.9	29.7	31.2
Attendance, N	18	65	118	93	125

Max. Temp. T ($^\circ$C)	36.3	33.4	27.8	24.2	23.3
Attendance, N	168	142	87	36	28

  a Determine the correlation coefficient r for this data.

  b Describe the relationship between the maximum temperature and attendance at the swimming pool.

  c Find the equation of the linear regression line for attendance as a function of temperature.

  d Use the equation of linear regression to estimate the number of people attending the pool on a day when the maximum temperature is: **i** 25°C   **ii** 40°C.

  e Which of the estimates in **d** is more reliable? Explain your answer.

  f Comment on the use of the model for a maximum temperature of 20°C.   (12 marks)

TRIAL EXAMINATION 3

Paper 1 - No calculators   (1 hour 30 minutes)

Section A

1 In a survey, 80 students were asked "Do you prefer computer games or playing sport?". The results are partially displayed in the following table.

	Girls	Boys	Total
Computer Games	10	12	
Sport			
Total		36	

a Copy and complete the table of values.

b Find the probability that a student selected at random:
  i prefers to play sport
  ii prefers to play sport, given that the student is a girl.
  (6 marks)

2 Consider the function $f(x) = x^2 e^{-x}$.

a $f'(x) = xe^{-x}(k - x)$. Find k.

b Find the equation of the tangent to $y = f(x)$ at the point where $x = -1$. (7 marks)

3

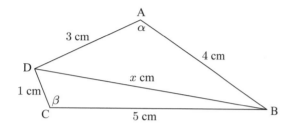

a Use the cosine rule in triangle ABD to show that
$$\cos \alpha = \frac{25 - x^2}{24}.$$

b If $\alpha = \beta$, find x in simplest form. (8 marks)

4 Copy the graph of $y = f(x)$ alongside.

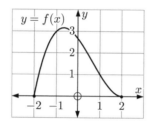

a On the same diagram, draw the graph of:
  i $y = f(x - 3)$
  ii $y = f(-x)$.

b Suppose the area between the graph and the x-axis is A. Write, in terms of A, the area between:
  i $y = f(-x)$ and the x-axis
  ii $y = 2f(x)$ and the x-axis. (8 marks)

5 The velocity of a moving object at time t seconds is given by $v = 30 - 6t^2$ m s^{-1}.

a Find its acceleration at the moment when $t = 5$ seconds.

b The initial displacement of the object is 15 metres. Find the displacement function $s(t)$. (6 marks)

6 The diagram shows the graph of $y = a\cos(bx) + c$ for $0 \leqslant x \leqslant \pi$.

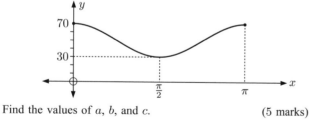

Find the values of a, b, and c. (5 marks)

7 X is a random variable with probability distribution table:

X	1	2	3	4	5
$P(X = x)$	0.1	0.2	p	0.15	0.3

a Find p. **b** Find $P(X$ is odd$)$.

c Find $E(X)$. (5 marks)

Section B

8 The graph of $f(x) = 2x^3 + ax^2 + 4x + 4$ is given below:

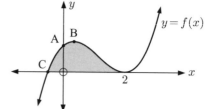

The graph cuts the x-axis at C and touches it at $x = 2$.

a Find the value of a.

b Find $f(-\frac{1}{2})$. Hence find the coordinates of point C.

c Find the x-coordinate of the local maximum B.

d Find intervals where $f(x)$ is increasing.

e Find the interval on which $f(x)$ is concave down.

f Write down an expression for the area of the shaded region. Do not attempt to evaluate it. (16 marks)

9 Consider $f(x) = \sqrt{\ln x}$.

a State the domain and range of f.

b Find the gradient of the tangent to the curve at the point where $x = e$.

c Differentiate $x \ln x$ and hence find $\int \ln x \, dx$.

d Find the volume of the solid generated when the region bounded by the curve $y = \sqrt{\ln x}$, the x-axis, and the line $x = e$, is rotated through $360°$ about the x-axis. (15 marks)

10 Two spotlights are located at A$(1, 0, 0)$ and B$(3, 4, 0)$. Each unit of the grid represents 10 m.
The light from A shines in the direction $\mathbf{i} + 3\mathbf{j} + 5\mathbf{k}$.
The light from B is represented by
$$\mathbf{r_B} = \begin{pmatrix} 3 \\ 4 \\ 0 \end{pmatrix} + t \begin{pmatrix} 1 \\ 1 \\ -5 \end{pmatrix}, \quad t \geqslant 0.$$

a Write a vector equation for the beam of light from A.

b Find the coordinates of the point where the beams meet.

c A bird flies through the intersection of the beams, and two seconds later is at $(4, 7, 9)$. Find the speed of the bird.

d Find the cosine of the angle between the beams. (14 marks)

Paper 2 - Calculators   (1 hour 30 minutes)

Section A

1 The heights of trees in a plantation are normally distributed with mean 3.18 metres and standard deviation 19.5 cm.

a Find the probability that a randomly selected tree will be:
  i taller than 3 metres
  ii between 2.8 and 3.3 metres tall.

b What height must a tree be to be in the tallest 20%? (5 marks)

2 The function $f(x) = \dfrac{ax + b}{x + d}$ is obtained by a vertical stretch of $y = \dfrac{1}{x}$ with scale factor 3, followed by a translation through $\begin{pmatrix} 5 \\ -2 \end{pmatrix}$.

a Find the values of a, b, and d.

b State the asymptotes of the function.

c Find the axes intercepts.

d Sketch $y = f(x)$, showing the details you have found.

(8 marks)

3 $20\,000$ is invested for 8 years. The rate of interest is fixed at 6.7% per annum, compounding annually.

a Write an expression for the value of the investment after n years.

b How much will the investment be worth at maturity?

c Find the total interest earned in these 8 years. (6 marks)

4 O is the centre of a circle that has a radius of 16 cm. Chord [AB] subtends an angle of $110°$ at the centre of the circle.

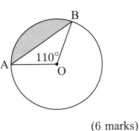

a Find the length of [AB].

b Find the shaded area. (6 marks)

5 Suppose $\cos\alpha = -\frac{2}{3}$ where $0 \leqslant \alpha \leqslant \pi$.
Find the exact value of:

a $\sin\alpha$ **b** $\tan 2\alpha$ (6 marks)

6 Consider the function $f(x) = a\ln x + b$ where $a > 0$. The normal to the curve at $x = 1$ and the tangent to the curve at $x = e^2$ both pass through the origin. Find a and b.

(7 marks)

7 A simple pendulum moves back and forth. Its period T is the number of seconds needed for it to return to its starting position.
The following table gives values of T for pendulums of different length l.

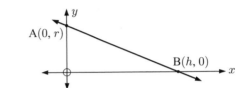

Length l (m)	0.30	0.40	0.50	0.60	0.80
Period T (s)	1.10	1.27	1.42	1.56	1.80
$\sqrt{l}$					

a Complete the table by calculating the value of $\sqrt{l}$ to 3 significant figures for each data point.

b Find the correlation coefficient r for the relationship between T and $\sqrt{l}$.

c The variables T and l are connected by the formula $T = m\sqrt{l}$ where m is a constant.
Calculate m using the mean values of $\sqrt{l}$ and T.

d Find the period of a pendulum of length 0.7 m. (7 marks)

Section B

8 **a** Consider $y(t) = 8 - 4\cos(\frac{\pi}{4}t)$, $0 \leqslant t \leqslant 8$.

i State the period of $y(t)$.

ii Find the minimum value of $y(t)$ and when it occurs.

iii Find the maximum value of $y(t)$ and when it occurs.

iv Sketch the graph of $y(t)$.

b A simplified model for the depth of water at the entrance to a harbour is $y(t) = p - q\cos\left(\frac{\pi}{r}t\right)$ metres, where p, q, and r are constants and t is the time measured in hours.

i The mean water depth is 6 metres, the difference between high and low tides is 4 metres, and the time between high and low tides is 6 hours.
Find p, q, and r.

ii A ship needs a depth of 7 metres of water to safely enter the harbour. During what fraction of the day can it make its entry? (14 marks)

9 **a** **i** Sketch the graph of $f(x) = \sqrt{2x+1}$ on $0 \leqslant x \leqslant 4$.

ii Find $\int f(x)\,dx$ using the substitution $u(x) = 2x + 1$.

iii Find the area bounded by $y = \sqrt{2x+1}$, the x-axis, and the lines $x = 0$ and $x = 4$.

iv Suppose $f(x) = \sqrt{2x+1}$ is revolved about the x-axis on $k \leqslant x \leqslant 2k$ to create a solid of revolution. Find k if the volume of the solid is 30 units^3.

b

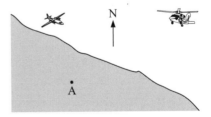

i Find the equation of the line (AB).

ii Illustrate what happens when the line segment [AB] is revolved about the x-axis.

iii Find a formula for the volume of the solid in **ii**. (15 marks)

10 In this question, distances are in kilometres and time is in hours. An airport is situated at the point $A(2, -1, 0)$.

The vectors $\begin{pmatrix} 1 \\ 0 \\ 0 \end{pmatrix}$ and $\begin{pmatrix} 0 \\ 1 \\ 0 \end{pmatrix}$ represent displacements of 1 km to the east and to the north of the airport respectively.

$\begin{pmatrix} 0 \\ 0 \\ 1 \end{pmatrix}$ represents a vertical displacement of 1 km above the airport.

A small airplane is flying along a straight stretch of coast on beach patrol. It is moving at a constant height with a speed of 200 km h^{-1} in the direction $\begin{pmatrix} 4 \\ -3 \\ 0 \end{pmatrix}$.

At 10:00 am, the airplane is at point B with coordinates $(-10, 50, 1)$.

Meanwhile, an emergency medical helicopter is returning to the airport after completing a mission to a distant island. The position vector of the helicopter t hours after 10:00 am is given by
$$\mathbf{h} = \begin{pmatrix} x \\ y \\ z \end{pmatrix} = \begin{pmatrix} 74 \\ 29 \\ 0.5 \end{pmatrix} + t\begin{pmatrix} -120 \\ -50 \\ 0.5 \end{pmatrix}.$$

a How far is the airplane from the airport at 10:00 am?

b Show that the position vector of the airplane t hours after 10:00 am is
$$\mathbf{r} = \begin{pmatrix} x \\ y \\ z \end{pmatrix} = \begin{pmatrix} -10 \\ 50 \\ 1 \end{pmatrix} + t\begin{pmatrix} 160 \\ -120 \\ 0 \end{pmatrix}.$$

c Find the coordinates of the airplane at 10:30 am.

d At what height is the helicopter flying when $t = 0$?

e Find the speed of the helicopter.

f At the moment that the helicopter pilot notices that he is directly beneath the airplane, he begins his descent (in a straight line) to the airport.

   i Find the time when the helicopter is directly beneath the airplane.

   ii Find the coordinates of the helicopter at this time.

   iii If the helicopter maintains an average speed equal to its present speed, find the time at which it will arrive at the airport.

                            (16 marks)

SOLUTIONS TO TOPIC 1 (ALGEBRA)

NO CALCULATORS

1 **a** The common difference $d = -6$.

  b
$$u_n = u_1 + (n-1)d$$
$$\therefore \; u_{20} = u_1 + 19d$$
$$= 51 + 19 \times -6$$
$$= 51 - 114$$
$$= -63$$

  c
$$S_n = \frac{n}{2}(u_1 + u_n)$$
$$\therefore \; S_{20} = \frac{20}{2}(51 - 63)$$
$$= 10 \times -12$$
$$= -120$$

2 **a** The common ratio $r = 2$.

  b
$$u_n = u_1 r^{n-1}$$
$$\therefore \; u_{20} = u_1 r^{19}$$
$$= \frac{1}{8} \times 2^{19}$$
$$= 2^{-3} \times 2^{19}$$
$$= 2^{16}$$

  c
$$S_n = \frac{u_1(r^n - 1)}{r - 1}$$
$$\therefore \; S_{10} = \frac{\frac{1}{8}(2^{10} - 1)}{2 - 1}$$
$$= \frac{1023}{8}$$

3 **a** $u_1 = 27$ and $u_4 = 8$
$$\therefore \; u_1 r^3 = 8$$
$$\therefore \; r^3 = \frac{8}{27}$$
$$\therefore \; r = \frac{2}{3}$$

  b
$$u_n = u_1 r^{n-1}$$
$$\therefore \; u_6 = 27 \times \left(\frac{2}{3}\right)^5$$
$$= \frac{3^3 \times 2^5}{3^5}$$
$$= \frac{32}{9}$$

  c $S = \sum_{k=1}^{\infty} u_n = \sum_{k=1}^{\infty} 27 \times \left(\frac{2}{3}\right)^{k-1}$

  d Since $|r| < 1$, the series converges.
$$S = \frac{u_1}{1 - r}$$
$$= \frac{27}{1 - \frac{2}{3}}$$
$$= 81$$

4 **a**
$$u_7 = 1 \quad \text{and} \quad u_{15} = -23$$
$$\therefore \; u_1 + 6d = 1 \quad \text{and} \quad u_1 + 14d = -23$$
$$\therefore \; (u_1 + 14d) - (u_1 + 6d) = -23 - 1$$
$$\therefore \; 8d = -24$$
$$\therefore \; d = -3$$
$$\text{and} \; u_1 = 1 - 6d$$
$$= 19$$

  b
$$u_n = u_1 + (n-1)d$$
$$\therefore \; u_{27} = u_1 + 26d$$
$$= 19 + 26(-3)$$
$$= -59$$

  c
$$S_n = \frac{n}{2}(u_1 + u_n)$$
$$\therefore \; S_{27} = \frac{27}{2}(u_1 + u_{27})$$
$$= \frac{27}{2}(19 - 59)$$
$$= -540$$

5 **a** $u_1 = 18$ and $d = -3$.

If the series has n terms, then
$$S_n = -210$$
$$\therefore \; \frac{n}{2}(2u_1 + (n-1)d) = -210$$
$$\therefore \; \frac{n}{2}(2 \times 18 + (n-1) \times (-3)) = -210$$
$$\therefore \; \frac{n}{2}(36 - 3n + 3) = -210$$
$$\therefore \; \frac{n}{2}(39 - 3n) = -210$$

  b From **a**, $\frac{3}{2}n(13 - n) = -210$
$$\therefore \; n(13 - n) = -140$$
$$\therefore \; n^2 - 13n - 140 = 0$$
$$\therefore \; (n - 20)(n + 7) = 0$$
$$\therefore \; n = 20 \quad \{\text{since} \; n > 0\}$$

6 **a**
$$\frac{x}{x^{-\frac{1}{2}}} = x^{1 - (-\frac{1}{2})} = x^{\frac{3}{2}}$$
$$\frac{x^{\frac{5}{2}}}{x} = x^{\frac{5}{2} - 1} = x^{\frac{3}{2}}$$
$$\therefore \; \text{the common ratio} \; r = x^{\frac{3}{2}}.$$

  b
$$u_n = u_1 r^{n-1}$$
$$\therefore \; u_{10} = u_1 r^9$$
$$= x^{-\frac{1}{2}} \left(x^{\frac{3}{2}}\right)^9$$
$$= x^{-\frac{1}{2} + \frac{27}{2}}$$
$$= x^{13}$$

  c The corresponding infinite geometric series will converge provided $|r| < 1$, $r \neq 0$.

Now $r = x^{\frac{3}{2}}$, so r is only defined for $x > 0$, and $|r| = 1$ when $x = 1$.

$\therefore$ the series will converge for $0 < x < 1$.

7 **a** There are 7 terms in the series.

  b $u_n = 3 \times 2^{n-1}$

$\therefore$ the first term $u_1 = 3 \times 2^0 = 3$
and the common ratio $r = 2$.

  c
$$S_n = \frac{u_1(r^n - 1)}{r - 1}$$
$$\therefore \; S_7 = \frac{3(2^7 - 1)}{2 - 1}$$
$$= 3 \times 127$$
$$= 381$$

8 **a** **i** $\sum_{k=1}^{\infty} 2\left(\frac{2}{3}\right)^k$ has general term
$$u_n = 2\left(\frac{2}{3}\right)^n$$
$$= \frac{4}{3}\left(\frac{2}{3}\right)^{n-1}$$
$$\therefore \; \text{the first term} \; u_1 = \frac{4}{3}$$
$$\text{and the common ratio} \; r = \frac{2}{3}.$$

  ii Since $|r| < 1$, the series converges.
$$S = \frac{u_1}{1 - r}$$
$$= \frac{\frac{4}{3}}{1 - \frac{2}{3}}$$
$$= 4$$

b **i** $\sum\limits_{k=1}^{n} (k-4)$ has general term $u_n = n - 4$

$\therefore$ the first term $u_1 = -3$
and the common difference $d = 1$.

ii $S_n = \dfrac{n}{2}(2u_1 + (n-1)d)$

$= \dfrac{n}{2}(2 \times -3 + (n-1)1)$

$= \dfrac{n}{2}(-6 + n - 1)$

$= \dfrac{n(n-7)}{2}$

c $\dfrac{n(n-7)}{2} = 4$

$\therefore n^2 - 7n - 8 = 0$

$\therefore (n-8)(n+1) = 0$

$\therefore n = 8 \quad \{\text{since } n > 0\}$

9 **a** The series has first term $u_1 = 1$
and common ratio $r = 0.6$.
Since $|r| < 1$, the series converges.

$S = \dfrac{u_1}{1-r}$

$= \dfrac{1}{1 - 0.6}$

$= \dfrac{5}{2}$

b

The total distance travelled
$= 1 + 1 \times 0.6 \times 2$
$\quad + 1 \times (0.6)^2 \times 2$
$\quad + 1 \times (0.6)^3 \times 2 + ...$
$= 1 + 0.6 \times 2(1 + 0.6 + (0.6)^2$
$\qquad\qquad\qquad\qquad + ...)$
$= 1 + \dfrac{3}{\cancel{5}} \times \dfrac{\cancel{5}}{\cancel{2}_1}$ $\quad \{\text{using } \mathbf{a}\}$
$= 4$ metres

10 **a** $9^x - 6(3^x) + 8 = 0$

$\therefore (3^x)^2 - 6(3^x) + 8 = 0$

$\therefore (3^x - 4)(3^x - 2) = 0$

$\therefore 3^x = 4 \quad \text{or} \quad 3^x = 2$

$\therefore x = \log_3 4 \quad \text{or} \quad \log_3 2$

b $8^{2x-3} = 16^{2-x}$

$\therefore (2^3)^{2x-3} = (2^4)^{2-x}$

$\therefore 2^{6x-9} = 2^{8-4x}$

$\therefore 6x - 9 = 8 - 4x$

$\therefore 10x = 17$

$\therefore x = \dfrac{17}{10}$

11 **a** $\log_5(2x-1) = -1$

$\therefore 5^{-1} = 2x - 1$

$\therefore \dfrac{1}{5} = 2x - 1$

$\therefore \dfrac{6}{5} = 2x$

$\therefore x = \dfrac{3}{5}$

b $25^x - 5^{x+1} + 6 = 0$

$\therefore (5^x)^2 - 5(5^x) + 6 = 0$

$\therefore (5^x - 2)(5^x - 3) = 0$

$\therefore 5^x = 2 \quad \text{or} \quad 5^x = 3$

$\therefore x = \log_5 2 \quad \text{or} \quad \log_5 3$

12 **a** $4^x + 4 = 17(2^{x-1})$

$\therefore (2^x)^2 - 17(2^{x-1}) + 4 = 0$

$\therefore 2(2^x)^2 - 17(2^x) + 8 = 0$

$\therefore (2(2^x) - 1)(2^x - 8) = 0$

$\therefore 2^x = \tfrac{1}{2} \text{ or } 8$

$\therefore 2^x = 2^{-1} \text{ or } 2^3$

$\therefore x = -1 \text{ or } 3$

b $\log_3 x + \log_3(x-2) = 1$

$\therefore \log_3(x(x-2)) = 1$

$\therefore x(x-2) = 3^1$

$\therefore x^2 - 2x = 3$

$\therefore x^2 - 2x - 3 = 0$

$\therefore (x-3)(x+1) = 0$

$\therefore x = 3 \quad \{\text{since } x > 2\}$

13 **a** $\tfrac{1}{4}\log 81 + \log 12 - \log 4$

$= \log\left(81^{\frac{1}{4}}\right) + \log\left(\tfrac{12}{4}\right)$

$= \log 3 + \log 3$

$= 2\log 3$

b $\log_a(5a) = \log_a 5 + \log_a a$

$= x + 1$

c $\log_a N = 2\log_a d - \log_a c$

$\therefore \log_a N = \log_a d^2 - \log_a c$

$\therefore \log_a N = \log_a\left(\dfrac{d^2}{c}\right)$

$\therefore N = \dfrac{d^2}{c}$

14 **a** $\log_{10}(P^2 Q \sqrt{R})$

$= \log P^2 + \log Q + \log R^{\frac{1}{2}}$

$= 2\log P + \log Q + \tfrac{1}{2}\log R$

$= 2A + B + \tfrac{1}{2}C$

b $\log_b a = \dfrac{\log_c a}{\log_c b}$

$\therefore \log_5 9 = \dfrac{\log_3 9}{\log_3 5}$

$\therefore \dfrac{8}{\log_5 9} = \dfrac{8}{\frac{\log_3 9}{\log_3 5}}$

$= \dfrac{8\log_3 5}{\log_3 9}$

$= \dfrac{8\log_3 5}{2}$

$= 4\log_3 5$

15 **a** There are 6 terms.

b
```
            1
          1   1
        1   2   1
      1   3   3   1
    1   4   6   4   1
  1   5  10  10   5   1   ← 5th row, for (a+b)⁵
```

Using the 5th row of Pascal's triangle,

$(a+b)^5 = a^5 + 5a^4 b + 10a^3 b^2 + 10a^2 b^3 + 5ab^4 + b^5$

$\therefore \left(x + \tfrac{1}{x}\right)^5 = x^5 + 5x^4\left(\tfrac{1}{x}\right) + 10x^3\left(\tfrac{1}{x}\right)^2 + 10x^2\left(\tfrac{1}{x}\right)^3$

$\qquad\qquad\qquad\qquad\qquad + 5x\left(\tfrac{1}{x}\right)^4 + \left(\tfrac{1}{x}\right)^5$

$= x^5 + 5x^3 + 10x + \dfrac{10}{x} + \dfrac{5}{x^3} + \dfrac{1}{x^5}$

16 a The general term is $\binom{6}{r} a^{6-r}b^r$.

b For the term a^4b^2, we have $r = 2$.

∴ the coefficient is $\binom{6}{2}$.

Now $\binom{6}{2} = \dfrac{6!}{2!4!} = \binom{6}{4} = 15$

∴ the coefficient is 15.

17 a There are 5 terms.

b The general term in the expansion of

$\left(3x - \dfrac{1}{x^2}\right)^4$ is $\binom{4}{r}(3x)^{4-r}\left(-\dfrac{1}{x^2}\right)^r$

$= \binom{4}{r} 3^{4-r}x^{4-r}(-1)^r x^{-2r}$

$= \binom{4}{r}(-1)^r 3^{4-r}x^{4-3r}$

The term in x occurs when $4 - 3r = 1$

∴ $r = 1$

∴ the term in x is $\binom{4}{1}(-1)^1 3^3 x$

$= -4 \times 27x$

$= -108x$

CALCULATORS

1 a $u_n = u_1 + (n-1)d$

$= 100 + (n-1)30$

b We want to find n where $100 + 30(n-1) > 1200$

∴ $30(n-1) > 1100$

∴ $n - 1 > 36.667$

∴ $n > 37.667$

∴ the first term is u_{38} which is 1210.

c The sum of the first k terms is

$S_k = \dfrac{k}{2}(2u_1 + (k-1)d) = 19\,140$

∴ $\dfrac{k}{2}(2 \times 100 + (k-1)30) = 19\,140$

∴ $15k^2 + 85k - 19\,140 = 0$

∴ $k = 33$ or $-\dfrac{116}{3}$ {technology}

∴ $k = 33$ {$k \in \mathbb{Z}^+$}

2 a $u_5 = u_1 r^4 = 18$ and $u_8 = u_1 r^7 = 486$

∴ $\dfrac{u_1 r^7}{u_1 r^4} = \dfrac{486}{18}$

∴ $r^3 = 27$ and so $r = 3$

Since $u_1 r^4 = 18$, $u_1 \times 81 = 18$

∴ $u_1 = \dfrac{2}{9}$

b $u_n = u_1 r^{n-1}$

∴ $u_{12} = u_1 r^{11}$

$= \dfrac{2}{9} \times 3^{11}$

$= 39\,366$

c $S_n = \dfrac{u_1(r^n - 1)}{r - 1}$

∴ $S_{10} = \dfrac{u_1(r^{10} - 1)}{r - 1}$

$= \dfrac{\frac{2}{9}(3^{10} - 1)}{3 - 1}$

≈ 6560

3 a Her annual amount is geometric with $u_1 = 800$,

$r = 107\% = 1.07$, and $n = 9$.

$u_9 = u_1 \times r^8 = 800 \times (1.07)^8$

≈ 1374.55 euro

b We need to solve $800 \times (1.07)^n = 4000$

∴ $(1.07)^n = 5$

∴ $\log(1.07)^n = \log 5$

∴ $n\log(1.07) = \log 5$

∴ $n = \dfrac{\log 5}{\log(1.07)}$

∴ $n \approx 23.79$

So, it will take 24 years.

4 a $u_1 = 10$

$u_2 = 10 \times 110\% = 10 \times 1.1$

$u_3 = u_2 \times 1.1 = 10 \times (1.1)^2$

$\vdots$

$u_7 = 10 \times (1.1)^6 = 17.715\,61$

So, Ying ran 17.7 km on day 7.

b Total distance ran $= u_1 + u_2 + u_3 + ... + u_7$

which is geometric with $u_1 = 10$, $r = 1.1$, $n = 7$

∴ $S_7 = \dfrac{10\left((1.1)^7 - 1\right)}{1.1 - 1}$

$= \dfrac{10\left((1.1)^7 - 1\right)}{0.1}$

≈ 94.8717

So, Ying ran a total of 94.9 km.

5 a $10 + 14 + 18 + ... + 138$ is arithmetic with

$u_1 = 10$, $d = 4$

Now $u_1 + (n-1)d = 138$

∴ $10 + 4(n-1) = 138$

∴ $4(n-1) = 128$

∴ $n - 1 = 32$

∴ $n = 33$

So, the sum is

$\dfrac{n}{2}(u_1 + u_{33})$

$= \dfrac{33}{2}(10 + 138)$

$= \dfrac{33}{2}(148)$

$= 2442$

b $6 - 12 + 24 - 48 + 96 - .... + 1536$ is geometric with

$u_1 = 6$, $r = -2$

Now $u_1 r^{n-1} = 1536$

∴ $6 \times (-2)^{n-1} = 1536$

∴ $(-2)^{n-1} = 256$

∴ $(-2)^{n-1} = (-2)^8$

∴ $n - 1 = 8$

∴ $n = 9$

So, the sum is

$\dfrac{u_1(1 - r^n)}{1 - r}$

$= \dfrac{6(1 - (-2)^9)}{1 - (-2)}$

$= \dfrac{6}{3}\left(1 - (-2)^9\right)$

$= 2 \times 513$

$= 1026$

6 a $\dfrac{u_1}{1 - r} = 1.5$

and $u_1 = 1$

∴ $1 - r = \dfrac{1}{1.5}$

∴ $1 - r = \dfrac{2}{3}$

∴ $r = \dfrac{1}{3}$

b $S_n = \dfrac{u_1(1 - r^n)}{1 - r}$

∴ $S_7 = \dfrac{u_1(1 - r^7)}{1 - r}$

$= \dfrac{1\left(1 - (\frac{1}{3})^7\right)}{1 - \frac{1}{3}}$

$= \dfrac{3}{2}\left(1 - \dfrac{1}{2187}\right)$

$= \dfrac{1093}{729}$

7 a $\dfrac{u_{n+1}}{u_n} = \dfrac{12\left(\frac{2}{3}\right)^n}{12\left(\frac{2}{3}\right)^{n-1}}$

$= \dfrac{2}{3}$ for all $n \in \mathbb{Z}^+$

Thus, the sequence is geometric with $r = \dfrac{2}{3}$.

b $u_5 = 12 \left(\frac{2}{3}\right)^4$

$\quad = 12 \left(\frac{16}{81}\right)$

$\quad = \frac{64}{27}$

c **i** $\displaystyle\sum_{n=1}^{\infty} u_n = \frac{u_1}{1-r}$ **ii** $\displaystyle\sum_{n=1}^{20} u_n = S_{20}$

$\quad = \dfrac{12\left(\frac{2}{3}\right)^0}{1-\frac{2}{3}}$ $S_n = \dfrac{u_1(1-r^n)}{1-r}$

$\quad = \dfrac{12}{\frac{1}{3}}$ $\therefore\; S_{20} = \dfrac{12\left(1-\left(\frac{2}{3}\right)^{20}\right)}{1-\frac{2}{3}}$

$\quad = 36$ ≈ 35.9892

8   Time period $= 33$ months $= 11$ quarters

Interest rate $= 8\%$ p.a. $= 2\%$ per quarter

$\therefore\; r = 1.02$

$\therefore\;$ the amount after 11 quarters is

$\qquad u_{12} = u_1 \times r^{11}$

$\qquad\quad = 3500 \times 1.02^{11}$

$\qquad\quad \approx 4351.8101$

So, the maturing value is £4351.81.

9   **a**   The series is geometric with first term $u_1 = 12$, and common ratio $r = (x-2)$.

The series converges provided $|r| < 1$

$\qquad \therefore\; 1 < x < 3$

b   Since $1 < \sqrt{5} < 3$, the series converges.

$S = \dfrac{u_1}{1-r}$

$\quad = \dfrac{12}{1-(\sqrt{5}-2)}$

$\quad \approx 15.7$

10   **a**   Pierre added $\$10 \times 8 = \$80$

Francesca added

$\qquad \$(0.50 + 1 + 1.50 + 2 + 2.5 + \ldots + 4) = \$18$

b $u_{52} = u_1 + 51d$

$\qquad = 0.50 + 51 \times 0.50$

$\qquad = 26$ So, she added $26.

c   Pierre had $\$10 \times 52 + \$100 = \$620$

Francesca had $(0.50 + 1 + 1.50 + \ldots + 26) + 100$

$\qquad = \frac{52}{2}(0.5 + 26) + 100$

$\qquad = 26 \times 26.5 + 100$

$\qquad = \$789$

11   **a**   Hayley: $u_5 = u_1 + 4d = 60 + 4 \times 20$

$\qquad\qquad\qquad\qquad\quad = 140$ km in week 5

Patrick: $u_5 = u_1 r^4 = 60 \times (1.2)^4$

$\qquad\qquad\qquad\qquad \approx 124$ km in week 5

b   For Hayley $u_8 = 60 + 7 \times 20 = 200$

$\qquad$ and $\quad u_9 = 60 + 8 \times 20 = 220$

For Patrick $u_7 = 60 \times (1.2)^6 \approx 179$

$\qquad$ and $\quad u_8 = 60 \times (1.2)^7 \approx 215$

So, Patrick was the first to cycle 210 km in a week.

c   Hayley: $S_{12} = \frac{12}{2}\left(2 \times 60 + 11 \times 20\right)$

$\qquad\qquad\qquad = 6 \times (120 + 220)$

$\qquad\qquad\qquad = 2040$ km

Patrick: $S_{12} = \dfrac{60\left(1.2^{12}-1\right)}{1.2-1} \approx 2370$ km

12   **a**   2002: $u_1 = 2000$

2003: $u_2 = 2000 + 2000 \times 1.0825$

2004: $u_3 = 2000 + [2000 + 2000 \times 1.0825] \times 1.0825$

$\qquad\quad = 2000 + 2000r + 2000r^2$ where $r = 1.0825$

$\qquad\quad = 2000(1 + r + r^2)$

2009: Total amount $= 2000(1 + r + r^2 + r^3 + \ldots + r^7)$

$\qquad\qquad\qquad\quad = 2000\left(\dfrac{r^8 - 1}{r - 1}\right)$

$\qquad\qquad\qquad\quad = \dfrac{2000\left(1.0825^8 - 1\right)}{0.0825}$

$\qquad\qquad\qquad\quad \approx 21\,466.32$ rupees

b   Each 2000 rupee investment earns

$2000 \times 0.09 = 180$ rupees simple interest per year.

$\therefore\;$ total amount in 2009

$= 8 \times 2000 + 1 \times 180 + 2 \times 180 + \ldots + 7 \times 180$

8 deposits   interest from 2008 investment   interest from 2007 investment   interest from 2002 investment

$= 16\,000 + \frac{7}{2}(180 + 1260)$

$= 21\,040$ rupees

So, Kapil will be 426.32 rupees better off with the compound interest option.

13   **a**   The interest rate $= 7.2\%$ per annum

$\qquad\qquad\qquad\qquad = 0.6\%$ per month

$\therefore\;$ the value of the investment is multiplied by $r = 1.006$ each month.

b   The value of the investment after n months is

$\qquad u_{n+1} = u_1 \times r^n$

$\qquad\qquad = 500 \times 1.006^n$

The value reaches €1000 when

$\qquad 500 \times 1.006^n = 1000$

$\qquad \therefore\; 1.006^n = 2$

$\qquad\qquad \therefore\; n = \log_{1.006} 2$

$\qquad\qquad\qquad \approx 115.9$ months

$\therefore\;$ it will take 116 months for Paige's investment to be worth €1000.

14   **a** $5 \times 2^x = 160$ **b** $(1.25)^x = 10$

$\therefore\; 2^x = 32$ $\therefore\; \log(1.25)^x = \log 10$

$\therefore\; 2^x = 2^5$ $\therefore\; x\log(1.25) = 1$

$\therefore\; x = 5$ $\therefore\; x = \dfrac{1}{\log(1.25)}$

$\qquad\qquad\qquad\qquad\qquad\quad \therefore\; x \approx 10.3$

c $7e^x = 100$

$\therefore\; e^x = \frac{100}{7}$

$\therefore\; x = \ln\left(\frac{100}{7}\right)$

$\therefore\; x \approx 2.66$

15   **a** $200e^{\frac{t}{4}} = 1500$

$\therefore\; e^{\frac{t}{4}} = 7.5$

$\therefore\; \frac{t}{4} = \ln(7.5)$

$\therefore\; t = 4 \times \ln(7.5)$

$\therefore\; t \approx 8.06$

b
$$A = 125 \times e^{-kt}$$
$$\therefore \quad 200 = 125e^{-3k}$$
$$\therefore \quad e^{-3k} = \tfrac{200}{125}$$
$$\therefore \quad e^{3k} = \tfrac{125}{200} \quad \{\text{reciprocals}\}$$
$$\therefore \quad 3k = \ln\left(\tfrac{125}{200}\right)$$
$$\therefore \quad k = \ln\left(\tfrac{125}{200}\right) \div 3 \approx -0.157$$

16 a
$$K(t) = 3200 \times (0.85)^t$$
$$\therefore \quad K(0) = 3200 \times 1 = 3200$$

So, at the beginning of 2000 there were 3200 kangaroos.

b $K(5) = 3200 \times (0.85)^5$ **c** $N(5) = 2400 + 250 \times 5$
       ≈ 1420 kangaroos $= 2400 + 1250$
                                         $= 3650$ koalas

d When $K(t) < 1000$
$$3200 \times (0.85)^t < 1000$$
$$\therefore \quad (0.85)^t < \tfrac{1000}{3200}$$
$$\therefore \quad t \log(0.85) < \log(0.3125)$$
$$\therefore \quad t > \frac{\log(0.3125)}{\log(0.85)} \quad \{\log(0.85) < 0\}$$
$$\therefore \quad t > 7.1570$$

The kangaroo population fell below 1000 about 7 years 2 months after the start of 2000, which is the end of February 2007.

e We need to solve $2400 + 250t > 3200 \times (0.85)^t$.
Using technology, $t > 1.102$.
So, the number of koalas exceeded the number of kangaroos about 1 year 1 month after the start of 2000, which is at the start of February 2001.

17 a There are 10 terms.

b $\left(x + \dfrac{3}{x^2}\right)^9$ has general term
$$T_{r+1} = \binom{9}{r} x^{9-r} \left(\tfrac{3}{x^2}\right)^r, \quad r = 0, 1, 2, ..., 9$$
$$= \binom{9}{r} x^{9-r} 3^r x^{-2r}$$
$$= \binom{9}{r} x^{9-3r} 3^r$$

The constant term occurs when $9 - 3r = 0$
$$\therefore \quad r = 3$$
$$\text{Now} \quad T_4 = \binom{9}{3} 3^3 = 2268$$
$$\therefore \quad \text{the constant term is } 2268.$$

18 a $(x + 2y^3)^7$ has general term
$$T_{r+1} = \binom{7}{r} x^{7-r} (2y^3)^r, \quad r = 0, 1, 2, ..., 7$$
$$= \binom{7}{r} x^{7-r} 2^r y^{3r}$$

b When $r = 3$, $T_4 = \binom{7}{3} 2^3 x^4 y^9$
$$\therefore \quad \text{the coefficient of } x^4 y^9 \text{ is } \binom{7}{3} 2^3 = 280.$$

19 a $\left(2x - \dfrac{1}{x^2}\right)^{12}$ has general term
$$T_{r+1} = \binom{12}{r} (2x)^{12-r} \left(\tfrac{-1}{x^2}\right)^r$$
$$= \binom{12}{r} 2^{12-r} x^{12-r} (-1)^r x^{-2r}$$
$$= \binom{12}{r} 2^{12-r} (-1)^r x^{12-3r}$$

b If $12 - 3r = 3$
then $r = 3$
$$\therefore \quad T_4 = \binom{12}{3} 2^{12-3} (-1)^3 x^3 = -112\,640 x^3$$
The coefficient of x^3 is $-112\,640$.

c If $12 - 3r = 0$
then $r = 4$
$$\therefore \quad T_5 = \binom{12}{4} 2^{12-4} (-1)^4 x^0 = 126\,720$$
The constant term is $126\,720$.

20 a $\left(kx + \dfrac{1}{\sqrt{x}}\right)^9$ has general term
$$T_{r+1} = \binom{9}{r} (kx)^{9-r} \left(\tfrac{1}{\sqrt{x}}\right)^r$$
$$= \binom{9}{r} k^{9-r} x^{9-r} \frac{1}{x^{\frac{r}{2}}}$$
$$= \binom{9}{r} k^{9-r} x^{9-\frac{3r}{2}}$$

b For the constant term, $9 - \dfrac{3r}{2} = 0$
$$\therefore \quad \frac{3r}{2} = 9$$
$$\therefore \quad r = 6$$
$$T_7 = \binom{9}{6} k^3 x^0$$
$$\therefore \quad 84k^3 = -10\tfrac{1}{2} \quad \{\text{constant term} = -10\tfrac{1}{2}\}$$
$$\therefore \quad k^3 = -\tfrac{1}{8}$$
$$\therefore \quad k = -\tfrac{1}{2}$$

21 $(x+2)(1-x)^{10}$
$$= (x+2)\left(\begin{matrix} 1^{10} + \binom{10}{1} 1^9(-x) + ... + \binom{10}{4} 1^6(-x)^4 \\ + \binom{10}{5} 1^5(-x)^5 + ... \end{matrix} \right)$$
$$= (x+2)\left(1 - 10x + ... + \binom{10}{4} x^4 - \binom{10}{5} x^5 + ... \right)$$

So, the terms containing x^5 are $\binom{10}{4} x^5$ and $-2\binom{10}{5} x^5$.
$$\therefore \quad \text{the coefficient of } x^5 \text{ is } \binom{10}{4} - 2\binom{10}{5} = -294.$$

SOLUTIONS TO TOPIC 2 (FUNCTIONS AND EQUATIONS)

NO CALCULATORS

1 a Yes, as any vertical line cuts the graph no more than once.

b Domain $= \{x \mid x \in \mathbb{R}\}$,   Range $= \{y \mid y \geqslant 0\}$

c

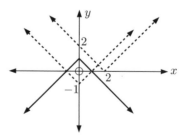

2 a The function passes the vertical line test. No vertical line cuts the graph more than once.

b Domain $= \{x \mid x \neq 0\}$,   Range $= \{y \mid y \neq 0\}$

c This is a self-inverse function.

3 a $(f \circ g)(x)$
$= f(g(x))$
$= f(2x + 7)$
$= 5(2x + 7) - 2$
$= 10x + 33$

b $(g \circ f)(x)$
$= g(f(x))$
$= g(5x - 2)$
$= 2(5x - 2) + 7$
$= 10x + 3$

c g is $y = 2x + 7$
$\therefore\ g^{-1}$ is $x = 2y + 7$
$\therefore\ x - 7 = 2y$
$\therefore\ y = \dfrac{x - 7}{2}$
$\therefore\ g^{-1}(x) = \dfrac{x - 7}{2}$

4 a f is $y = x - 2$
$\therefore\ f^{-1}$ is $x = y - 2$
$\therefore\ x + 2 = y$
$\therefore\ f^{-1}(x) = x + 2$

b $(g \circ f)(x) = g(f(x))$
$= g(x - 2)$
$= 3 - (x - 2) - 2(x - 2)^2$
$= 3 - x + 2 - 2(x^2 - 4x + 4)$
$= -2x^2 + 7x - 3$

c Using **b**, $(g \circ f)(-1)$
$= -2(-1)^2 + 7(-1) - 3$
$= -12$

5 a $(f \circ g)(x) = f(g(x))$
$= f(2x + 1)$
$= (2x + 1)^2 - 3$
$= 4x^2 + 4x + 1 - 3$
$= 4x^2 + 4x - 2$

b Since $y = h(x)$ is a translation of $(f \circ g)(x)$ 1 unit left and 2 units up,
$h(x) = (f \circ g)(x + 1) + 2$
$= 4(x + 1)^2 + 4(x + 1) - 2 + 2$
$= 4(x^2 + 2x + 1) + 4x + 4$
$= 4x^2 + 8x + 4 + 4x + 4$
$= 4x^2 + 12x + 8$

c $h(x) = 4x^2 + 12x + 8$ has axis of symmetry
$x = -\dfrac{b}{2a} = -\dfrac{12}{2 \times 4} = -\dfrac{12}{8} = -\dfrac{3}{2}$
Now $h(-\tfrac{3}{2}) = 4(-\tfrac{3}{2})^2 + 12(-\tfrac{3}{2}) + 8$
$= 9 - 18 + 8$
$= -1$
$\therefore$ the vertex is $(-\tfrac{3}{2},\ -1)$.

d When $x = 0$, $y = 8$.
$\therefore$ the y-intercept is 8.
When $y = 0$, $4x^2 + 12x + 8 = 0$
$\therefore\ x^2 + 3x + 2 = 0$
$\therefore\ (x + 2)(x + 1) = 0$
$\therefore\ x = -2$ or $x = -1$
$\therefore$ the x-intercepts are -2 and -1.

e

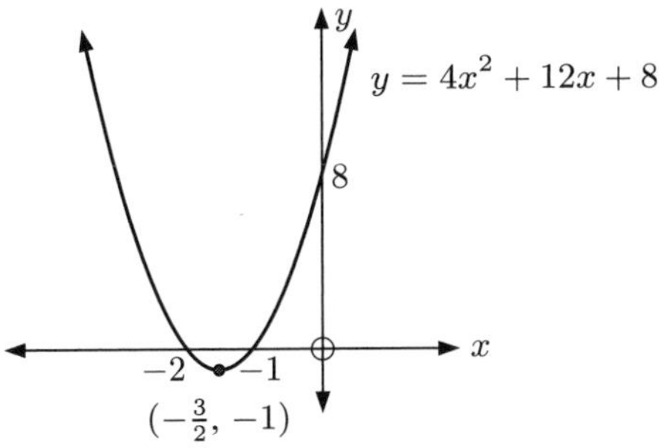

6 a $f(g(x)) = f(4 - x)$
$= 3(4 - x) + 1$
$= -3x + 13$

b $(g \circ f)(x) = g(3x + 1)$
$= 4 - (3x + 1)$
$= 3 - 3x$
$\therefore\ (g \circ f)(-4) = 3 - 3(-4)$
$= 15$

c f is $y = 3x + 1$,
so f^{-1} is $x = 3y + 1$
$\therefore\ y = \dfrac{x - 1}{3}$
$\therefore\ f^{-1}(x) = \dfrac{x - 1}{3}$
$\therefore\ f^{-1}(\tfrac{1}{2}) = \dfrac{\tfrac{1}{2} - 1}{3} = -\tfrac{1}{6}$

7 a $f(1) = 2^{1-1} = 1$
$f(2) = 2^{2-1} = 2$

b

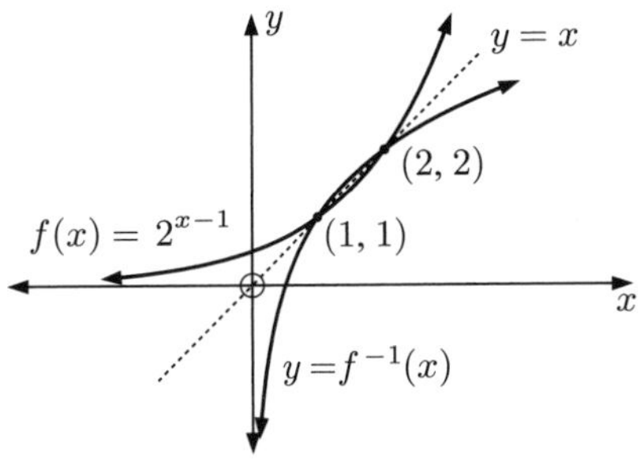

c $f(x)$ is $y = 2^{x-1}$
so $f^{-1}(x)$ is $x = 2^{y-1}$
$\therefore\ \log x = (y - 1)\log 2$
$\therefore\ \dfrac{\log x}{\log 2} = y - 1$
$\therefore\ y = \log_2 x + 1$
$\therefore\ f^{-1}(x) = \log_2 x + 1$

d Domain $= \{x \mid x > 0\}$, Range $= \{y \mid y \in \mathbb{R}\}$

8 a Domain $= \{x \mid x \geqslant -1,\ x \neq 1\}$

b $(f \circ g)(x) = f(g(x))$
$= f(x^2)$
$= \dfrac{1}{x^2 - 1} + \sqrt{x^2 + 1}$

c $(f \circ g)(x)$ is undefined when $x^2 - 1 = 0$, which is when $x = \pm 1$.
$\therefore$ the domain of $(f \circ g)$ is $\{x \mid x \neq \pm 1\}$.
This is not the same as the domain of either f or g.

d The function which is a vertical stretch of f with scale factor 2, is

$$y = 2f(x)$$
$$= 2\left(\frac{1}{x-1} + \sqrt{x+1}\right)$$
$$= \frac{2}{x-1} + 2\sqrt{x+1}$$

9 a

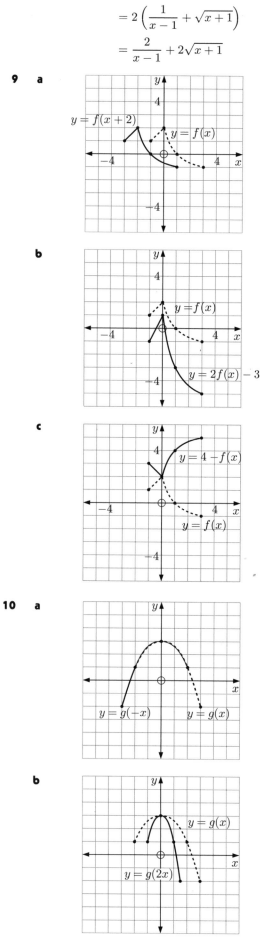

b

c

10 a

b

11 a Domain $= \{x \mid x > 2\}$,   Range $= \{y \mid y \in \mathbb{R}\}$

b $y = g(x)$ has the vertical asymptote $x = 2$.

c $y = g(2x)$ is a horizontal stretch of g with scale factor $\frac{1}{2}$.

$$\therefore \quad h(x) = g(2x)$$
$$= 4 - \ln(2x - 2)$$
or $h : x \mapsto 4 - \ln(2x - 2)$

d $y = h(x)$ is defined when $2x - 2 > 0$
$$\therefore \quad x > 1$$
$\therefore \quad y = h(x)$ has the vertical asymptote $x = 1$.

12 a $y = -4x(x + 3)$

   i The graph cuts the x-axis when $y = 0$
$$\therefore \quad -4x(x + 3) = 0$$
$$\therefore \quad x = 0 \text{ or } -3$$
$\therefore$ the x-intercepts are 0 and -3.

   ii The axis of symmetry is $x = -1\frac{1}{2}$

   iii $f(-\frac{3}{2}) = -4(-\frac{3}{2})(\frac{3}{2}) = 9$
$\therefore$ the vertex is at $(-1\frac{1}{2}, 9)$.

   iv When $x = 0$, $y = 0$, so the y-intercept is 0.

   v

b $y = \frac{1}{2}(x + 6)(x - 4)$

   i When $y = 0$, $x = -6$ or 4
$\therefore$ the x-intercepts are -6 and 4.

   ii The axis of symmetry is $x = -1$.

   iii $f(-1) = \frac{1}{2}(5)(-5) = -12\frac{1}{2}$
$\therefore$ the vertex is at $(-1, -12\frac{1}{2})$.

   iv When $x = 0$, $y = \frac{1}{2}(6)(-4) = -12$
$\therefore$ the y-intercept is -12.

   v

c $y = -3(x - 2)^2$

   i The graph cuts x-axis when $y = 0$
$$\therefore \quad (x - 2)^2 = 0$$
$\therefore$ the graph touches the x-axis when $x = 2$.

   ii The axis of symmetry is $x = 2$.

   iii $f(2) = 0$
$\therefore$ the vertex is at $(2, 0)$.

   iv The y-intercept is $f(0) = -3(-2)^2 = -12$.

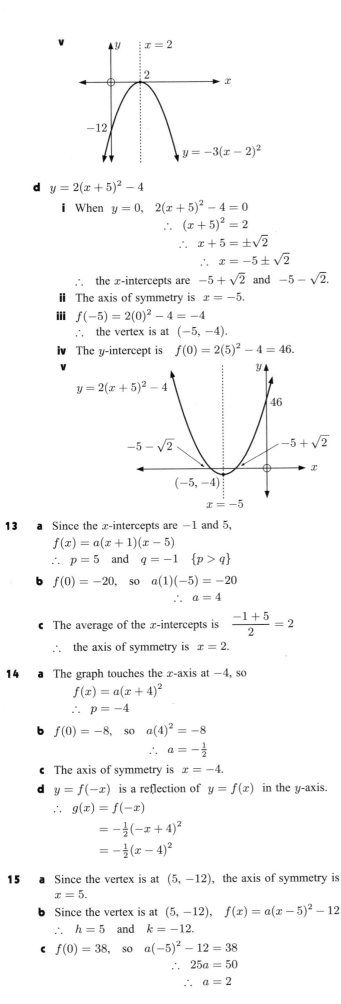

v

$y = -3(x-2)^2$

d $y = 2(x+5)^2 - 4$

  i When $y = 0$, $2(x+5)^2 - 4 = 0$

      $\therefore (x+5)^2 = 2$

      $\therefore x+5 = \pm\sqrt{2}$

      $\therefore x = -5 \pm \sqrt{2}$

    $\therefore$ the x-intercepts are $-5+\sqrt{2}$ and $-5-\sqrt{2}$.

  ii The axis of symmetry is $x = -5$.

  iii $f(-5) = 2(0)^2 - 4 = -4$

    $\therefore$ the vertex is at $(-5, -4)$.

  iv The y-intercept is $f(0) = 2(5)^2 - 4 = 46$.

  v

13 **a** Since the x-intercepts are -1 and 5,

    $f(x) = a(x+1)(x-5)$

    $\therefore p = 5$ and $q = -1$ $\{p > q\}$

  b $f(0) = -20$, so $a(1)(-5) = -20$

                  $\therefore a = 4$

  c The average of the x-intercepts is $\dfrac{-1+5}{2} = 2$

    $\therefore$ the axis of symmetry is $x = 2$.

14 **a** The graph touches the x-axis at -4, so

    $f(x) = a(x+4)^2$

    $\therefore p = -4$

  b $f(0) = -8$, so $a(4)^2 = -8$

               $\therefore a = -\frac{1}{2}$

  c The axis of symmetry is $x = -4$.

  d $y = f(-x)$ is a reflection of $y = f(x)$ in the y-axis.

    $\therefore g(x) = f(-x)$

          $= -\frac{1}{2}(-x+4)^2$

          $= -\frac{1}{2}(x-4)^2$

15 **a** Since the vertex is at $(5, -12)$, the axis of symmetry is $x = 5$.

  b Since the vertex is at $(5, -12)$, $f(x) = a(x-5)^2 - 12$

    $\therefore h = 5$ and $k = -12$.

  c $f(0) = 38$, so $a(-5)^2 - 12 = 38$

                  $\therefore 25a = 50$

                    $\therefore a = 2$

16 **a** **i** When $x = 0$, $y = 9$.

      $\therefore$ the y-intercept is 9.

  ii $y = x^2 - 4x + 9$

    $= x^2 - 4x + 2^2 + 9 - 2^2$

    $= (x-2)^2 + 5$

  iii The vertex is at $(2, 5)$.

  iv

b **i** When $x = 0$, $y = -2$.

    $\therefore$ the y-intercept is -2.

  ii $y = x^2 - 6x - 2$

    $= x^2 - 6x + 3^2 - 2 - 3^2$

    $= (x-3)^2 - 11$

  iii The vertex is at $(3, -11)$.

  iv

c **i** When $x = 0$, $y = 11$.

    $\therefore$ the y-intercept is 11.

  ii $y = 4x^2 + 16x + 11$

    $= 4(x^2 + 4x) + 11$

    $= 4(x^2 + 4x + 2^2) + 11 - 4 \times 2^2$

    $= 4(x+2)^2 - 5$

  iii The vertex is at $(-2, -5)$.

  iv

d **i** When $x = 0$, $y = -10$.

    $\therefore$ the y-intercept is -10.

  ii $y = -3x^2 + 12x - 10$

    $= -3(x^2 - 4x) - 10$

    $= -3(x^2 - 4x + 2^2) - 10 + 3 \times 2^2$

    $= -3(x-2)^2 + 2$

  iii The vertex is at $(2, 2)$.

  iv

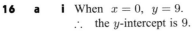

17 a When $x = 0$, $y = 8$.

$\therefore$ the y-intercept is 8.

b $x^2 + 12x + 8 = 0$

$\therefore \quad x = \dfrac{-12 \pm \sqrt{144 - 4(1)(8)}}{2}$

$\qquad = \dfrac{-12 \pm \sqrt{112}}{2}$

$\qquad = \dfrac{-12 \pm 4\sqrt{7}}{2}$

$\qquad = -6 \pm 2\sqrt{7}$

c $y = x^2 + 12x + 8$

$\quad = x^2 + 12x + 6^2 + 8 - 6^2$

$\quad = (x + 6)^2 - 28$

So, the vertex is at $(-6, -28)$.

d Range $= \{y \mid y \geqslant -28\}$

e

18 a $x^2 + 8x + k = 0$ has $\Delta = b^2 - 4ac$

$\qquad\qquad = 8^2 - 4(1)(k)$

$\qquad\qquad = 64 - 4k$

b i There are no real roots when $\Delta < 0$

$\therefore \quad 64 - 4k < 0$

$\therefore \quad 64 < 4k$

$\therefore \quad k > 16$

ii There are two distinct real roots when $\Delta > 0$

$\therefore \quad k < 16$

19 $y = mx^2 + 4x + 6$ lies entirely above the x-axis when $m > 0$ *and* $\Delta < 0$

So, $m > 0$ *and* $4^2 - 4(m)(6) < 0$

$\therefore \quad 16 - 24m < 0$

$\therefore \quad -24m < -16$

$\therefore \quad m > \frac{2}{3}$

So, $m > \frac{2}{3}$.

20 Since $mx^2 + (m - 2)x + m = 0$ has a repeated root, $\Delta = 0$.

$\therefore \quad (m - 2)^2 - 4 \times m \times m = 0$

$\therefore \quad -3m^2 - 4m + 4 = 0$

$\therefore \quad -(3m - 2)(m + 2) = 0$

$\therefore \quad m = \frac{2}{3}$ or -2

21 a $(-2)^2 + b(-2) + (b - 2) = 0 \qquad \{-2 \text{ is a solution}\}$

$\therefore \quad 4 - 2b + b - 2 = 0$

$\therefore \quad b = 2$

b Since $b = 2$, the equation is $x^2 + 2x = 0$

$\therefore \quad x(x + 2) = 0$

$\therefore \quad x = 0$ is the other solution.

22 a Domain $= \{x \mid x \neq 1\}$, Range $= \{y \mid y \neq 1\}$

b $f(x) = \dfrac{x + 2}{x - 1}$ is undefined when $x = 1$, so $x = 1$ is a vertical asymptote.

Now $f(x) = \dfrac{x + 2}{x - 1} = \dfrac{1 + \frac{2}{x}}{1 - \frac{1}{x}}$

$\therefore$ as $|x| \to \infty$, $f(x) \to \frac{1}{1} = 1$

$\therefore \quad y = 1$ is a horizontal asymptote.

c $f(0) = \dfrac{0 + 2}{0 - 1} = -2$

So, the y-intercept is -2.

$f(x) = 0$ when $\dfrac{x + 2}{x - 1} = 0$

$\therefore \quad x + 2 = 0$

$\therefore \quad x = -2$

So, the x-intercept is -2.

d

23 a Domain $= \{x \mid x \neq 2\}$, Range $= \{y \mid y \neq 4\}$

b $f(x) = 4 - \dfrac{1}{x - 2}$ is undefined when $x = 2$, so $x = 2$ is a vertical asymptote.

As $|x| \to \infty$, $\dfrac{1}{x - 2} \to 0$, so $f(x) \to 4$.

$\therefore \quad y = 4$ is a horizontal asymptote.

c $f(0) = 4 - \frac{1}{0 - 2} = \frac{9}{2}$

So, the y-intercept is $\frac{9}{2}$.

$f(x) = 0$ when $4 - \dfrac{1}{x - 2} = 0$

$\therefore \quad \dfrac{1}{x - 2} = 4$

$\therefore \quad x - 2 = \frac{1}{4}$

$\therefore \quad x = \frac{9}{4}$

So, the x-intercept is $\frac{9}{4}$.

d

24 a

b $y = f(x - 1) + 2$ is a translation of $y = f(x)$ through $\binom{1}{2}$.

$y = \frac{1}{2}f(x) - 1$ is a vertical stretch of $y = f(x)$ with scale factor $\frac{1}{2}$, followed by a vertical translation of 1 unit downwards.

25 a

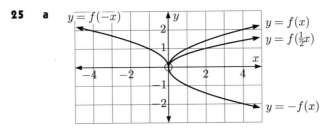

b $y = -f(x)$ is a reflection of $y = f(x)$ in the x-axis.

$y = f(-x)$ is a reflection of $y = f(x)$ in the y-axis.

$y = f\left(\frac{1}{2}x\right)$ is a horizontal stretch of $y = f(x)$ with scale factor 2.

26 a Domain $= \{x \mid -1 < x < 1\}$

b $f(-x) = \ln(1 - (-x)^2)$
   $= \ln(1 - x^2)$
   $= f(x)$ as required

This means $f(x)$ is symmetrical about the y-axis.

c From the graph, there are two values of x for which $\ln(1 - x^2) = -2$.

$\therefore$ there are two solutions.

CALCULATORS

1

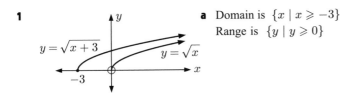

a Domain is $\{x \mid x \geqslant -3\}$
   Range is $\{y \mid y \geqslant 0\}$

b $y = \sqrt{x + 3}$ is a translation of $y = \sqrt{x}$ through $\binom{-3}{0}$.

2

a Domain is $\{x \mid x > 2\}$
   Range is $\{y \mid y \in \mathbb{R}\}$

b $f(x) = \ln(x - 2)$ is undefined when $x = 2$, so $x = 2$ is a vertical asymptote.

c $y = 3f(-x)$ is a vertical stretch of $y = f(x)$ with scale factor 3, followed by a reflection in the y-axis.

$\therefore$ the function is $y = 3\ln(-x - 2)$.

3

a Domain is $\{x \mid x > 4\}$
   Range is $\{y \mid y > 3\}$

b $y = \dfrac{1}{\sqrt{x - 4}} + 3$ is a translation of $y = \dfrac{1}{\sqrt{x}}$ through $\binom{4}{3}$.

c $f(x) = \dfrac{1}{\sqrt{x - 4}} + 3$ is undefined when $x = 4$, so $x = 4$ is a vertical asymptote.

As $x \to \infty$, $\dfrac{1}{\sqrt{x - 4}} \to 0$, so $f(x) \to 3$.

$\therefore$ $y = 3$ is a horizontal asymptote.

4 $f(x) = e^x$, $g(x) = 2x + 1$

a $(f \circ g)(x) = f(g(x))$
   $= f(2x + 1)$
   $= e^{2x+1}$

b $(f \circ g)(x)$ is $y = e^{2x+1}$
   so $(f \circ g)^{-1}(x)$ is $x = e^{2y+1}$
   $\therefore \ln x = 2y + 1$
   $\therefore y = \dfrac{\ln x - 1}{2}$
   $\therefore (f \circ g)^{-1}(x) = \dfrac{\ln x - 1}{2}$

c $(f \circ g)^{-1}(7) = \dfrac{\ln 7 - 1}{2}$
   ≈ 0.473

5

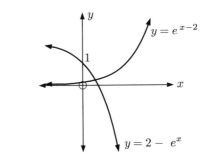

Using technology, the point of intersection is $\approx (0.566, 0.238)$.

6 $f(x) = \ln x$, $g(x) = x^3$

a $(f \circ g)(2)$
   $= f(g(2))$
   $= f(8)$
   $= \ln 8$
   ≈ 2.08

b $(g \circ f)(2)$
   $= g(f(2))$
   $= g(\ln 2)$
   $= (\ln 2)^3$
   ≈ 0.333

c $f(x) = \ln x$
   $\therefore f^{-1}(x) = e^x$ {definition of $\ln$ }
   So, $(f^{-1} \circ g)(1.2) = f^{-1}(g(1.2))$
   $= f^{-1}((1.2)^3)$
   $= e^{1.2^3}$
   ≈ 5.63

d $g \circ f$ is $y = g(f(x))$
   $= g(\ln x)$
   $= (\ln x)^3$
   $\therefore (g \circ f)^{-1}$ is $x = (\ln y)^3$
   $\therefore \ln y = \sqrt[3]{x}$
   $\therefore y = e^{\sqrt[3]{x}}$
   $\therefore (g \circ f)^{-1}(x) = e^{\sqrt[3]{x}}$
   $\therefore (g \circ f)^{-1}(8) = e^{\sqrt[3]{8}} = e^2$

7 a f is $y = \ln(x+2) - 5$, $x > -2$

$\therefore\ f^{-1}$ is $x = \ln(y+2) - 5$, $y > -2$

$\therefore\ \ln(y+2) = x + 5$

$\therefore\ y + 2 = e^{x+5}$

So, $f^{-1}(x) = e^{x+5} - 2$, $x \in \mathbb{R}$

b

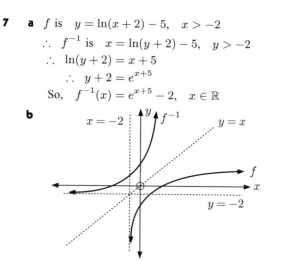

c f has domain $\{x \mid x > -2\}$ and range $\{y \mid y \in \mathbb{R}\}$.
f^{-1} has domain $\{x \mid x \in \mathbb{R}\}$ and range $\{y \mid y > -2\}$.

8 a The axis of symmetry is $x = -\dfrac{b}{2a}$ which is $x = \frac{9}{4}$.

b When $x = \frac{9}{4}$, $y = 2(\frac{9}{4})^2 - 9(\frac{9}{4}) + 3$

$= -7\frac{1}{8}$

$\therefore$ the vertex is at $(2\frac{1}{4}, -7\frac{1}{8})$.

c The graph cuts the y-axis at $f(0) = 3$

and the x-axis when $y = 0$

$\therefore\ 2x^2 - 9x + 3 = 0$

$\therefore\ x \approx 0.363$ or 4.137

$\therefore$ the y-intercept is 3, and the x-intercepts are 0.363 and 4.137.

d

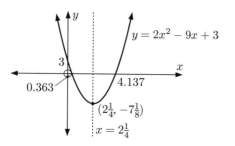

9 a $f(x) = \dfrac{6-2x}{x+4}$ has vertical asymptote $x = -4$ and horizontal asymptote $y = -2$.

b $f(0) = \frac{3}{2}$ so the y-intercept is $\frac{3}{2}$.

When $y = 0$, $\dfrac{6-2x}{x+4} = 0$

$\therefore\ x = 3$

$\therefore$ the x-intercept is 3.

c

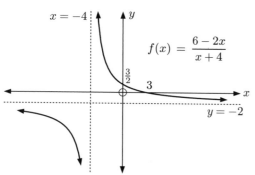

d $f(x)$ is $y = \dfrac{6-2x}{x+4}$

so $f^{-1}(x)$ is $x = \dfrac{6-2y}{y+4}$

$\therefore\ xy + 4x = 6 - 2y$

$\therefore\ xy + 2y = 6 - 4x$

$\therefore\ y(x+2) = 6 - 4x$

$\therefore\ y = \dfrac{6-4x}{x+2}$

$\therefore\ f^{-1}(x) = \dfrac{6-4x}{x+2}$

10 a $(g \circ f)(x) = g(f(x))$

$= g(25 - x^2)$

$= \dfrac{2}{\sqrt{25-x^2}}$

b Domain $= \{x \mid -5 < x < 5\}$

c $\sqrt{25-x^2} = 0$ when $x = \pm 5$, so $x = -5$ and $x = 5$ are the vertical asymptotes.

11 a The graph cuts the y-axis at $f(0) = 0$.
So, the x-intercept and y-intercept are both 0.

b As $x \to \infty$, $2^{-x} \to 0$, so $y \to -1$.
$\therefore\ y = -1$ is a horizontal asymptote.

c Domain $= \{x \mid x \in \mathbb{R}\}$, Range $= \{y \mid y > -1\}$

d

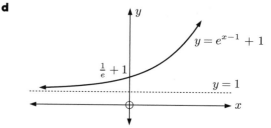

12 a $f(0) = \frac{1}{e} + 1$, so the y-intercept is $\frac{1}{e} + 1$.
Since $\neq 0$ for all $x \in \mathbb{R}$, there are no x-intercepts.

b As $x \to -\infty$, $e^{x-1} \to 0$, so $y \to 1$.
$\therefore\ y = 1$ is a horizontal asymptote.

c Domain $= \{x \mid x \in \mathbb{R}\}$, Range $= \{y \mid y > 1\}$

d

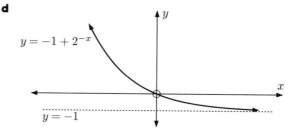

13 a $I(0) = 40e^{-0.1 \times 0} = 40$ amps
So, the initial current was 40 amps.

b $I(100) = 40e^{-0.1 \times 100} = 40e^{-10} \approx 0.001\,82$ amps
So, the current after 100 milliseconds is about $0.001\,82$ amps.

c

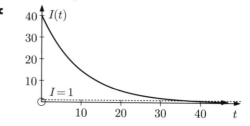

d Using technology, $40e^{-0.1t} = 1$ when
$t \approx 36.9$ milliseconds.
So, it will take about 36.9 milliseconds.

14 a Suppose the equilateral triangle ends have side length
x cm.

$\therefore$ each end has area

$$= \frac{x}{2} \times \sqrt{x^2 - \left(\frac{x}{2}\right)^2}$$

$$= \frac{x}{2} \times \sqrt{x^2 \left(1 - \frac{1}{4}\right)}$$

$$= \frac{\sqrt{3}}{4}x^2 \text{ cm}^2$$

b Suppose the prism has height y cm.

$\therefore$ the sum of the side lengths of
the prism is

$$6x + 3y = 180$$
$$\therefore \quad 2x + y = 60$$
$$\therefore \quad y = 60 - 2x$$

c Each side has area $= xy$

$$= x(60 - 2x) \text{ cm}^2$$

$\therefore$ the total area $= 2 \times \frac{\sqrt{3}}{4}x^2 + 3x(60 - 2x)$

$$= \left(\frac{\sqrt{3}}{2} - 6\right)x^2 + 180x \text{ cm}^2$$

d Since $\frac{\sqrt{3}}{2} - 6 < 0$, the area is maximised when

$$x = -\frac{180}{2\left(\frac{\sqrt{3}}{2} - 6\right)} \approx 17.5$$

and $y = 60 - 2x \approx 24.9$

So, the aquarium should have
the dimensions shown:

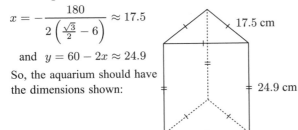

SOLUTIONS TO TOPIC 3
(CIRCULAR FUNCTIONS AND TRIGONOMETRY)

NO CALCULATORS

1

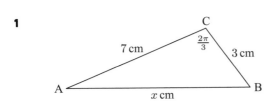

a Using the cosine rule,

$$x^2 = 7^2 + 3^2 - 2 \times 7 \times 3 \times \cos\left(\frac{2\pi}{3}\right)$$
$$\therefore \quad x^2 = 49 + 9 - (-21)$$
$$= 79$$
$$\therefore \quad x = \sqrt{79} \quad \{x > 0\}$$

So, AB is $\sqrt{79}$ cm.

b Area of $\triangle ABC = \frac{1}{2} \times 7 \times 3 \times \sin\left(\frac{2\pi}{3}\right)$

$$= \frac{21}{2} \times \frac{\sqrt{3}}{2}$$

$$= \frac{21\sqrt{3}}{4} \text{ cm}^2$$

2

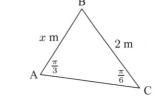

a Area of $\triangle PQR$ is 2.5 cm².

$$\therefore \quad \frac{1}{2} \times x \times 5 \times \sin\left(\frac{3\pi}{4}\right) = 2.5$$

$$\therefore \quad \frac{5}{2}x \times \frac{1}{\sqrt{2}} = \frac{5}{2}$$

$$\therefore \quad x = \sqrt{2}$$

So, PQ is $\sqrt{2}$ cm.

b Using the cosine rule,

$$y^2 = (\sqrt{2})^2 + 5^2 - 2 \times \sqrt{2} \times 5 \times \cos\left(\frac{3\pi}{4}\right)$$
$$\therefore \quad y^2 = 2 + 25 - 10\sqrt{2} \times \left(-\frac{1}{\sqrt{2}}\right)$$
$$= 27 + 10$$
$$= 37$$
$$\therefore \quad y = \sqrt{37} \quad \{y > 0\}$$

So, PR is $\sqrt{37}$ cm.

3

a Using the sine rule,

$$\frac{x}{\sin\left(\frac{\pi}{6}\right)} = \frac{2}{\sin\left(\frac{\pi}{3}\right)}$$

$$\therefore \quad \frac{x}{\left(\frac{1}{2}\right)} = \frac{2}{\left(\frac{\sqrt{3}}{2}\right)}$$

$$\therefore \quad x = \frac{4}{\left(\frac{\sqrt{3}}{2}\right)} = \frac{8}{\sqrt{3}}$$

So, AB is $\frac{8\sqrt{3}}{3}$ m.

b $\quad A\widehat{B}C = \pi - \frac{\pi}{3} - \frac{\pi}{6}$ {sum of angles in $\triangle$}

$$\therefore \quad A\widehat{B}C = \frac{\pi}{2}$$

Area of $\triangle ABC = \frac{1}{2} \times \frac{8}{\sqrt{3}} \times 2$

$$= \frac{8\sqrt{3}}{3} \text{ m}^2$$

4

a Using the cosine rule,

$$7^2 = x^2 + 5^2 - 2 \times x \times 5 \times \cos 60°$$
$$\therefore \quad 49 = x^2 + 25 - 5x$$
$$\therefore \quad x^2 - 5x - 24 = 0$$
$$\therefore \quad (x - 8)(x + 3) = 0$$
$$\therefore \quad x = 8 \quad \{x > 0\}$$

So, PQ = 8 cm.

b Area of $\triangle PQR = \frac{1}{2} \times 8 \times 5 \times \sin 60°$

$$= 20 \times \frac{\sqrt{3}}{2}$$

$$= 10\sqrt{3} \text{ cm}^2$$

Mathematics SL – Exam Preparation & Practice Guide (3ʳᵈ edition)

5 a Length of arc AB $= \theta \times$ radius

$$\therefore \ \pi = \theta \times 3$$
$$\therefore \ \theta = \frac{\pi}{3}$$

b Area of circle $= \pi r^2$
$$= \pi \times 3^2$$
$$= 9\pi \ \text{cm}^2$$
Area of sector $= \frac{1}{2}\theta r^2$
$$= \frac{1}{2} \times \frac{\pi}{3} \times 3^2$$
$$= \frac{3\pi}{2} \ \text{cm}^2$$
$$\therefore \ \text{shaded area} = 9\pi - \frac{3\pi}{2}$$
$$= \frac{15\pi}{2} \ \text{cm}^2$$

6

a perimeter $= 40$ cm
$$\therefore \ 10 + 10 + l = 40$$
$$\therefore \ l = 20$$
So, the arc length is 20 cm.

b area $= \frac{1}{2}\theta r^2$
$$= \frac{1}{2}lr \quad \{l = \theta r\}$$
$$= \frac{1}{2} \times 20 \times 10$$
$$= 100 \ \text{cm}^2$$

7 a area $= 20 \ \text{cm}^2$
$$\therefore \ \frac{1}{2}\theta r^2 = 20$$
$$\therefore \ \frac{1}{2}lr = 20 \quad \{l = \theta r\}$$
$$\therefore \ \frac{1}{2}(6)r = 20$$
$$\therefore \ r = \frac{20}{3} \ \text{cm}$$

b $\theta = \frac{l}{r}$
$$= \frac{6}{\frac{20}{3}}$$
$$= 0.9$$

8 a Length of arc PQ $= \frac{\theta}{360} \times 2\pi r$
$$= \frac{135}{360} \times 2\pi \times 4$$
$$= 3\pi \ \text{m}$$

b Area of whole sector POQ $= \frac{\theta}{360} \times \pi r^2$
$$= \frac{135}{360} \times \pi \times 4^2$$
$$= 6\pi \ \text{m}^2$$
Area of unshaded sector $= \frac{135}{360} \times \pi \times 2^2$
$$= \frac{3\pi}{2} \ \text{m}^2$$
So, shaded area $= 6\pi - \frac{3\pi}{2}$
$$= \frac{9\pi}{2} \ \text{m}^2$$

9 a $\cos^2\left(\frac{\pi}{4}\right) - \sin^2\left(\frac{5\pi}{6}\right) = \left(\frac{1}{\sqrt{2}}\right)^2 - \left(\frac{1}{2}\right)^2$
$$= \frac{1}{2} - \frac{1}{4}$$
$$= \frac{1}{4}$$

b $\tan 60° = \sqrt{3}$
$$\therefore \ \text{the equation is} \ y = \sqrt{3}x$$

10 a $\tan\left(-\frac{\pi}{6}\right) - \cos\left(\frac{4\pi}{3}\right) = -\frac{1}{\sqrt{3}} - \left(-\frac{1}{2}\right)$
$$= \frac{1}{2} - \frac{\sqrt{3}}{3}$$

b $\tan\left(\frac{2\pi}{3}\right) = -\sqrt{3}$
$$\therefore \ \text{the equation is}$$
$$y = -\sqrt{3}x + c$$
But when $x = 4$, $y = 0$
$$\therefore \ 0 = -4\sqrt{3} + c$$
$$\therefore \ c = 4\sqrt{3}$$
So, $y = -\sqrt{3}x + 4\sqrt{3}$

11 a i amplitude $= 2$
ii principal axis is $y = 0$
iii period $= \frac{2\pi}{1} = 2\pi$
iv

b i amplitude $= 1$
ii principal axis is $y = 2$
iii period $= \frac{2\pi}{1} = 2\pi$
iv

c i amplitude $= 3$
ii principal axis is $y = 0$
iii period $= \frac{2\pi}{2} = \pi$
iv

d i amplitude $= 1$
ii principal axis is $y = -1$
iii period $= \frac{2\pi}{\frac{1}{2}} = 4\pi$
iv

e i amplitude $= 1$
ii principal axis is $y = 2$

iii period $= \frac{2\pi}{2} = \pi$

iv

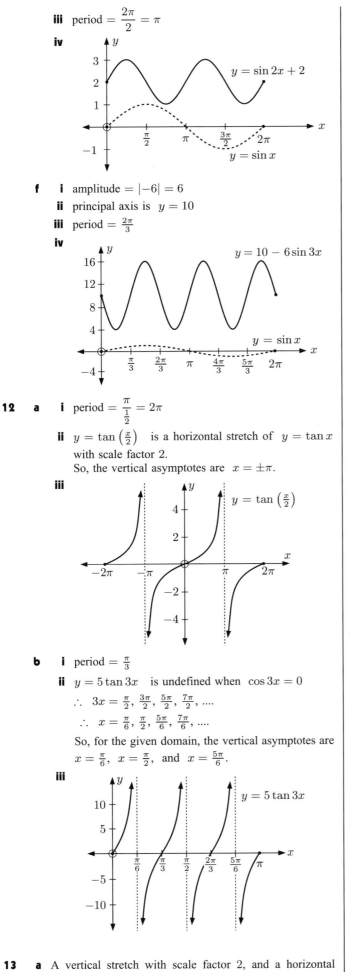

f **i** amplitude $= |-6| = 6$
ii principal axis is $y = 10$
iii period $= \frac{2\pi}{3}$

iv

12 **a** **i** period $= \frac{\pi}{\frac{1}{2}} = 2\pi$

ii $y = \tan\left(\frac{x}{2}\right)$ is a horizontal stretch of $y = \tan x$ with scale factor 2.
So, the vertical asymptotes are $x = \pm\pi$.

iii

b **i** period $= \frac{\pi}{3}$

ii $y = 5\tan 3x$ is undefined when $\cos 3x = 0$
$\therefore \ 3x = \frac{\pi}{2}, \frac{3\pi}{2}, \frac{5\pi}{2}, \frac{7\pi}{2}, \dots$
$\therefore \ x = \frac{\pi}{6}, \frac{\pi}{2}, \frac{5\pi}{6}, \frac{7\pi}{6}, \dots$
So, for the given domain, the vertical asymptotes are $x = \frac{\pi}{6}$, $x = \frac{\pi}{2}$, and $x = \frac{5\pi}{6}$.

iii

13 **a** A vertical stretch with scale factor 2, and a horizontal stretch with scale factor 3.

b

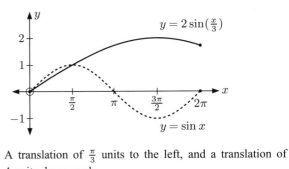

14 **a** A translation of $\frac{\pi}{3}$ units to the left, and a translation of 4 units downwards.

b

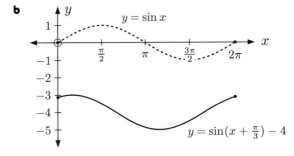

15 **a** $y(0) = 4$ so $a + b\sin 0 = 4$
$\therefore \ a = 4$

b $y\left(\frac{\pi}{2}\right) = 1$
$\therefore \ 4 + b\sin\left(\frac{\pi}{2}\right) = 1$
$\therefore \ b(1) = -3$
$\therefore \ b = -3$
Check: $y = 4 - 3\sin x$
$y(\pi) = 4 - 3\sin\pi = 4 - 0 = 4$ ✓

16 Period $= \frac{2\pi}{b} = \pi$, so $b = 2$
Amplitude is 10, so $a = 10$.
Principal axis is $y = 15$, so $c = 15$.
$\therefore \ y = 10\sin 2x + 15$
Check: $y\left(\frac{\pi}{4}\right) = 10\sin\left(\frac{\pi}{2}\right) + 15$
$= 10(1) + 15$
$= 25$ ✓

17 **a** $\sqrt{2}\cos x + 1 = 0$
$\therefore \ \cos x = -\frac{1}{\sqrt{2}}$
$\therefore \ x = \frac{3\pi}{4}$ or $\frac{5\pi}{4}$

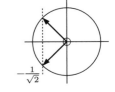

b $2\sin x = \sqrt{3}$
$\therefore \ \sin x = \frac{\sqrt{3}}{2}$
$\therefore \ x = \frac{\pi}{3}$ or $\frac{2\pi}{3}$

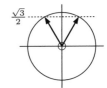

c $2\sin^2 x + 3\cos x = 3$
$2(1 - \cos^2 x) + 3\cos x - 3 = 0$
$\therefore \ 2 - 2\cos^2 x + 3\cos x - 3 = 0$
$\therefore \ -2\cos^2 x + 3\cos x - 1 = 0$
$\therefore \ 2\cos^2 x - 3\cos x + 1 = 0$
$\therefore \ (2\cos x - 1)(\cos x - 1) = 0$
$\therefore \ \cos x = \frac{1}{2}$ or 1
$\therefore \ x = 0, \frac{\pi}{3}, \frac{5\pi}{3}, 2\pi$

d
$$\sin 2x + \sin x = 0$$
$$\therefore\ 2\sin x \cos x + \sin x = 0$$
$$\therefore\ \sin x(2\cos x + 1) = 0$$
$$\therefore\ \sin x = 0 \ \text{ or } \ \cos x = -\tfrac{1}{2}$$
$$\therefore\ x = 0, \tfrac{2\pi}{3}, \pi, \tfrac{4\pi}{3}, 2\pi$$

e
$$\sin x = -\sqrt{3}\cos x$$
$$\therefore\ \frac{\sin x}{\cos x} = -\sqrt{3}$$
$$\therefore\ \tan x = -\sqrt{3}$$
$$\therefore\ x = \tfrac{2\pi}{3}, \tfrac{5\pi}{3}$$

f
$$\tfrac{1}{\sqrt{3}}\cos x - \sin x = 0$$
$$\therefore\ \sin x = \tfrac{1}{\sqrt{3}}\cos x$$
$$\therefore\ \frac{\sin x}{\cos x} = \tfrac{1}{\sqrt{3}}$$
$$\therefore\ \tan x = \tfrac{1}{\sqrt{3}}$$
$$\therefore\ x = \tfrac{\pi}{6}, \tfrac{7\pi}{6}$$

18 a $y = a\cos(b(x-c)) + d$

  i The amplitude is 5, so $a = 5$.

  ii The period is 4, so $\dfrac{2\pi}{b} = 4$
$$\therefore\ b = \tfrac{\pi}{2}$$

  iii The principal axis is $y = 2$, so $d = 2$.

  iv So far, the curve is $\ y = 5\cos(\tfrac{\pi}{2}(x-c)) + 2$

     A maximum occurs when $x = 4$.
$$\therefore\ \tfrac{\pi}{2}(4 - c) \ \text{ is a multiple of } 2\pi$$
$$\therefore\ \text{we can choose } c = 0.$$

b From **a**, $\ y = 5\cos(\tfrac{\pi}{2}x) + 2$

Since $\ \cos\theta = \sin(\theta + \tfrac{\pi}{2})$, the sine function of this curve is $\ y = 5\sin(\tfrac{\pi}{2}x + \tfrac{\pi}{2}) + 2$.

19 a $\sin^2\theta + \cos^2\theta = 1$
$$\therefore\ \sin^2\theta + \tfrac{9}{64} = 1$$
$$\therefore\ \sin^2\theta = \tfrac{55}{64}$$
$$\therefore\ \sin\theta = \pm\tfrac{\sqrt{55}}{8}$$
$$\therefore\ \sin\theta = \tfrac{\sqrt{55}}{8} \ \{\theta \text{ is acute}\}$$

b $\sin 2\theta = 2\sin\theta\cos\theta$
$$= 2\left(\tfrac{\sqrt{55}}{8}\right)\left(\tfrac{3}{8}\right)$$
$$= \tfrac{3}{32}\sqrt{55}$$

20 a $\cos^2\alpha + \sin^2\alpha = 1$
$$\therefore\ \cos^2\alpha + \tfrac{4}{9} = 1$$
$$\therefore\ \cos^2\alpha = \tfrac{5}{9}$$
$$\therefore\ \cos\alpha = \pm\tfrac{\sqrt{5}}{3}$$
$$\therefore\ \cos\alpha = -\tfrac{\sqrt{5}}{3} \ \{\alpha \text{ is obtuse}\}$$

b $\cos 2\alpha = 1 - 2\sin^2\alpha$
$$= 1 - 2\left(\tfrac{2}{3}\right)^2$$
$$= 1 - \tfrac{8}{9}$$
$$= \tfrac{1}{9}$$

21 a
$$\cos 2\alpha = \tfrac{5}{13}$$
$$\therefore\ 1 - 2\sin^2\alpha = \tfrac{5}{13}$$
$$\therefore\ 2\sin^2\alpha = \tfrac{8}{13}$$
$$\therefore\ \sin^2\alpha = \tfrac{4}{13}$$
$$\therefore\ \sin\alpha = \pm\tfrac{2}{\sqrt{13}}$$

But α is acute and so $\sin\alpha > 0$
$$\therefore\ \sin\alpha = \tfrac{2}{\sqrt{13}}$$

b $\cos^2\alpha + \sin^2\alpha = 1$
$$\therefore\ \cos^2\alpha + \tfrac{4}{13} = 1 \qquad \{\text{from } \mathbf{a}\}$$
$$\therefore\ \cos^2\alpha = \tfrac{9}{13}$$
$$\therefore\ \cos\alpha = \pm\tfrac{3}{\sqrt{13}}$$
$$\therefore\ \cos\alpha = \tfrac{3}{\sqrt{13}} \qquad \{\alpha \text{ is acute}\}$$

c $\tan\alpha = \dfrac{\sin\alpha}{\cos\alpha}$
$$= \frac{\tfrac{2}{\sqrt{13}}}{\tfrac{3}{\sqrt{13}}}$$
$$= \tfrac{2}{3}$$

22 a $\theta = \tfrac{7\pi}{6}$

b $\tan\theta = \dfrac{\sin\theta}{\cos\theta}$
$$= \tfrac{1}{\sqrt{3}}$$

c Since $\ \theta = \tfrac{7\pi}{6}$,
$$2\theta = \tfrac{7\pi}{3}$$
$$\therefore\ \tan 2\theta = \frac{\tfrac{\sqrt{3}}{2}}{\tfrac{1}{2}} = \sqrt{3}$$

23 a

S	A
②	①
③	④
T	C

$\tan\theta > 0$ and $\cos\theta < 0$ in the third quadrant.

b
$$\tan\theta = \frac{\sin\theta}{\cos\theta} = 2$$
$$\therefore\ \sin\theta = 2\cos\theta$$
Now $\ \cos^2\theta + \sin^2\theta = 1$
$$\therefore\ \cos^2\theta + (2\cos\theta)^2 = 1$$
$$\therefore\ 5\cos^2\theta = 1$$
$$\therefore\ \cos\theta = \pm\tfrac{1}{\sqrt{5}}$$
But $\cos\theta < 0$ in Q3
$$\therefore\ \cos\theta = -\tfrac{1}{\sqrt{5}}$$

c $y = \tan(x + \tfrac{\pi}{6}) + 2$ is a translation of $y = \tan x$ through $\begin{pmatrix} -\tfrac{\pi}{6} \\ 2 \end{pmatrix}$.

24 a For the sine function $\ y = a\sin b(x-c) + d$:

- the amplitude $= 2$, so $a = 2$
- the period $= \pi$, so $\tfrac{2\pi}{b} = \pi \quad \therefore\ b = 2$
- the principal axis is $y = 1$, so $d = 1$
- there is no horizontal translation, so $c = 0$.

b The function is $\ y = 2\sin 2x + 1$.
$$\therefore\ \text{we need to solve } 2\sin 2x + 1 = 0, \quad 0 \leqslant x \leqslant \pi$$
$$\therefore\ \sin 2x = -\tfrac{1}{2}$$
$$\therefore\ 2x = \tfrac{7\pi}{6} \text{ or } \tfrac{11\pi}{6}$$
$$\therefore\ x = \tfrac{7\pi}{12} \text{ or } \tfrac{11\pi}{12}$$
So, P is $\left(\tfrac{7\pi}{12}, 0\right)$ and Q is $\left(\tfrac{11\pi}{12}, 0\right)$.

25 a $f(x) = \dfrac{1}{\sin x}$ is defined when

$\sin x \neq 0$

$\therefore \ x \neq 0 + k\pi$

$(-1, 0) \qquad (1, 0)$

So, the domain is $\{x \mid x \neq k\pi, \ k \in \mathbb{Z}\}$

Since the range of $\sin x$ is $\{y \mid -1 \leqslant y \leqslant 1\}$, the values of $\dfrac{1}{\sin x}$ are $\leqslant -1$ or $\geqslant 1$.

So, the range is $\{y \mid y \leqslant -1 \text{ or } y \geqslant 1\}$.

b $f(x)$ is undefined when $x = k\pi, \ k \in \mathbb{Z}$

So, $x = 0$, $x = \pm\pi$, $x = \pm 2\pi$, ...

are all vertical asymptotes.

26 a $\tan\theta = \dfrac{\sin\theta}{\cos\theta} \quad \therefore \quad \cos\theta = \dfrac{\sin\theta}{\tan\theta} = \dfrac{-\frac{4}{5}}{-\frac{4}{3}} = \dfrac{3}{5}$

b $\cos 2\theta = \cos^2\theta - \sin^2\theta = \left(\frac{3}{5}\right)^2 - \left(-\frac{4}{5}\right)^2$

$\qquad = -\frac{7}{25}$

27 We label points W, X, Y and Z as shown, and let $Y\widehat{X}Z = \beta$ and $W\widehat{Z}X = \alpha$.

Now $\tan\beta = \dfrac{b}{c}$ {from $\triangle$XYZ}

$\therefore \quad \beta = \tan^{-1}\left(\dfrac{b}{c}\right)$

Likewise, $\tan\alpha = \dfrac{a}{c}$ {from $\triangle$XWZ}

$\therefore \quad \alpha = \tan^{-1}\left(\dfrac{a}{c}\right)$

Now $\theta = \alpha + \beta$ {external angle of a triangle}

$\therefore \quad \theta = \tan^{-1}\left(\dfrac{a}{c}\right) + \tan^{-1}\left(\dfrac{b}{c}\right)$ as required.

28

$B\widehat{C}A = \tan^{-1}\left(\dfrac{7}{x}\right)$ and $P\widehat{C}A = \tan^{-1}\left(\dfrac{2}{x}\right)$

Now $\theta = B\widehat{C}A - P\widehat{C}A$

$\therefore \quad \theta = \tan^{-1}\left(\dfrac{7}{x}\right) - \tan^{-1}\left(\dfrac{2}{x}\right)$

29 a $\cos 2x = \dfrac{5}{8}$

$\therefore \ 1 - 2\sin^2 x = \dfrac{5}{8}$ {double angle formula}

$\therefore \ 2\sin^2 x = \dfrac{3}{8}$

$\therefore \ \sin x = \pm\dfrac{\sqrt{3}}{4}$

$\therefore \ \sin x = \dfrac{\sqrt{3}}{4}$ {x is acute}

b $\sin^2 x + \cos^2 x = 1$

$\therefore \ \left(\dfrac{\sqrt{3}}{4}\right)^2 + \cos^2 x = 1$

$\therefore \ \dfrac{3}{16} + \cos^2 x = 1$

$\therefore \ \cos^2 x = \dfrac{13}{16}$

$\therefore \ \cos x = \pm\dfrac{\sqrt{13}}{4}$

$\therefore \ \cos x = \dfrac{\sqrt{13}}{4}$ {x is acute}

Now, $\sin 2x = 2\sin x \cos x$

$\qquad = 2\left(\dfrac{\sqrt{3}}{4}\right)\left(\dfrac{\sqrt{13}}{4}\right)$

$\qquad = \dfrac{\sqrt{39}}{8}$

$\therefore \ \tan 2x = \dfrac{\sin 2x}{\cos 2x}$

$\qquad = \dfrac{\frac{\sqrt{39}}{8}}{\frac{5}{8}}$

$\qquad = \dfrac{\sqrt{39}}{5}$

30 a $\sin^2\theta + \cos^2\theta = 1$

$\therefore \ \left(\dfrac{2}{3}\right)^2 + \cos^2\theta = 1$

$\therefore \ \cos^2\theta = \dfrac{5}{9}$

$\therefore \ \cos\theta = -\dfrac{\sqrt{5}}{3}$ {θ is obtuse}

$\sin 2\theta = 2\sin\theta\cos\theta$

$\qquad = 2 \times \dfrac{2}{3} \times -\dfrac{\sqrt{5}}{3}$

$\qquad = -\dfrac{4\sqrt{5}}{9}$

b $\cos 2\theta = 1 - 2\sin^2\theta$

$\qquad = 1 - 2\left(\dfrac{2}{3}\right)^2$

$\qquad = 1 - 2\left(\dfrac{4}{9}\right)$

$\qquad = \dfrac{1}{9}$

31
$(\sin x + \cos x)^2 = \sin^2 x + \cos^2 x$

$\therefore \ \sin^2 x + 2\sin x \cos x + \cos^2 x = \sin^2 x + \cos^2 x$

$\therefore \ 2\sin x \cos x = 0$

$\therefore \ \sin x = 0 \text{ or } \cos x = 0$

Since $0 \leqslant x \leqslant \pi$, $x = 0, \dfrac{\pi}{2}$, or π.

32
$\sin^2 t + \cos^2 t = 1$,

$\therefore \ \sin^2 t = 1 - \cos^2 t$

For $0 < t < \pi$, $\sin t > 0$

$\therefore \ \sin t = \sqrt{1 - \cos^2 t}$

$\therefore \ \tan t = \dfrac{\sin t}{\cos t} = \dfrac{\sqrt{1 - \cos^2 t}}{\cos t}$ for $0 < t < \pi$

33 a $\sin^{-1}(3x^2 - 2x) = \dfrac{5\pi}{6}$

$\therefore \ 3x^2 - 2x = \sin\left(\dfrac{5\pi}{6}\right) = \dfrac{1}{2}$

$\therefore \ 6x^2 - 4x - 1 = 0$

$\therefore \quad x = \dfrac{4 \pm \sqrt{(-4)^2 - 4 \times 6(-1)}}{2 \times 6}$

$\qquad = \dfrac{4 \pm \sqrt{40}}{12} = \dfrac{2 \pm \sqrt{10}}{6}$

b $\sin x + \sqrt{3}\cos x = 0$

$\therefore \ \sin x = -\sqrt{3}\cos x$

$\therefore \ \dfrac{\sin x}{\cos x} = -\sqrt{3}$

$\therefore \ \tan x = -\sqrt{3}$

$\therefore$ for $0 \leqslant x \leqslant 2\pi$, $x = \dfrac{2\pi}{3}, \dfrac{5\pi}{3}$

34 a $\dfrac{1 - \cos 2\theta}{\sin 2\theta} = \dfrac{1 - (1 - 2\sin^2\theta)}{2\sin\theta\cos\theta}$

$\qquad = \dfrac{2\sin^2\theta}{2\sin\theta\cos\theta}$

$\qquad = \dfrac{\sin\theta}{\cos\theta}$

$\qquad = \tan\theta$

b $\dfrac{1-\cos 2\theta}{\sin 2\theta} = \sqrt{3}$

$\therefore \quad \tan\theta = \sqrt{3}$

$\therefore \quad \theta = \dfrac{\pi}{3} \quad \text{as} \ 0 < \theta < \dfrac{\pi}{2}$

$\left(\dfrac{1}{2}, \dfrac{\sqrt{3}}{2}\right)$

35 a $\dfrac{\sin^2\theta}{1+\cos\theta} = \dfrac{1-\cos^2\theta}{1+\cos\theta}$

$= \dfrac{(1+\cos\theta)(1-\cos\theta)}{(1+\cos\theta)}$

$= (1-\cos\theta) \quad \text{provided} \ \cos\theta \neq -1$

b $\dfrac{\sin^2\theta}{1+\cos\theta} = \dfrac{1}{2}$

$\therefore \quad 1 - \cos\theta = \dfrac{1}{2}$

$\therefore \quad \cos\theta = \dfrac{1}{2}$

$\therefore \quad \theta = -\dfrac{\pi}{3}, \dfrac{\pi}{3}$

36 a $\quad -3\cos 2\theta - 14\sin\theta + 11$

$= -3(1 - 2\sin^2\theta) - 14\sin\theta + 11$

$= -3 + 6\sin^2\theta - 14\sin\theta + 11$

$= 6\sin^2\theta - 14\sin\theta + 8$

b $\quad -3\cos 2\theta - 14\sin\theta + 11 = 0$

$\therefore \quad 6\sin^2\theta - 14\sin\theta + 8 = 0$

$\therefore \quad 3\sin^2\theta - 7\sin\theta + 4 = 0$

$\therefore \quad (3\sin\theta - 4)(\sin\theta - 1) = 0$

$\therefore \quad \sin\theta = 1 \quad \{-1 \leqslant \sin\theta \leqslant 1\}$

$\therefore \quad \theta = \dfrac{\pi}{2}$

37 a $\quad \cos 2\theta + 2\sqrt{2}\cos\theta - 2$

$= (2\cos^2\theta - 1) + 2\sqrt{2}\cos\theta - 2$

$= 2\cos^2\theta - 1 + 2\sqrt{2}\cos\theta - 2$

$= 2\cos^2\theta + 2\sqrt{2}\cos\theta - 3 \quad \text{as required}$

b $\quad \cos 2\theta + 2\sqrt{2}\cos\theta - 2 = 0$

$\therefore \quad 2\cos^2\theta + 2\sqrt{2}\cos\theta - 3 = 0$

Using the quadratic formula,

$\cos\theta = \dfrac{-2\sqrt{2} \pm \sqrt{(2\sqrt{2})^2 - 4\times 2\times(-3)}}{2\times 2}$

$= \dfrac{-2\sqrt{2} \pm \sqrt{32}}{4}$

$= -\dfrac{\sqrt{2}}{2} \pm \dfrac{4\sqrt{2}}{4}$

$= -\dfrac{1}{\sqrt{2}} \pm \dfrac{2}{\sqrt{2}}$

$= \dfrac{1}{\sqrt{2}} \ \text{ or } \ -\dfrac{3}{\sqrt{2}}$

$\therefore \quad \theta = -\dfrac{\pi}{4}, \dfrac{\pi}{4} \quad \{-1 \leqslant \cos\theta \leqslant 1\}$

38 a $\quad \tan 2A = \sin A$

$\therefore \quad \dfrac{\sin 2A}{\cos 2A} = \sin A$

$\therefore \quad \dfrac{2\sin A\cos A}{2\cos^2 A - 1} = \sin A \quad \{\text{double angle formula}\}$

$\therefore \quad \dfrac{2\cos A}{2\cos^2 A - 1} = 1 \quad \{\sin A \neq 0\}$

$2\cos A = 2\cos^2 A - 1$

$\therefore \quad 2\cos^2 A - 2\cos A - 1 = 0$

---

b $\cos A = \dfrac{2 \pm \sqrt{(-2)^2 - 4\times 2\times(-1)}}{2\times 2}$

$= \dfrac{1 \pm \sqrt{3}}{2}$

But $-1 \leqslant \cos A \leqslant 1$, so $\cos A = \dfrac{1-\sqrt{3}}{2}$

CALCULATORS

1 a Length of arc $= \dfrac{\theta}{360} \times 2\pi r$

$= \dfrac{40}{360} \times 2\pi \times 8$

≈ 5.59 cm

So, perimeter $\approx 8 + 8 + 5.59$

≈ 21.6 cm

b Area of sector $= \dfrac{\theta}{360} \times \pi r^2$

$= \dfrac{40}{360} \times \pi \times 8^2$

$\approx 22.3 \text{ cm}^2$

2 a Length of arc $= \theta r$

$= 2.4 \times 12$

$= 28.8$ cm

b Area of sector $= \dfrac{1}{2}\theta r^2$

$= \dfrac{1}{2} \times 2.4 \times 12^2$

$= 172.8 \text{ cm}^2$

Area of circle $= \pi r^2$

$= \pi \times 12^2$

$= 144\pi \text{ cm}^2$

So, shaded area $= 144\pi - 172.8$

$\approx 280 \text{ cm}^2$

3 a Area $= \dfrac{1}{2}ab\sin\theta$

$= \dfrac{1}{2} \times 4 \times 4 \times \sin\theta$

$\therefore \quad 4 = 8\sin\theta$

$\therefore \quad \sin\theta = \dfrac{1}{2}$

$\therefore \quad \theta = \dfrac{5\pi}{6} \quad \{\text{since } \theta \text{ is obtuse}\}$

b Using the cosine rule,

$x^2 = 4^2 + 4^2 - 2\times 4 \times 4 \times \cos\left(\dfrac{5\pi}{6}\right)$

$\therefore \quad x = \sqrt{4^2 + 4^2 - 2\times 4 \times 4 \times \cos\left(\dfrac{5\pi}{6}\right)}$

$\therefore \quad x \approx 7.73$

4 a

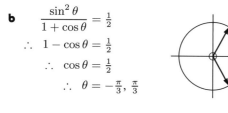

$\sin\alpha = \dfrac{25}{32}$

$\therefore \quad \alpha = \sin^{-1}\left(\dfrac{25}{32}\right)$

$\theta = 2\alpha$

$= 2\sin^{-1}\left(\dfrac{25}{32}\right)$

≈ 1.793 radians

b Area of segment

$= \text{area of sector} - \text{area of triangle}$

$= \dfrac{1}{2}\theta r^2 - \dfrac{1}{2}r^2\sin\theta \quad \{\text{where } \theta \text{ is in radians}\}$

$= \dfrac{1}{2} \times 1.793 \times 32^2 - \dfrac{1}{2} \times 32^2 \times \sin(1.793)$

$\approx 419 \text{ cm}^2$

5 a Area $= \dfrac{1}{2} \times 5.4 \times 7.8 \times \sin 125° \approx 17.3 \text{ cm}^2$

b Using the cosine rule,

$AC^2 = 5.4^2 + 7.8^2 - 2 \times 5.4 \times 7.8 \times \cos 125°$

$\therefore \quad AC = \sqrt{5.4^2 + 7.8^2 - 2 \times 5.4 \times 7.8 \times \cos 125°}$

$\therefore \quad AC \approx 11.8 \text{ cm}$

6 a

The largest angle is opposite the longest side.

$\cos \theta = \dfrac{9^2 + 7^2 - 11^2}{2 \times 9 \times 7}$ {cosine rule}

$\therefore \quad \cos \theta = \dfrac{9}{126}$

$\therefore \quad \theta \approx 85.9°$

b Area of triangle $\approx \frac{1}{2} \times 7 \times 9 \times \sin 85.9°$

$\approx 31.4 \text{ cm}^2$

7 a

$\dfrac{\sin C}{15} = \dfrac{\sin 30°}{12}$ {sine rule}

$\therefore \quad C = \sin^{-1}\left(\dfrac{15 \sin 30°}{12}\right)$

$\therefore \quad C \approx 38.7°$ or $141.3°$

b From **a**, $A\widehat{C}B \approx 38.7°$ or $141.3°$

$\therefore \quad B\widehat{A}C \approx 180° - 30° - 38.7°$ or $180° - 30° - 141.3°$

$\therefore \quad B\widehat{A}C \approx 111°$ or $8.68°$

$\therefore \quad B\widehat{A}C \approx 8.68°$ {since $B\widehat{A}C$ is acute}

8 a

$\dfrac{\sin 2\theta}{8} = \dfrac{\sin \theta}{5}$ {sine rule}

$\therefore \quad \dfrac{2 \sin \theta \cos \theta}{8} = \dfrac{\sin \theta}{5}$

$\therefore \quad \cos \theta = \dfrac{4}{5}$

b $A\widehat{B}C = \pi - 3\theta$

$= \pi - 3 \cos^{-1}\left(\frac{4}{5}\right)$

≈ 1.211

Area of triangle

$\approx \frac{1}{2} \times 5 \times 8 \times \sin(1.211)$

$\approx 18.7 \text{ cm}^2$

9 a $\sin x = 0.785$

$\therefore \quad x \approx 0.9027$ or $\pi - 0.9027$

$\therefore \quad x \approx 0.903$ or 2.24

b $2 \cos x = 5 \sin x$

$\therefore \quad \dfrac{2}{5} = \dfrac{\sin x}{\cos x}$

$\therefore \quad \tan x = \dfrac{2}{5}$

$\therefore \quad x \approx 0.380\,51$ or $\pi + 0.380\,51$

$\therefore \quad x \approx 0.381$ or 3.52

c $\tan 3x = 0.9$

Since $0 \leqslant x \leqslant 2\pi$,

$0 \leqslant 3x \leqslant 6\pi$

$\therefore \quad 3x \approx 0.733, \ 0.733 + \pi,$

$0.733 + 2\pi, \ 0.733 + 3\pi,$

$0.733 + 4\pi, \ 0.733 + 5\pi$

$\therefore \quad x \approx 0.244, \ 1.29, \ 2.34,$

$3.39, \ 4.43, \ 5.48$

d $4 \sin^2 x = \cos^2 x$

$\therefore \quad \dfrac{\sin^2 x}{\cos^2 x} = \frac{1}{4}$

$\therefore \quad \tan^2 x = \frac{1}{4}$

$\therefore \quad \tan x = \pm\frac{1}{2}$

$\therefore \quad x \approx 0.464, \ 2.68,$

$3.61, \ 5.82$

10 a $2 \sin \theta = \sqrt{3}, \quad -2\pi \leqslant \theta \leqslant 2\pi$

$\therefore \quad \sin \theta = \dfrac{\sqrt{3}}{2}$

$\therefore \quad \theta = -\dfrac{5\pi}{3}, \ -\dfrac{4\pi}{3}, \ \dfrac{\pi}{3}, \ \dfrac{2\pi}{3}$

b $2 \sin \theta \leqslant \sqrt{3}, \quad -2\pi \leqslant \theta \leqslant 2\pi$

$\therefore \quad \sin \theta \leqslant \dfrac{\sqrt{3}}{2}$

$\therefore \quad -2\pi \leqslant \theta \leqslant -\dfrac{5\pi}{3}, \ -\dfrac{4\pi}{3} \leqslant \theta \leqslant \dfrac{\pi}{3},$ or $\dfrac{2\pi}{3} \leqslant \theta \leqslant 2\pi$

11 a $\sqrt{2} \cos \theta = -1, \quad -2\pi \leqslant \theta \leqslant 2\pi$

$\therefore \quad \cos \theta = -\dfrac{1}{\sqrt{2}}$

$\therefore \quad \theta = -\dfrac{5\pi}{4}, \ -\dfrac{3\pi}{4}, \ \dfrac{3\pi}{4}, \ \dfrac{5\pi}{4}$

b $\sqrt{2} \cos \theta \leqslant -1, \quad -2\pi \leqslant \theta \leqslant 2\pi$

$\therefore \quad \cos \theta \leqslant -\dfrac{1}{\sqrt{2}}$

$\therefore \quad -\dfrac{5\pi}{4} \leqslant \theta \leqslant -\dfrac{3\pi}{4}$ or $\dfrac{3\pi}{4} \leqslant \theta \leqslant \dfrac{5\pi}{4}$

12 $d = a + b \sin\left(\dfrac{2\pi t}{k}\right)$

a The period $= \dfrac{2\pi}{\frac{2\pi}{k}} = 12$, so $k = 12$

b When $t = 3$ and 15, $d_{\max} = 12.5$

At this time, $\sin\left(\dfrac{2\pi t}{k}\right) = 1$

$\therefore \quad 12.5 = a + b$ .... (1)

When $t = 9$ and 21, $d_{\min} = 8.7$

At this time, $\sin\left(\dfrac{2\pi t}{k}\right) = -1$

$\therefore \quad 8.7 = a - b$ .... (2)

Adding (1) and (2), we get $2a = 21.2$

$\therefore \quad a = 10.6$ and $b = 1.9$

Check: $d = 10.6 + 1.9 \sin\left(\dfrac{\pi t}{6}\right)$ has max. value

$10.6 + 1.9 = 12.5$ when $\sin\left(\dfrac{\pi t}{6}\right) = 1$

$$\therefore \quad \frac{\pi t}{6} = \frac{\pi}{2} + c2\pi$$

$$\therefore \quad \frac{t}{6} = \frac{1}{2} + 2c$$

$$\therefore \quad t = 3 + 12c \quad \checkmark$$

c For the depth of water to be 10 m,

$$10 = 10.6 + 1.9 \sin\left(\frac{2\pi t}{12}\right)$$

$$\therefore \quad t \approx 6.6136, \ 11.386, \ 18.614, \ 23.386$$

So, the first time after 9 pm that the depth of water is 10 m, is at 23.386 hours after midnight, or 11:23 pm.

13

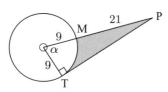

a In $\triangle$OTP, $\cos\alpha = \frac{9}{30} = 0.3$

$$\therefore \quad \alpha = \cos^{-1}(0.3)$$

$$\therefore \quad \alpha \approx 72.542°$$

$$\therefore \quad \alpha \approx 72.5°$$

b
$$\text{Area of } \triangle\text{OTP} \approx \frac{1}{2} \times 9 \times 30 \times \sin 72.542°$$

$$\approx 128.78 \text{ cm}^2$$

$$\text{Area of sector OTM} = \left(\frac{\alpha}{360}\right) \times \pi \times 9^2$$

$$\approx \frac{72.542}{360} \times \pi \times 81$$

$$\approx 51.28 \text{ cm}^2$$

$$\therefore \quad \text{area of shaded region} \approx 128.78 - 51.28$$

$$\approx 77.5 \text{ cm}^2$$

14 a

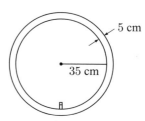

$$AB = 400 \times \frac{3}{4} = 300 \text{ km}$$

$$BC = 400 \times 1\frac{1}{2} = 600 \text{ km}$$

Using the cosine rule,

$$x^2 = 300^2 + 600^2 - 2 \times 300 \times 600 \cos 135°$$

$$\therefore \quad x = \sqrt{300^2 + 600^2 - 600^2 \times \cos 135°}$$

$$\therefore \quad x \approx 839.38$$

$$\therefore \quad \text{the distance is about 839 km.}$$

b
$$\text{time} = \frac{\text{distance}}{\text{speed}} \approx \frac{839.38}{400}$$

$$\approx 2.098$$

$$\approx 2 \text{ hours 6 minutes}$$

15 a We need to solve

$$I = \frac{\sin t}{t^2 + 1} = 0, \quad -4\pi \leqslant t \leqslant 4\pi$$

$$\therefore \quad \sin t = 0$$

$$\therefore \quad t = 0, \pm\pi, \pm 2\pi, \pm 3\pi, \pm 4\pi \text{ milliseconds}$$

There is zero electrical impulse when $t = 0, \pm\pi, \pm 2\pi, \pm 3\pi, \pm 4\pi$ milliseconds.

b Consider the graphs of $y = \dfrac{\sin t}{t^2 + 1}$ and $y = 0.3$.

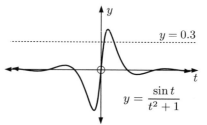

Using technology, the t-coordinates of the points of intersection are about 0.342 and 1.526.

$$\therefore \quad \text{the solutions of } \frac{\sin t}{t^2 + 1} = 0.3$$

$$\text{are } t \approx 0.342 \text{ and } t \approx 1.526$$

c The two solutions in **b** represent the times at which the electrical impulse is 0.3 units. Between these times, the electrical impulse reaches its maximum.

16 a
$$\tan\theta = 2\cos\theta$$

$$\therefore \quad \frac{\sin\theta}{\cos\theta} = 2\cos\theta$$

$$\therefore \quad \sin\theta = 2\cos^2\theta \quad \{\text{as } 0 < \theta < \tfrac{\pi}{2}, \ \cos\theta \neq 0\}$$

$$\therefore \quad \sin\theta = 2(1 - \sin^2\theta)$$

$$\therefore \quad \sin\theta = 2 - 2\sin^2\theta$$

$$\therefore \quad 2\sin^2\theta + \sin\theta - 2 = 0$$

b
$$\sin\theta = \frac{-1 \pm \sqrt{1^2 - 4 \times 2(-2)}}{2 \times 2} = \frac{-1 \pm \sqrt{17}}{4}$$

But $-1 \leqslant \sin\theta \leqslant 1$,

so $\sin\theta = \dfrac{-1 + \sqrt{17}}{4} \approx 0.7808$

$$\therefore \quad \theta \approx 0.896 \text{ or } 2.25$$

$$\therefore \quad \theta \approx 0.896 \quad \{\text{as } 0 < \theta < \tfrac{\pi}{2}\}$$

17

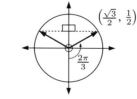

5 cm

35 cm

a i At 0 seconds, the valve is at its lowest position, closest to the road, so the height of the valve above the road is 5 cm.

ii The wheel rotates at a constant speed of 4 revolutions per second.

$$\therefore \quad \text{after } \frac{1}{12} \text{ second, the wheel has rotated}$$

$$\frac{1}{12} \times 4 = \frac{1}{3} \text{ revolution.}$$

$$\therefore \quad \text{the valve will have moved through an angle of } \frac{2\pi}{3}.$$

So, the valve will be at a height of $1\frac{1}{2}$ times the radius of the wheel, plus 5 cm.

$$\therefore \quad \text{the height of the valve above the road}$$

$$= 1.5 \times 35 + 5$$

$$= 57.5 \text{ cm}$$

b $H(t) = a\sin(b(t-c)) + d$ cm

  i Amplitude = radius of the wheel
$$= 35 \text{ cm}$$
$$\therefore \ a = 35$$

  ii The centre of the wheel is 40 cm above the ground, so the principal axis is at $H = 40$ cm.
$$\therefore \ d = 40$$

  iii There are 4 revolutions per second, so the period is $\frac{1}{4}$ second.

    The period $= \dfrac{2\pi}{b}$
$$\therefore \ \frac{1}{4} = \frac{2\pi}{b}$$
$$\therefore \ b = 8\pi$$

  iv $H(t) = 35\sin(8\pi(t-c)) + 40$

    Now from **a i**, $H(0) = 5$
$$\therefore \ 5 = 35\sin(8\pi(-c)) + 40$$
$$\therefore \ -1 = \sin(8\pi(-c))$$
$$\therefore \ -\frac{\pi}{2} = 8\pi(-c)$$
$$\therefore \ c = \frac{1}{16}$$

c From **b**, $H(t) = 35\sin(8\pi(t-\frac{1}{16})) + 40$

  Now $H(t) = 60$ when
$$35\sin(8\pi(t-\tfrac{1}{16})) + 40 = 60$$
$$\therefore \ \sin(8\pi(t-\tfrac{1}{16})) = \frac{20}{35}$$
$$\therefore \ t \approx 0.0867$$

It takes approximately 0.0867 seconds for the valve to rise to 60 cm above the road.

SOLUTIONS TO TOPIC 4 (VECTORS)

NO CALCULATORS

1 **a** $p = \begin{pmatrix} -4 \\ 1 \end{pmatrix}$, $q = \begin{pmatrix} 2 \\ 3 \end{pmatrix}$

  b $p + q = \begin{pmatrix} -4 \\ 1 \end{pmatrix} + \begin{pmatrix} 2 \\ 3 \end{pmatrix}$
$$= \begin{pmatrix} -2 \\ 4 \end{pmatrix}$$

  So, R is $(-2, 4)$.

  c Since R is defined by $p + q$,
$\overrightarrow{PR} = \overrightarrow{OQ} = q$ and
$\overrightarrow{QR} = \overrightarrow{OP} = p$
$$\therefore \ OPRQ \text{ is a parallelogram.}$$

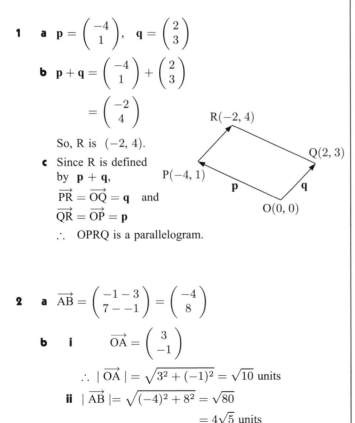

2 **a** $\overrightarrow{AB} = \begin{pmatrix} -1-3 \\ 7--1 \end{pmatrix} = \begin{pmatrix} -4 \\ 8 \end{pmatrix}$

  b **i** $\overrightarrow{OA} = \begin{pmatrix} 3 \\ -1 \end{pmatrix}$
$$\therefore \ |\overrightarrow{OA}| = \sqrt{3^2 + (-1)^2} = \sqrt{10} \text{ units}$$

    ii $|\overrightarrow{AB}| = \sqrt{(-4)^2 + 8^2} = \sqrt{80}$
$$= 4\sqrt{5} \text{ units}$$

c $\overrightarrow{AO} = \begin{pmatrix} -3 \\ 1 \end{pmatrix}$

Let the angle between $\overrightarrow{AO}$ and $\overrightarrow{AB}$ be θ.

Now $\cos\theta = \dfrac{\overrightarrow{AO} \bullet \overrightarrow{AB}}{|\overrightarrow{AO}||\overrightarrow{AB}|}$

$$= \frac{\begin{pmatrix} -3 \\ 1 \end{pmatrix} \bullet \begin{pmatrix} -4 \\ 8 \end{pmatrix}}{\sqrt{10} \times 4\sqrt{5}}$$
$$= \frac{12 + 8}{20\sqrt{2}}$$
$$= \frac{1}{\sqrt{2}}$$
$$\therefore \ \theta = \frac{\pi}{4}$$
$$\therefore \ \widehat{OAB} = \frac{\pi}{4}$$

d Area of $\triangle OAB = \frac{1}{2} \times \sqrt{10} \times 4\sqrt{5} \times \sin(\frac{\pi}{4})$
$$= \frac{20\sqrt{2}}{2} \times \frac{1}{\sqrt{2}}$$
$$= 10 \text{ units}^2$$

3 **a** $a = i - 2j + 3k$

  b $|a| = \sqrt{1^2 + (-2)^2 + 3^2} = \sqrt{14}$ units

  c The unit vector in the opposite direction is $\frac{-1}{\sqrt{14}}\begin{pmatrix} 1 \\ -2 \\ 3 \end{pmatrix}$.

4 **a** $\begin{pmatrix} k \\ 1 \\ 3 \end{pmatrix}$ and $\begin{pmatrix} 4 \\ k \\ 3k \end{pmatrix}$ are parallel if $\begin{pmatrix} 4 \\ k \\ 3k \end{pmatrix} = a\begin{pmatrix} k \\ 1 \\ 3 \end{pmatrix}$

  for some a.

  Thus, $4 = ak$ .... (1)
$$k = a \quad .... (2)$$
$$3k = 3a \quad .... (3)$$

  From (1) and (2), $k^2 = 4$ and so $k = \pm 2$.
  Hence the vectors are parallel if $k = \pm 2$.

  b The vectors are perpendicular if $\begin{pmatrix} k \\ 1 \\ 3 \end{pmatrix} \bullet \begin{pmatrix} 4 \\ k \\ 3k \end{pmatrix} = 0$
$$\therefore \ 4k + k + 9k = 0$$
$$\therefore \ k = 0$$

5 **a** $\overrightarrow{BC} = \begin{pmatrix} 4--1 \\ 4-2 \end{pmatrix} = \begin{pmatrix} 5 \\ 2 \end{pmatrix}$

  b $\overrightarrow{OD} = \overrightarrow{OA} + \overrightarrow{AD}$
$$= \overrightarrow{OA} + \overrightarrow{BC}$$
$$= \begin{pmatrix} 1 \\ 7 \end{pmatrix} + \begin{pmatrix} 5 \\ 2 \end{pmatrix}$$
$$= \begin{pmatrix} 6 \\ 9 \end{pmatrix}$$
$$\therefore \ D \text{ is } (6, 9).$$

  c $\overrightarrow{AC} = \begin{pmatrix} 3 \\ -3 \end{pmatrix}$ and $\overrightarrow{BD} = \begin{pmatrix} 7 \\ 7 \end{pmatrix}$

  Now $\overrightarrow{AC} \bullet \overrightarrow{BD} = 3 \times 7 + (-3) \times 7$
$$= 0$$
$$\therefore \ \text{the angle between the diagonals is } 90°.$$

d Opposite sides are parallel, and the diagonals are perpendicular.

∴ ABCD is a rhombus.

6 a $\overrightarrow{AC} = \overrightarrow{AB} + \overrightarrow{BC} = \mathbf{a} + \mathbf{b}$

$\overrightarrow{BD} = \overrightarrow{BC} + \overrightarrow{CD} = \mathbf{b} - \mathbf{a}$

b $\overrightarrow{AC} \bullet \overrightarrow{BD} = (\mathbf{a} + \mathbf{b}) \bullet (\mathbf{b} - \mathbf{a})$

$= \mathbf{a} \bullet \mathbf{b} - \mathbf{a} \bullet \mathbf{a} + \mathbf{b} \bullet \mathbf{b} - \mathbf{b} \bullet \mathbf{a}$

$= \mathbf{b} \bullet \mathbf{b} - \mathbf{a} \bullet \mathbf{a}$ {as $\mathbf{a} \bullet \mathbf{b} = \mathbf{b} \bullet \mathbf{a}$}

$= |\mathbf{b}|^2 - |\mathbf{a}|^2$

c If the parallelogram is a rhombus, then $|\mathbf{b}| = |\mathbf{a}|$

and so $\overrightarrow{AC} \bullet \overrightarrow{BD} = |\mathbf{b}|^2 - |\mathbf{b}|^2 = 0$

∴ $\overrightarrow{AC}$ and $\overrightarrow{BD}$ are perpendicular.

7 $\begin{pmatrix} t \\ 1 \end{pmatrix} \bullet \begin{pmatrix} t-4 \\ -5 \end{pmatrix} = 0$

∴ $t(t-4) + -5 = 0$

∴ $t^2 - 4t - 5 = 0$

∴ $(t-5)(t+1) = 0$

∴ $t = 5$ or -1

8 a $\overrightarrow{OM} = \mathbf{a} + \frac{1}{2}\overrightarrow{AB}$

$= \mathbf{a} + \frac{1}{2}(-\mathbf{a} + \mathbf{b})$

$= \frac{1}{2}\mathbf{a} + \frac{1}{2}\mathbf{b}$

$= \frac{1}{2}(\mathbf{a} + \mathbf{b})$

b $\overrightarrow{OM} = \frac{1}{2}(\mathbf{a} + \mathbf{b})$

$= \frac{1}{2}\left(\begin{pmatrix} 1 \\ 3 \end{pmatrix} + \begin{pmatrix} 5 \\ -1 \end{pmatrix}\right)$

$= \frac{1}{2}\begin{pmatrix} 6 \\ 2 \end{pmatrix}$

$= \begin{pmatrix} 3 \\ 1 \end{pmatrix}$

So, M is $(3, 1)$.

c $\begin{pmatrix} x \\ y \end{pmatrix} = \begin{pmatrix} 0 \\ 0 \end{pmatrix} + t\begin{pmatrix} 3 \\ 1 \end{pmatrix}, \quad t \in \mathbb{R}$

∴ $\begin{pmatrix} x \\ y \end{pmatrix} = t\begin{pmatrix} 3 \\ 1 \end{pmatrix}, \quad t \in \mathbb{R}$

d Any point P on (OM) has coordinates $(3t, t)$.

If $|\overrightarrow{PM}| = 2\sqrt{10}$

then $\sqrt{(3-3t)^2 + (1-t)^2} = 2\sqrt{10}$

∴ $9 - 18t + 9t^2 + 1 - 2t + t^2 = 40$

∴ $10t^2 - 20t + 10 = 40$

∴ $t^2 - 2t - 3 = 0$

∴ $(t-3)(t+1) = 0$

∴ $t = -1$ or 3

Letting $t = -1$, $\begin{pmatrix} x \\ y \end{pmatrix} = \begin{pmatrix} -3 \\ -1 \end{pmatrix}$.

Letting $t = 3$, $\begin{pmatrix} x \\ y \end{pmatrix} = \begin{pmatrix} 9 \\ 3 \end{pmatrix}$.

So, the two points are $(-3, -1)$ and $(9, 3)$.

9 $\overrightarrow{OC} = \begin{pmatrix} 5 \\ 22 \end{pmatrix}$

So, $\begin{pmatrix} 5 \\ 22 \end{pmatrix} = r\begin{pmatrix} 3 \\ -6 \end{pmatrix} + s\begin{pmatrix} 7 \\ 2 \end{pmatrix}$

$= \begin{pmatrix} 3r + 7s \\ -6r + 2s \end{pmatrix}$

∴ $3r + 7s = 5$ .... (1)

$-6r + 2s = 22$ .... (2)

∴ $6r + 14s = 10$ {$2 \times$ (1)}

$\underline{-6r + 2s = 22}$

Adding, $16s = 32$ and so $s = 2$

Substituting into (1), $3r + 7(2) = 5$

∴ $3r = -9$

∴ $r = -3$

So, $r = -3$, $s = 2$.

10 a $\begin{pmatrix} x \\ y \end{pmatrix} = \begin{pmatrix} -5 \\ -2 \end{pmatrix} + t\begin{pmatrix} 2 \\ 3 \end{pmatrix}, \quad t \in \mathbb{R}$

b $x = -5 + 2t = -1$

∴ $2t = 4$

∴ $t = 2$

Now, $y = -2 + 3t$

$= -2 + 3(2)$

$= 4$

So, the point is $(-1, 4)$.

c i L_2 is perpendicular to $\begin{pmatrix} 2 \\ 3 \end{pmatrix}$,

so L_2 has direction vector $\begin{pmatrix} -3 \\ 2 \end{pmatrix}$.

∴ its vector equation is

$\begin{pmatrix} x \\ y \end{pmatrix} = \begin{pmatrix} 4 \\ 5 \end{pmatrix} + s\begin{pmatrix} -3 \\ 2 \end{pmatrix}, \quad s \in \mathbb{R}$.

ii L_1 meets L_2 where

$\begin{pmatrix} -5 \\ -2 \end{pmatrix} + t\begin{pmatrix} 2 \\ 3 \end{pmatrix} = \begin{pmatrix} 4 \\ 5 \end{pmatrix} + s\begin{pmatrix} -3 \\ 2 \end{pmatrix}$

∴ $t\begin{pmatrix} 2 \\ 3 \end{pmatrix} - s\begin{pmatrix} -3 \\ 2 \end{pmatrix} = \begin{pmatrix} 4 \\ 5 \end{pmatrix} - \begin{pmatrix} -5 \\ -2 \end{pmatrix}$

$= \begin{pmatrix} 9 \\ 7 \end{pmatrix}$

So, $2t + 3s = 9$ .... (1)

$3t - 2s = 7$ .... (2)

∴ $4t + 6s = 18$ {$2 \times$ (1)}

$\underline{9t - 6s = 21}$ {$3 \times$ (2)}

Adding, $13t = 39$

∴ $t = 3$

Substituting $t = 3$ into L_1 gives:

$\begin{pmatrix} x \\ y \end{pmatrix} = \begin{pmatrix} -5 \\ -2 \end{pmatrix} + 3\begin{pmatrix} 2 \\ 3 \end{pmatrix} = \begin{pmatrix} 1 \\ 7 \end{pmatrix}$

So, the lines meet at $(1, 7)$.

iii The shortest distance from $(4, 5)$ to the line L_1 is found when the line joining point $(4, 5)$ to L_1 is perpendicular to L_1.

Since L_2 passes through $(4, 5)$ and is perpendicular to L_1, we need the distance from $(4, 5)$ to the point of intersection of L_1 and L_2, which is $(1, 7)$. {from **ii**}

$$\text{Distance} = \sqrt{(1-4)^2 + (7-5)^2}$$
$$= \sqrt{9+4} = \sqrt{13} \text{ units}$$

11 **a**
$$r(\mathbf{v} - \mathbf{w}) = (r+s)\mathbf{i} - 20\mathbf{j}$$
$$\therefore \quad r(5\mathbf{i} - 2\mathbf{j} - \mathbf{i} - 3\mathbf{j}) = (r+s)\mathbf{i} - 20\mathbf{j}$$
$$\therefore \quad r(4\mathbf{i} - 5\mathbf{j}) = (r+s)\mathbf{i} - 20\mathbf{j}$$
$$\therefore \quad 4r\mathbf{i} - 5r\mathbf{j} = (r+s)\mathbf{i} - 20\mathbf{j}$$
$$\therefore \quad 4r = r+s \quad \text{and} \quad -5r = -20$$
$$\therefore \quad r = 4$$
$$\therefore \quad 16 = 4 + s$$
So, $r = 4, \quad s = 12$.

b $\cos\theta = \dfrac{\begin{pmatrix} 5 \\ -2 \end{pmatrix} \bullet \begin{pmatrix} 1 \\ 3 \end{pmatrix}}{\left| \begin{pmatrix} 5 \\ -2 \end{pmatrix} \right| \left| \begin{pmatrix} 1 \\ 3 \end{pmatrix} \right|}$

$$= \frac{5-6}{\sqrt{25+4}\sqrt{1+9}}$$
$$= \frac{-1}{\sqrt{29}\sqrt{10}}$$
$$= -\frac{1}{\sqrt{290}}$$

12 **a** The line has direction vector $= \begin{pmatrix} 3 \\ 1 \end{pmatrix}$
∴ its vector equation is
$$\begin{pmatrix} x \\ y \end{pmatrix} = \begin{pmatrix} -2 \\ -1 \end{pmatrix} + t\begin{pmatrix} 3 \\ 1 \end{pmatrix}, \quad t \in \mathbb{R}$$

b The line $x = 1 + kt$, $y = 2 - t$, $t \in \mathbb{R}$ has direction vector $\begin{pmatrix} k \\ -1 \end{pmatrix}$.

$\therefore \begin{pmatrix} 3 \\ 1 \end{pmatrix} \bullet \begin{pmatrix} k \\ -1 \end{pmatrix} = \left| \begin{pmatrix} 3 \\ 1 \end{pmatrix} \right| \left| \begin{pmatrix} k \\ -1 \end{pmatrix} \right| \cos(\frac{\pi}{3})$

$$\therefore \quad 3k - 1 = \sqrt{3^2 + 1^2}\sqrt{k^2 + (-1)^2} \times \tfrac{1}{2}$$
$$\therefore \quad 6k - 2 = \sqrt{10(k^2 + 1)}$$
$$\therefore \quad (6k-2)^2 = 10(k^2 + 1)$$
$$\therefore \quad 36k^2 - 24k + 4 = 10k^2 + 10$$
$$\therefore \quad 26k^2 - 24k - 6 = 0$$
$$\therefore \quad 13k^2 - 12k - 3 = 0 \quad \text{as required}$$

13 **a** **i** $\overrightarrow{OA} = -2\mathbf{i} + 4\mathbf{j}$
∴ A is $(-2, 4)$.

ii $\overrightarrow{OC} = \overrightarrow{OA} + \overrightarrow{AC}$
$$= \overrightarrow{OA} - \overrightarrow{CA}$$
$$= -2\mathbf{i} + 4\mathbf{j} - (-6\mathbf{i} + 2\mathbf{j})$$
$$= 4\mathbf{i} + 2\mathbf{j}$$
∴ C is $(4, 2)$.

iii $\overrightarrow{CB}$ is parallel to $\mathbf{j}$, so (BC) is vertical.
∴ B and C have the same x-coordinate, which is 4.
Suppose B has y-coordinate b.
Since $\overrightarrow{AB} \bullet \overrightarrow{OA} = 0$,
$$\begin{pmatrix} 4 - -2 \\ b - 4 \end{pmatrix} \bullet \begin{pmatrix} -2 \\ 4 \end{pmatrix} = 0$$
$$\therefore \quad 6(-2) + 4(b-4) = 0$$
$$\therefore \quad 4b - 28 = 0$$
$$\therefore \quad 4b = 28$$
$$\therefore \quad b = 7$$
∴ B is $(4, 7)$.

b Since P lies on [BC], P has x-coordinate 4.
Since [BC] is vertical and $\overrightarrow{AP}$ is perpendicular to $\overrightarrow{BC}$, [AP] must be horizontal.
∴ A and P have the same y-coordinate, which is 4.
∴ P is $(4, 4)$.

c BC $= 5$ units
AP $= 6$ units
∴ area of triangle ABC
$$= \tfrac{1}{2} \times \text{base} \times \text{height}$$
$$= \tfrac{1}{2} \times 5 \times 6$$
$$= 15 \text{ units}^2$$

14 **a** $\mathbf{m} + \mathbf{n} = \mathbf{i} + 6\mathbf{j} - 2\mathbf{k}$
$$\therefore \quad |\mathbf{m} + \mathbf{n}| = \sqrt{1 + 36 + 4}$$
$$= \sqrt{41} \text{ units}$$

b $\mathbf{m} \bullet \mathbf{n} = (3 \times -2) + (1 \times 5) + (2 \times -4)$
$$= -6 + 5 - 8$$
$$= -9$$

c $\begin{pmatrix} x \\ y \\ z \end{pmatrix} = \begin{pmatrix} 1 \\ -1 \\ 2 \end{pmatrix} + t\begin{pmatrix} 3 \\ 1 \\ 2 \end{pmatrix}, \quad t \in \mathbb{R}$

15 The vectors are perpendicular, so $\begin{pmatrix} 2t \\ -4 \\ 7 \end{pmatrix} \bullet \begin{pmatrix} 3 \\ t \\ -8 \end{pmatrix} = 0$
$$\therefore \quad 6t - 4t - 56 = 0$$
$$\therefore \quad 2t = 56$$
$$\therefore \quad t = 28$$

16 **a** $\begin{pmatrix} x \\ y \\ z \end{pmatrix} = \begin{pmatrix} 5 \\ 0 \\ -2 \end{pmatrix} + t\begin{pmatrix} 1 \\ 2 \\ 3 \end{pmatrix}, \quad t \in \mathbb{R}$

b $\begin{pmatrix} x \\ y \\ z \end{pmatrix} = \begin{pmatrix} -2 \\ 5 \\ 4 \end{pmatrix} + t\begin{pmatrix} 2 \\ -3 \\ 4 \end{pmatrix}, \quad t \in \mathbb{R}$

c $\mathbf{j} = \begin{pmatrix} 0 \\ 1 \\ 0 \end{pmatrix}$ is perpendicular to the XOZ plane.
$$\therefore \quad \begin{pmatrix} x \\ y \\ z \end{pmatrix} = \begin{pmatrix} 2 \\ -4 \\ 1 \end{pmatrix} + t\begin{pmatrix} 0 \\ 1 \\ 0 \end{pmatrix},$$
$$t \in \mathbb{R}$$

17 **a** $x = 5 + 7t$, $y = -1 + 2t$, $z = 2 - 3t$, $t \in \mathbb{R}$
b $x = 2t$, $y = 2 - 3t$, $z = -6 + t$, $t \in \mathbb{R}$
c The direction vector $= \begin{pmatrix} 8 - 2 \\ 6 - 5 \\ 2 - 1 \end{pmatrix} = \begin{pmatrix} 6 \\ 1 \\ 1 \end{pmatrix}$
$$\therefore \quad x = 2 + 6t, \quad y = 5 + t, \quad z = 1 + t, \quad t \in \mathbb{R}$$

18 **a** $\mathbf{a} - 4\mathbf{x} = 2\mathbf{b}$
$$\therefore \quad -4\mathbf{x} = 2\mathbf{b} - \mathbf{a}$$
$$\therefore \quad \mathbf{x} = \tfrac{1}{4}(\mathbf{a} - 2\mathbf{b})$$
$$= \tfrac{1}{4}\left(\begin{pmatrix} 4 \\ -2 \\ 1 \end{pmatrix} - \begin{pmatrix} 6 \\ 4 \\ -8 \end{pmatrix} \right)$$
$$= \tfrac{1}{4}\begin{pmatrix} -2 \\ -6 \\ 9 \end{pmatrix} = \begin{pmatrix} -\frac{1}{2} \\ -1\frac{1}{2} \\ 2\frac{1}{4} \end{pmatrix}$$

b If the vectors are parallel,

then $\begin{pmatrix} p \\ q \\ -3 \end{pmatrix} = k \begin{pmatrix} 4 \\ -2 \\ 1 \end{pmatrix}$ for some scalar k

$\therefore$ $p = 4k$, $q = -2k$, and $-3 = k$

$\therefore$ $p = -12$ and $q = 6$

c If the vectors are perpendicular,

then $\begin{pmatrix} -10 \\ k^2 \\ k+10 \end{pmatrix} \bullet \begin{pmatrix} 3 \\ 2 \\ -4 \end{pmatrix} = 0$

$\therefore$ $-30 + 2k^2 - 4(k+10) = 0$

$\therefore$ $-30 + 2k^2 - 4k - 40 = 0$

$\therefore$ $2k^2 - 4k - 70 = 0$

$\therefore$ $k^2 - 2k - 35 = 0$

$\therefore$ $(k-7)(k+5) = 0$

$\therefore$ $k = 7$ or -5

19 a i $\overrightarrow{AB} = \begin{pmatrix} 5-1 \\ -1--1 \\ -1-2 \end{pmatrix} = \begin{pmatrix} 4 \\ 0 \\ -3 \end{pmatrix}$

So, L_1 has equation

$\begin{pmatrix} x \\ y \\ z \end{pmatrix} = \begin{pmatrix} 1 \\ -1 \\ 2 \end{pmatrix} + t \begin{pmatrix} 4 \\ 0 \\ -3 \end{pmatrix}$, $t \in \mathbb{R}$.

ii Any point P on L_1 has coordinates $(1+4t, -1, 2-3t)$.

$\therefore$ $\overrightarrow{AP} = \begin{pmatrix} 4t \\ 0 \\ -3t \end{pmatrix}$

Now $|\overrightarrow{AP}| = 20$, so $\sqrt{(4t)^2 + (-3t)^2} = 20$

$\therefore$ $16t^2 + 9t^2 = 400$

$\therefore$ $t^2 = 16$

$\therefore$ $t = \pm 4$

So, letting $t = 4$, a point on L_1 which is 20 units from A is

$(1+4(4), -1, 2-3(4)) = (17, -1, -10)$.

iii L_1 meets the YOZ plane when $x = 0$

$\therefore$ $1 + 4t = 0$

$\therefore$ $t = -\frac{1}{4}$

When $t = -\frac{1}{4}$, P is $(0, -1, 2\frac{3}{4})$.

$\therefore$ L_1 meets the YOZ plane at $(0, -1, \frac{11}{4})$.

b i $\begin{pmatrix} x \\ y \\ z \end{pmatrix} = \begin{pmatrix} 4 \\ 1 \\ -\frac{13}{2} \end{pmatrix} + s \begin{pmatrix} -3 \\ 2 \\ -4 \end{pmatrix}$, $s \in \mathbb{R}$

ii The direction vectors of the lines are

$\begin{pmatrix} 4 \\ 0 \\ -3 \end{pmatrix}$ and $\begin{pmatrix} -3 \\ 2 \\ -4 \end{pmatrix}$.

Now $\begin{pmatrix} 4 \\ 0 \\ -3 \end{pmatrix} \bullet \begin{pmatrix} -3 \\ 2 \\ -4 \end{pmatrix} = -12 + 0 + 12 = 0$

$\therefore$ L_1 is perpendicular to L_2.

c i The y-coordinate of P will be the same as the y-coordinate of any point on L_1 which is -1.

ii L_1 meets L_2 at the point on L_2 where $y = -1$.

$\therefore$ $1 + 2s = -1$

$\therefore$ $2s = -2$

$\therefore$ $s = -1$

$\therefore$ $x = 4 - 3s$ and $z = -\frac{13}{2} - 4s$

$= 4 - 3(-1)$ $\qquad = -\frac{13}{2} - 4(-1)$

$= 7$ $\qquad = -\frac{5}{2}$

$\therefore$ L_1 meets L_2 at $(7, -1, -\frac{5}{2})$.

d The shortest distance from C to the line L_1 is the distance from C to the point of intersection of L_1 and L_2, which is $(7, -1, -\frac{5}{2})$.

Distance $= \sqrt{(7-4)^2 + (-1-1)^2 + (-\frac{5}{2} - -\frac{13}{2})^2}$

$= \sqrt{9 + 4 + 16}$

$= \sqrt{29}$ units

20 a $\mathbf{p} = \left(1 - \frac{t}{12}\right)\mathbf{a} + t\mathbf{b}$

At time $t = 0$, $\mathbf{p} = (1-0)\mathbf{a} + 0\mathbf{b}$

$\therefore$ $\mathbf{p} = \mathbf{a}$

So, the train is at point A at time $t = 0$.

b The train is at point B when

$\mathbf{p} = 0\mathbf{a} + 1\mathbf{b} = \mathbf{b}$

$\therefore$ $t = 12$

It takes 12 minutes for the train to reach B.

c i Distance from A to B

$= \sqrt{(2-1)^2 + (2-3)^2 + (1-0)^2}$

$= \sqrt{1 + 1 + 1}$

$= \sqrt{3}$ km

ii 12 minutes $= \frac{1}{5}$ hour

speed $= \dfrac{\text{distance}}{\text{time}}$

$= \dfrac{\sqrt{3} \text{ km}}{\frac{1}{5} \text{ hour}}$

$= 5\sqrt{3}$ km h^{-1}

21 $\mathbf{b} = \begin{pmatrix} 2 \\ 0 \\ -1 \end{pmatrix}$, $\mathbf{c} - 2\mathbf{a} = \begin{pmatrix} -1 \\ 2 \\ 3 \end{pmatrix} - 2\begin{pmatrix} 1 \\ 3 \\ k \end{pmatrix}$

$= \begin{pmatrix} -3 \\ -4 \\ 3 - 2k \end{pmatrix}$

Now $\mathbf{b}$ is perpendicular to $\mathbf{c} - 2\mathbf{a}$

$\therefore$ $\begin{pmatrix} 2 \\ 0 \\ -1 \end{pmatrix} \bullet \begin{pmatrix} -3 \\ -4 \\ 3 - 2k \end{pmatrix} = 0$

$\therefore$ $-6 - 3 + 2k = 0$

$\therefore$ $2k = 9$

$\therefore$ $k = \frac{9}{2}$

22 a $\overrightarrow{AB} = \begin{pmatrix} 0--1 \\ 1-2 \\ 3-1 \end{pmatrix} = \begin{pmatrix} 1 \\ -1 \\ 2 \end{pmatrix}$

$\therefore$ line (AB) has equation

$\mathbf{r} = \begin{pmatrix} -1 \\ 2 \\ 1 \end{pmatrix} + t \begin{pmatrix} 1 \\ -1 \\ 2 \end{pmatrix}$, $t \in \mathbb{R}$

b The line L has direction vector $\begin{pmatrix} 2 \\ 0 \\ -1 \end{pmatrix}$

and (AB) has direction vector $\begin{pmatrix} 1 \\ -1 \\ 2 \end{pmatrix}$.

If θ is the angle between the lines, then

$$\cos \theta = \frac{\left| \begin{pmatrix} 2 \\ 0 \\ -1 \end{pmatrix} \bullet \begin{pmatrix} 1 \\ -1 \\ 2 \end{pmatrix} \right|}{\left| \begin{pmatrix} 2 \\ 0 \\ -1 \end{pmatrix} \right| \left| \begin{pmatrix} 1 \\ -1 \\ 2 \end{pmatrix} \right|}$$

$$= \frac{|\, 2 + 0 - 2 \,|}{\sqrt{2^2 + (-1)^2} \sqrt{1^2 + (-1)^2 + 2^2}}$$

$$= 0$$

$$\therefore \quad \theta = 90°$$

So, the angle between (AB) and L is $90°$.

CALCULATORS

1 a $\overrightarrow{AC} = \begin{pmatrix} 16 - 2 \\ 6 - 10 \end{pmatrix} = \begin{pmatrix} 14 \\ -4 \end{pmatrix}$

b M is $\left(\dfrac{-2 + 16}{2}, \dfrac{2 + 6}{2} \right)$ which is $(7, 4)$.

$$\therefore \quad \overrightarrow{AM} = \begin{pmatrix} 7 - 2 \\ 4 - 10 \end{pmatrix} = \begin{pmatrix} 5 \\ -6 \end{pmatrix}$$

c

$\overrightarrow{AB} = \begin{pmatrix} -2 - 2 \\ 2 - 10 \end{pmatrix} = \begin{pmatrix} -4 \\ -8 \end{pmatrix}$

$\overrightarrow{AC} = \begin{pmatrix} 14 \\ -4 \end{pmatrix}$

$$\cos \theta = \frac{\overrightarrow{AB} \bullet \overrightarrow{AC}}{|\,\overrightarrow{AB}\,|\,|\,\overrightarrow{AC}\,|}$$

$$= \frac{-56 + 32}{\sqrt{16 + 64} \sqrt{196 + 16}}$$

$$= \frac{-24}{\sqrt{80 \times 212}}$$

$$\therefore \quad \theta = \cos^{-1}\left(\frac{-24}{\sqrt{80 \times 212}} \right) \approx 101°$$

2 $\mathbf{p} = 4\mathbf{i} - 9\mathbf{j}, \quad \mathbf{q} = -12\mathbf{i} + 5\mathbf{j}$

a $|\,\mathbf{q}\,| = \sqrt{144 + 25}$
$\qquad = \sqrt{169}$
$\qquad = 13$ units

b $\mathbf{p} \bullet \mathbf{q}$
$\quad = \begin{pmatrix} 4 \\ -9 \end{pmatrix} \bullet \begin{pmatrix} -12 \\ 5 \end{pmatrix}$
$\quad = -48 + -45$
$\quad = -93$

c The angle θ between $\mathbf{p}$ and $\mathbf{q}$ has

$$\cos \theta = \frac{\mathbf{p} \bullet \mathbf{q}}{|\,\mathbf{p}\,|\,|\,\mathbf{q}\,|}$$

$$= \frac{-93}{\sqrt{16 + 81} \times 13}$$

$$= \frac{-93}{13\sqrt{97}}$$

$$\therefore \quad \theta \approx 137°$$

d A unit vector parallel to $\mathbf{q}$

$$= \frac{1}{|\,\mathbf{q}\,|} \mathbf{q}$$

$$= \tfrac{1}{13}(-12\mathbf{i} + 5\mathbf{j})$$

$$= -\tfrac{12}{13}\mathbf{i} + \tfrac{5}{13}\mathbf{j}$$

3 a $\overrightarrow{QR} = \begin{pmatrix} 10 - 4 \\ 6 - 10 \end{pmatrix} = \begin{pmatrix} 6 \\ -4 \end{pmatrix} = \overrightarrow{OP}$ as required

Since one pair of opposite sides are equal in length and direction, the other pair of opposite sides must also be equal in length and parallel.

$\therefore$ OPRQ is a parallelogram.

b M is $\left(\dfrac{6 + 4}{2}, \dfrac{-4 + 10}{2} \right)$ or $(5, 3)$.

c $\overrightarrow{OM} = \begin{pmatrix} 5 \\ 3 \end{pmatrix}$

$\overrightarrow{MR} = \begin{pmatrix} 10 - 5 \\ 6 - 3 \end{pmatrix} = \begin{pmatrix} 5 \\ 3 \end{pmatrix}$

$\therefore \quad \overrightarrow{OM} = \overrightarrow{MR}$, so O, M, and R are collinear.

d The direction vector of (OR) is $\begin{pmatrix} 10 \\ 6 \end{pmatrix}$, and the line passes through $(0, 0)$.

$\therefore$ its vector equation is $\begin{pmatrix} x \\ y \end{pmatrix} = t \begin{pmatrix} 10 \\ 6 \end{pmatrix}, \quad t \in \mathbb{R}$.

4 a $\begin{pmatrix} x \\ y \end{pmatrix} = \begin{pmatrix} 6 \\ 17 \end{pmatrix} + s \begin{pmatrix} -1 \\ -2 \end{pmatrix}, \quad s \in \mathbb{R}$

b i The direction vector of L_2 is $\begin{pmatrix} 4 - 0 \\ 2 - 5 \end{pmatrix} = \begin{pmatrix} 4 \\ -3 \end{pmatrix}$.

ii $\begin{pmatrix} x \\ y \end{pmatrix} = \begin{pmatrix} 0 \\ 5 \end{pmatrix} + t \begin{pmatrix} 4 \\ -3 \end{pmatrix}, \quad t \in \mathbb{R}$

c The acute angle θ between L_1 and L_2 has

$$\cos \theta = \frac{\left| \begin{pmatrix} -1 \\ -2 \end{pmatrix} \bullet \begin{pmatrix} 4 \\ -3 \end{pmatrix} \right|}{\left| \begin{pmatrix} -1 \\ -2 \end{pmatrix} \right| \left| \begin{pmatrix} 4 \\ -3 \end{pmatrix} \right|}$$

$$= \frac{|-4 + 6|}{\sqrt{1 + 4} \sqrt{16 + 9}}$$

$$= \frac{2}{5\sqrt{5}}$$

$$\therefore \quad \theta = \cos^{-1}\left(\frac{2}{5\sqrt{5}} \right) \approx 79.7°$$

5 a $\mathbf{a} \bullet \mathbf{b} = |\,\mathbf{a}\,|\,|\,\mathbf{b}\,| \cos \theta$ where θ is the angle between $\mathbf{a}$ and $\mathbf{b}$.

If $\mathbf{a} \bullet \mathbf{b} < 0$, then $\cos \theta < 0$ and so $90° < \theta < 180°$.

b i $\mathbf{a} \bullet \mathbf{b} = \begin{pmatrix} -2 \\ 1 \\ 3 \end{pmatrix} \bullet \begin{pmatrix} 3 \\ -1 \\ 1 \end{pmatrix} = -6 - 1 + 3 = -4$

ii $|\,\mathbf{a}\,| = \sqrt{(-2)^2 + 1^2 + 3^2} = \sqrt{14}$ and

$|\,\mathbf{b}\,| = \sqrt{3^2 + (-1)^2 + 1^2} = \sqrt{11}$

and $\cos \theta = \dfrac{\mathbf{a} \bullet \mathbf{b}}{|\,\mathbf{a}\,|\,|\,\mathbf{b}\,|} = \dfrac{-4}{\sqrt{14}\sqrt{11}}$

$$\approx -0.3223$$

$$\therefore \quad \theta \approx 108.8°$$

iii Area of triangle $= \frac{1}{2} |\mathbf{a}||\mathbf{b}| \sin \theta$

$\approx \frac{1}{2} \sqrt{14} \sqrt{11} \sin 108.8°$

$\approx 5.87 \text{ units}^2$

6 a i $\overrightarrow{AB} = 2\mathbf{a}$ **ii** $\overrightarrow{AC} = 2\mathbf{b}$

    iii $\overrightarrow{MN} = \overrightarrow{MA} + \overrightarrow{AN}$ **iv** $\overrightarrow{BC} = \overrightarrow{BA} + \overrightarrow{AC}$

$\qquad\qquad = -\mathbf{a} + \mathbf{b} \qquad\qquad\qquad = -2\mathbf{a} + 2\mathbf{b}$

$\qquad\qquad = \mathbf{b} - \mathbf{a} \qquad\qquad\qquad = 2\mathbf{b} - 2\mathbf{a}$

b From **a iii** and **iv**, $\overrightarrow{MN} = \mathbf{b} - \mathbf{a}$

$\qquad\qquad\qquad\qquad = \frac{1}{2}(2\mathbf{b} - 2\mathbf{a})$

$\qquad\qquad\qquad\qquad = \frac{1}{2}\overrightarrow{BC}$

So, $\overrightarrow{MN}$ is parallel to $\overrightarrow{BC}$ and half its length.

7 $\overrightarrow{AC} = \begin{pmatrix} 11 - 2 \\ 5 - 10 \end{pmatrix} = \begin{pmatrix} 9 \\ -5 \end{pmatrix}$,

$\overrightarrow{BD} = \begin{pmatrix} -1 - 12 \\ 2 - 8 \end{pmatrix} = \begin{pmatrix} -13 \\ -6 \end{pmatrix}$

The acute angle θ between the diagonals has

$\cos \theta = \dfrac{|\overrightarrow{AC} \bullet \overrightarrow{BD}|}{|\overrightarrow{AC}||\overrightarrow{BD}|}$

$\qquad = \dfrac{|-117 + 30|}{\sqrt{81 + 25}\sqrt{169 + 36}}$

$\qquad = \dfrac{87}{\sqrt{106 \times 205}}$

$\therefore \quad \theta \approx 53.8°$

8 $x = 3 + t, \quad y = 4t - 3, \quad t \geqslant 0$

a When $t = 0, \quad x = 3, \quad y = -3$

$\therefore$ the boat's initial position is $(3, -3)$.

b When $t = 3, \quad x = 6, \quad y = 9$

$\therefore$ the boat's position after 3 seconds is $(6, 9)$.

c The velocity vector is $\begin{pmatrix} 1 \\ 4 \end{pmatrix}$.

d The boat's speed is $\sqrt{1 + 16} = \sqrt{17} \text{ m s}^{-1}$.

9 a 8:30 am corresponds to time $t = 0$ hours.

$x = 3 - 2t, \quad y = 3t + 1 \quad \therefore \quad x(0) = 3, \quad y(0) = 1$

So, at 8:30 am the ship is at $(3, 1)$.

b i The ship's velocity vector is $\begin{pmatrix} -2 \\ 3 \end{pmatrix}$.

   ii The ship's speed is $\sqrt{4 + 9} = \sqrt{13} \text{ km h}^{-1}$.

c At 10:30 am, $t = 2$

So, the ship is at $(3 - 2(2), 3(2) + 1)$ or $(-1, 7)$

and the distance to $(0, 10)$

$= \sqrt{(0 - -1)^2 + (10 - 7)^2}$

$= \sqrt{1 + 9}$

$= \sqrt{10} \text{ km}$

d When the ship is directly west of the lighthouse,

$3t + 1 = 10$

$\therefore \quad 3t = 9$

$\therefore \quad t = 3 \qquad \therefore$ the time is 11:30 am.

e

L(0, 10)

$\quad\quad$ S(3−2t, 3t+1)

$\begin{pmatrix} -2 \\ 3 \end{pmatrix}$

$\overrightarrow{LS} = \begin{pmatrix} 3 - 2t - 0 \\ 3t + 1 - 10 \end{pmatrix}$

$\qquad = \begin{pmatrix} 3 - 2t \\ 3t - 9 \end{pmatrix}$

The ship is nearest when

$\overrightarrow{LS} \perp \begin{pmatrix} -2 \\ 3 \end{pmatrix}$.

$\therefore \quad \overrightarrow{LS} \bullet \begin{pmatrix} -2 \\ 3 \end{pmatrix} = 0$

$\therefore \quad -2(3 - 2t) + 3(3t - 9) = 0$

$\therefore \quad -6 + 4t + 9t - 27 = 0$

$\therefore \quad 13t = 33$

$\therefore \quad t = \frac{33}{13} \approx 2.538\,46 \text{ h}$

$\therefore \quad t \approx 2 \text{ h } 32 \text{ mins}$

So, the time is about 11:02 am.

10 a i The direction vector is $\begin{pmatrix} -2 \\ 3 \end{pmatrix}$ which has length

$\sqrt{4 + 9} = \sqrt{13}$ units.

$\therefore$ the velocity vector is $\frac{\sqrt{13}}{\sqrt{13}} \begin{pmatrix} -2 \\ 3 \end{pmatrix} = \begin{pmatrix} -2 \\ 3 \end{pmatrix}$.

$\therefore \quad \begin{pmatrix} x \\ y \end{pmatrix} = \begin{pmatrix} 9 \\ -3 \end{pmatrix} + t \begin{pmatrix} -2 \\ 3 \end{pmatrix}, \quad t \in \mathbb{R}$

   ii The direction vector is $\begin{pmatrix} 5 - -1 \\ 7 - 4 \end{pmatrix} = \begin{pmatrix} 6 \\ 3 \end{pmatrix}$

and it takes 3 seconds to get there.

$\therefore$ the velocity vector is $\frac{1}{3} \begin{pmatrix} 6 \\ 3 \end{pmatrix} = \begin{pmatrix} 2 \\ 1 \end{pmatrix}$

$\therefore \quad \begin{pmatrix} x \\ y \end{pmatrix} = \begin{pmatrix} -1 \\ 4 \end{pmatrix} + t \begin{pmatrix} 2 \\ 1 \end{pmatrix}, \quad 0 \leqslant t \leqslant 3 \text{ s}$

b Car A has coordinates $(9 - 2t, -3 + 3t)$.

$\therefore \quad x = 3 \quad$ when $\quad 9 - 2t = 3$

$\therefore \quad 2t = 6$

$\therefore \quad t = 3$

At this time, $\quad y = -3 + 3 \times 3 = 6$

$\therefore$ car A passes through $(3, 6)$ when $t = 3$ seconds.

Car B has coordinates $(-1 + 2t, 4 + t)$.

$\therefore \quad x = 3 \quad$ when $\quad -1 + 2t = 3$

$\therefore \quad 2t = 4$

$\therefore \quad t = 2$

At this time, $\quad y = 4 + 2 = 6$

$\therefore$ car B passes through $(3, 6)$ when $t = 2$ seconds.

So, both cars will pass through $(3, 6)$.

c The cars pass through $(3, 6)$ at different times, so they will not collide.

11 a $\overrightarrow{AB} = \begin{pmatrix} -3 - 2 \\ 1 - 0 \\ 7 - 5 \end{pmatrix} = \begin{pmatrix} -5 \\ 1 \\ 2 \end{pmatrix}$

b $\overrightarrow{AC} = \begin{pmatrix} 4 - 2 \\ -2 - 0 \\ 9 - 5 \end{pmatrix} = \begin{pmatrix} 2 \\ -2 \\ 4 \end{pmatrix}$

c

B

θ

A $\qquad$ C

$$\cos\theta = \frac{\overrightarrow{AB} \bullet \overrightarrow{AC}}{|\overrightarrow{AB}||\overrightarrow{AC}|}$$

$$= \frac{-10 - 2 + 8}{\sqrt{25 + 1 + 4}\sqrt{4 + 4 + 16}}$$

$$= \frac{-4}{\sqrt{30 \times 24}}$$

$$\therefore \quad \theta = \cos^{-1}\left(\frac{-4}{\sqrt{30 \times 24}}\right) \approx 98.6°$$

12 a
$$\overrightarrow{AB} = \begin{pmatrix} 7 - 2 \\ -3 - -5 \\ -1 - 3 \end{pmatrix} = \begin{pmatrix} 5 \\ 2 \\ -4 \end{pmatrix}$$

$$\overrightarrow{DC} = \begin{pmatrix} 1 - -4 \\ 3 - 1 \\ 0 - 4 \end{pmatrix} = \begin{pmatrix} 5 \\ 2 \\ -4 \end{pmatrix}$$

$$\therefore \quad \overrightarrow{AB} = \overrightarrow{DC}$$

Thus AB ∥ DC and $|\overrightarrow{AB}| = |\overrightarrow{DC}|$
which is sufficient to deduce that ABCD is a parallelogram.

b
$$\overrightarrow{AD} = \begin{pmatrix} -4 - 2 \\ 1 - -5 \\ 4 - 3 \end{pmatrix} = \begin{pmatrix} -6 \\ 6 \\ 1 \end{pmatrix}$$

$$\cos\theta = \frac{\overrightarrow{AB} \bullet \overrightarrow{AD}}{|\overrightarrow{AB}||\overrightarrow{AD}|}$$

$$= \frac{-30 + 12 - 4}{\sqrt{25 + 4 + 16}\sqrt{36 + 36 + 1}}$$

$$= \frac{-22}{\sqrt{45 \times 73}}$$

$$\therefore \quad \theta = \cos^{-1}\left(\frac{-22}{\sqrt{45 \times 73}}\right) \approx 112.6°$$

$\therefore$ the smaller angles are $180° - 112.6° \approx 67.4°$.

13 a
$$\overrightarrow{LK} = \begin{pmatrix} 4 - 6 \\ -2 - 1 \\ 7 - -1 \end{pmatrix} = \begin{pmatrix} -2 \\ -3 \\ 8 \end{pmatrix}$$

$$\overrightarrow{LM} = \begin{pmatrix} 3 - 6 \\ -2 - 1 \\ 5 - -1 \end{pmatrix} = \begin{pmatrix} -3 \\ -3 \\ 6 \end{pmatrix}$$

$$\cos\phi = \frac{\overrightarrow{LK} \bullet \overrightarrow{LM}}{|\overrightarrow{LK}||\overrightarrow{LM}|}$$

$$= \frac{6 + 9 + 48}{\sqrt{4 + 9 + 64}\sqrt{9 + 9 + 36}}$$

$$= \frac{63}{\sqrt{77 \times 54}}$$

$$\therefore \quad \phi = \cos^{-1}\left(\frac{63}{\sqrt{77 \times 54}}\right) \approx 12.3°$$

$\therefore \quad K\widehat{L}M \approx 12.3°$

b The direction vector of the line is
$$\overrightarrow{KL} = \begin{pmatrix} 6 - 4 \\ 1 - -2 \\ -1 - 7 \end{pmatrix} = \begin{pmatrix} 2 \\ 3 \\ -8 \end{pmatrix}$$

The parametric equations are
$$x = 4 + 2t, \quad y = -2 + 3t, \quad z = 7 - 8t, \quad t \in \mathbb{R}$$

c Suppose N lies on (KL) such that $\overrightarrow{MN} \perp \overrightarrow{KL}$.

N has coordinates
$(4 + 2t, -2 + 3t, 7 - 8t)$ for some $t \in \mathbb{R}$,

and $\overrightarrow{MN}$ is
$$\begin{pmatrix} 4 + 2t - 3 \\ -2 + 3t - -2 \\ 7 - 8t - 5 \end{pmatrix} = \begin{pmatrix} 2t + 1 \\ 3t \\ 2 - 8t \end{pmatrix}$$

Now, $\overrightarrow{MN} \bullet \overrightarrow{KL} = 0$

$$\therefore \quad \begin{pmatrix} 2t + 1 \\ 3t \\ 2 - 8t \end{pmatrix} \bullet \begin{pmatrix} 2 \\ 3 \\ -8 \end{pmatrix} = 0$$

$$\therefore \quad 2(2t + 1) + 3(3t) - 8(2 - 8t) = 0$$
$$\therefore \quad 4t + 2 + 9t - 16 + 64t = 0$$
$$\therefore \quad 77t - 14 = 0$$
$$\therefore \quad 11t - 2 = 0$$
$$\therefore \quad t = \tfrac{2}{11}$$

So, $\overrightarrow{MN} = \begin{pmatrix} \frac{4}{11} + 1 \\ \frac{6}{11} \\ 2 - \frac{16}{11} \end{pmatrix} = \begin{pmatrix} \frac{15}{11} \\ \frac{6}{11} \\ \frac{6}{11} \end{pmatrix} = \frac{3}{11}\begin{pmatrix} 5 \\ 2 \\ 2 \end{pmatrix}$

and $|\overrightarrow{MN}| = \frac{3}{11}\left|\begin{pmatrix} 5 \\ 2 \\ 2 \end{pmatrix}\right|$

$$= \frac{3}{11}\sqrt{25 + 4 + 4}$$

$$= \frac{3\sqrt{33}}{11} \text{ units}$$

The shortest distance from M to (KL) is $\frac{3\sqrt{33}}{11}$ units.

14 a L_1 and L_2 have direction vectors $\begin{pmatrix} 3 \\ -6 \\ -3 \end{pmatrix}$ and $\begin{pmatrix} -1 \\ 2 \\ 1 \end{pmatrix}$ respectively.

Since $\begin{pmatrix} 3 \\ -6 \\ -3 \end{pmatrix} = -3\begin{pmatrix} -1 \\ 2 \\ 1 \end{pmatrix}$, L_1 is parallel to L_2.

b L_1 and L_3 meet if
$$\begin{cases} 2 + 3t = 5 - 3s \\ 1 - 6t = 5 + 4s \\ -1 - 3t = 1 + 2s \end{cases}$$

$$\therefore \quad \begin{cases} 3s + 3t = 3 \\ 4s + 6t = -4 \\ 2s + 3t = -2 \end{cases}$$

Solving this system using technology, $s = 5$ and $t = -4$.
$\therefore$ the lines meet at $(-10, 25, 11)$.

L_3 has direction vector $\begin{pmatrix} -3 \\ 4 \\ 2 \end{pmatrix}$.

Now $\cos\phi = \dfrac{\left|\begin{pmatrix} 3 \\ -6 \\ -3 \end{pmatrix} \bullet \begin{pmatrix} -3 \\ 4 \\ 2 \end{pmatrix}\right|}{\sqrt{9 + 36 + 9}\sqrt{9 + 16 + 4}}$

$$= \frac{|-9 - 24 - 6|}{\sqrt{54 \times 29}}$$

$$= \frac{39}{\sqrt{54}\sqrt{29}}$$

$$\therefore \quad \phi = \cos^{-1}\left(\frac{39}{\sqrt{54}\sqrt{29}}\right) \approx 9.76°$$

$\therefore$ the angle between L_1 and L_3 is about $9.76°$.

SOLUTIONS TO TOPIC 5 (STATISTICS AND PROBABILITY)

NO CALCULATORS

1 a There are 72 cars in total.
$$\therefore\ 4 + 11 + x + 18 + 12 + 6 + 4 + 2 = 72$$
$$\therefore\ x + 57 = 72$$
$$\therefore\ x = 15$$

b The modal class is $60 \leqslant v < 70$ km h^{-1}.

c

Speed (km h^{-1})	Frequency	Cumul. Frequency
$v < 30$	0	0
$30 \leqslant v < 40$	4	4
$40 \leqslant v < 50$	11	15
$50 \leqslant v < 60$	15	30
$60 \leqslant v < 70$	18	48
$70 \leqslant v < 80$	12	60
$80 \leqslant v < 90$	6	66
$90 \leqslant v < 100$	4	70
$100 \leqslant v < 110$	2	72

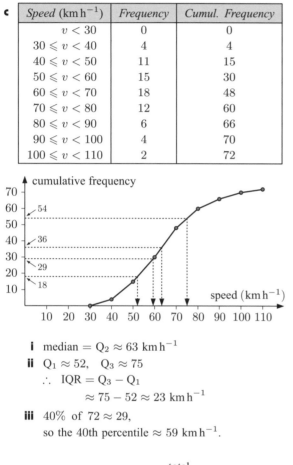

i median $= Q_2 \approx 63$ km h^{-1}

ii $Q_1 \approx 52$, $Q_3 \approx 75$
$$\therefore\ IQR = Q_3 - Q_1$$
$$\approx 75 - 52 \approx 23\ \text{km h}^{-1}$$

iii 40% of $72 \approx 29$,
so the 40th percentile ≈ 59 km h^{-1}.

2 a
$$\text{mean} = \frac{\text{total}}{7} = 11$$
$$\therefore\ \frac{7 + 9 + 9 + x + 13 + 13 + 16}{7} = 11$$
$$\therefore\ x + 67 = 77$$
$$\therefore\ x = 10$$

b The total of the scores is $67 + 10 = 77$.
If Kai scores t goals in the next game,

then $12 = \dfrac{77 + t}{8}$
$$\therefore\ 96 = 77 + t$$
$$\therefore\ t = 19$$

So, she must score 19 goals next time.

3

$$\overset{Q_1}{\overbrace{}}\qquad\overset{Q_2}{\overbrace{}}$$
85 96 98 100 105 106 108 108 112 112 118 120 123
125 126 128 133 $\underset{Q_3}{\underbrace{135\ 140}}$ 144 144 148 148 156

a **i** $Q_1 = 107$ **ii** median $= Q_2 = 121.5$
iii $Q_3 = 137.5$ **iv** IQR $= 30.5$
v range $= 156 - 85 = 71$

b upper boundary $= Q_3 + 1.5 \times IQR$
$$= 137.5 + 1.5 \times 30.5$$
$$= 183.25$$

lower boundary $= Q_1 - 1.5 \times IQR$
$$= 107 - 1.5 \times 30.5$$
$$= 61.25$$

There are no data values which are either greater than the upper boundary or less than the lower boundary, so there are no outliers.

c

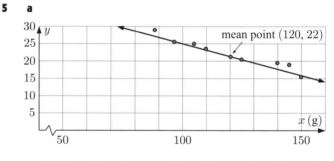

4 a From the graph, 100 units were sold for $< \$200\,000$.

b   When $N = \frac{1}{2}$ of $800 = 400$,
the value $= 300$ thousand
$\therefore$ the median $= \$300\,000$

c IQR $= Q_3 - Q_1$
$$= \$375\,000 - \$250\,000$$
$$= \$125\,000$$

d From the graph, 500 units were sold for $< \$330\,000$, so 300 units were sold for $> \$330\,000$.
P(selling price $> \$330\,000$) $= \frac{300}{800} = \frac{3}{8}$

5 a

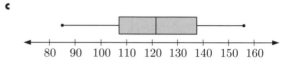

The line of best fit passes through $(120, 22)$ and $(80, 28)$.
The line has gradient $m = \dfrac{28 - 22}{80 - 120}$
$$= -0.15$$

Its equation is $\dfrac{y - 28}{x - 80} = -0.15$
$$\therefore\ y - 28 = -0.15x + 12$$
$$\therefore\ y = -0.15x + 40$$

b   **i** $y = -0.15(100) + 40 = 25$
ii $y = -0.15(200) + 40 = 10$

c The first calculation is likely to be more reliable, as it is an interpolated value. 200 grams is outside the domain, however so the second calculation is an extrapolation and less reliable.

6 a **i** 22 cm   **ii** 4 cm   **iii** 19 cm   **iv** 17 cm
b **i** range $= 22 - 4$ **ii** IQR $= 19 - 11$
$= 18$ cm $= 8$ cm

c 75% of seedlings were taller than 11 cm.

d No, the distribution is negatively skewed (skewed to the left).

7 a

Die 2						
6	5	4	③	2	1	0
5	4	③	2	1	0	1
4	③	2	1	0	1	2
3	2	1	0	1	2	③
2	1	0	1	2	③	4
1	0	1	2	③	4	5
	1	2	3	4	5	6 Die 1

b There are 6 outcomes where the difference is 3.
As all outcomes are equally possible, the probability of the difference being 3 is $\frac{6}{36} = \frac{1}{6}$.

8 There are $11 + 8 + 4 + 2 = 25$ students.

a $P(H)$
$= \frac{11 + 8}{25}$
$= \frac{19}{25}$

b $P(T')$
$= \frac{11 + 2}{25}$
$= \frac{13}{25}$

c P(plays at least one sport)
$= \frac{11 + 8 + 4}{25}$
$= \frac{23}{25}$

d $P(T \mid H)$
$= \frac{8}{11 + 8}$
$= \frac{8}{19}$

9 a $f(x) \geqslant 0$ on a given interval $a \leqslant x \leqslant b$,
and $\int_a^b f(x)\,dx = 1$.

b $P(x_1 \leqslant X \leqslant x_2) = \int_{x_1}^{x_2} f(x)\,dx$

10 a The random variable is discrete.

b $\frac{1}{3} + \frac{1}{6} + k + \frac{1}{12} = 1$
$\therefore k + \frac{7}{12} = 1$
$\therefore k = \frac{5}{12}$

c $E(X) = -2(\frac{1}{3}) + 0(\frac{1}{6}) + 3(\frac{5}{12}) + 5(\frac{1}{12}) = 1$

11 a $a + b = 71 \quad \therefore \quad b = 71 - a$
$a + c = 44 \quad \therefore \quad c = 44 - a$
$a + d = 21 \quad \therefore \quad d = 21 - a$
Now $a + b + c + d = 100$
$\therefore a + (71 - a) + (44 - a) + (21 - a) = 100$
$\therefore 136 - 2a = 100$
$\therefore a = 18$
So, $b = 53$, $c = 26$, $d = 3$

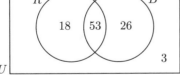

b i $P(R \cap B') = \frac{18}{100} = 0.18$
ii $P(R \cap B) = \frac{53}{100} = 0.53$
iii $P(R \cup B) = \frac{18 + 53 + 26}{100} = 0.97$

12 a

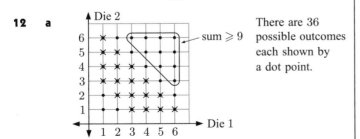

There are 36 possible outcomes each shown by a dot point.

b i P(sum more than 8)
$= P(\text{sum} \geqslant 9)$
$= \frac{10}{36}$
$= \frac{5}{18}$

ii P(more than 3, but less than 8)
$= P(4 \leqslant \text{sum} \leqslant 7)$
$= \frac{18}{36}$ {marked ×}
$= \frac{1}{2}$

iii $P(\text{sum} = 6) = \frac{5}{36}$
$\{1 + 5,\ 2 + 4,\ 3 + 3,\ 4 + 2,\ 5 + 1\}$

13 a

```
        1/2        1/3    E
          ---- T <
         /         2/3   E'
        /                    E
        \         1/3  ----
         \       /
       1/2 ---- T'
                 \
                  2/3   E'
```

b i $P(T \cap E') = \frac{1}{2} \times \frac{2}{3}$
$= \frac{1}{3}$

ii $P(T \cup E') = 1 - P(T' \cap E)$
$= 1 - \frac{1}{2} \times \frac{1}{3}$
$= 1 - \frac{1}{6} = \frac{5}{6}$

14

```
1st      2nd       3rd
                    B
              B <
             /      G ✓
        B <
       /     \      B ✓
      /       G <
     /              G ✓
     \              B ✓
      \       B <
       \     /      G ✓
        G <
             \      B ✓
              G <
                    G
```

P(at least one of each sex) $= \frac{6}{8} = \frac{3}{4}$

15 a The scatter diagram suggests there is a very strong positive relationship between age and annual income.

b The mean point is $(27, 20)$.
The line of best fit passes through $(27, 20)$ and $(39, 30)$.
The line has gradient $m = \frac{30 - 20}{39 - 27}$
$= \frac{10}{12}$
$= \frac{5}{6}$
Its equation is $\frac{y - 20}{x - 27} = \frac{5}{6}$
$\therefore y - 20 = \frac{5}{6}x - \frac{45}{2}$
$\therefore y = \frac{5}{6}x - \frac{5}{2}$

c i When $x = 30$, $y = \frac{5}{6}(30) - \frac{5}{2} = 22.5$
So, the annual income is approximately \$22 500.

ii When $x = 60$, $y = \frac{5}{6}(60) - \frac{5}{2} = 47.5$
So, the annual income is approximately \$47 500.

d The age of 30 is within the given data range but 60 is outside the range. Predicting the income at 30 years is an interpolation and is more reliable than the extrapolation required for 60.

71

16

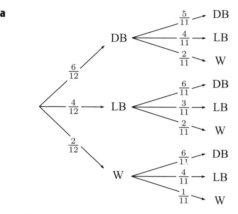

Tom   Jerry

a   P(only one of them is successful)
= $(0.7)(0.4) + (0.3)(0.6)$
= 0.46

b   P(at least one is successful)
= $1 - $ P(both miss)
= $1 - (0.3)(0.4)$
= $1 - 0.12$
= 0.88

17 **a**

```
                                    5/11 → DB
                      DB ←          4/11 → LB
                6/12               2/11 → W
                                    6/11 → DB
        ← 4/12 → LB ←              3/11 → LB
                                    2/11 → W
                2/12               6/11 → DB
                      W ←           4/11 → LB
                                    1/11 → W
```

b   **i**   P(2 whites) $= \frac{2}{12} \times \frac{1}{11} = \frac{1}{66}$

   ii   P(different colours)
   $= 1 - $ P(both the same colour)
   $= 1 - \left[\left(\frac{6}{12}\right)\left(\frac{5}{11}\right) + \left(\frac{4}{12}\right)\left(\frac{3}{11}\right) + \left(\frac{2}{12}\right)\left(\frac{1}{11}\right) \right]$
   $= 1 - \frac{44}{12 \times 11} = \frac{2}{3}$

18

Venn diagram: Br, Bl with regions a, b, c and d outside, in universal set U.

$a + b + c + d = 30$
$a + b = 17$
$b + c = 12$
$d = 4$
$\therefore \quad a + b + c = 26$

Since $a + b = 17$, $\quad 17 + c = 26$
$\therefore \quad c = 9$

Since $b + c = 12$, $\quad b + 9 = 12$
$\therefore \quad b = 3$

Venn diagram: Br, Bl with regions 14, 3, 9 and 4 outside, in U.

$a + b = 17$
$\therefore \quad a + 3 = 17$
$\therefore \quad a = 14$

a   3 students have both brown hair and blue eyes.

b   **i**   P(Bl but not Br) $= \frac{9}{30} = 0.3$
   ii   P($Br \mid Bl$) $= \frac{3}{12} = 0.25$

CALCULATORS

1   **a**   Using technology, $\overline{x} = 7.52$ marks

b   The mode = 8 marks

c   There are 25 data values, so the median is the $\frac{25+1}{2} = 13$th data value.
$\therefore$ the median is 8 marks.

---

2   **a** $\overline{x} = \frac{\sum fx}{\sum f}$ $\therefore$ $\frac{0 + 4 + 6 + 3a + 8}{6 + 4 + 3 + a + 2} = 1.65$

$\therefore \quad \frac{3a + 18}{a + 15} = 1.65$

$\therefore \quad 3a + 18 = 1.65a + 24.75$

$\therefore \quad 1.35a = 6.75$

$\therefore \quad a = \frac{6.75}{1.35}$

$\therefore \quad a = 5$

b   The standard deviation ≈ 1.39 {technology}

3   Using technology
a $\mu \approx 3.56$, $\quad \sigma \approx 0.512$ **b** $\mu \approx 67.9$, $\quad \sigma \approx 12.2$

4   **a** $\frac{90 + 100 + 93 + 96 + p + 107 + 98 + 98 + 92}{9} = 97$

$\therefore \quad 774 + p = 873$

$\therefore \quad p = 99$

b   The ordered data is:
90, 92, 93, 96, 98, 98, 99, 100, 107
$\therefore$ the median is 98.

5   **a**   The sum of the frequencies is 30, so 30 drives were chosen.

b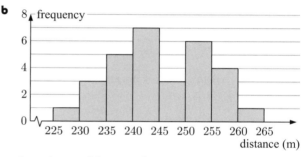

c   An estimate of the mean is 245.
An estimate of the median is 243.
The modal class is $240 \leqslant d < 245$.
Since the mean, median, and mode are about equal, the data appears to be symmetric.

d

Distance (m)	Frequency	Cumul. Frequency
$225 \leqslant d < 230$	1	1
$230 \leqslant d < 235$	3	4
$235 \leqslant d < 240$	5	9
$240 \leqslant d < 245$	7	16
$245 \leqslant d < 250$	3	19
$250 \leqslant d < 255$	6	25
$255 \leqslant d < 260$	4	29
$260 \leqslant d < 265$	1	30

e $\frac{19}{30} \approx 63.3\%$

f   The golfer hit a distance of more than 235 metres on 26 out of the 30 drives sampled.
So, if the golfer hit 100 drives, we would expect
$100 \times \frac{26}{30} \approx 87$ drives to travel more than 235 metres.

6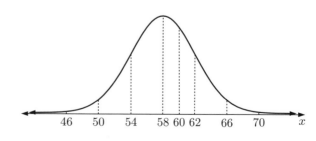

a $P(X > 60) \approx 0.309$

Over a 100 year period we would expect more than 60 mm of rain to occur 31 times.

b $P(50 < X < 60) \approx 0.669$

Over a 100 year period we would expect between 50 mm and 60 mm of rain to occur 67 times.

7 The tree diagram uses: F for female L for left-handed

                               M for male R for right-handed

                      0.13 → L

            0.38 → F

                      0.87 → R

                      0.24 → L

            0.62 → M

                      0.76 → R

a $P(L) = (0.38)(0.13) + (0.62)(0.24) \approx 0.198$

b $P(F \mid L) = \dfrac{P(F \cap L)}{P(L)} = \dfrac{(0.38)(0.13)}{0.1982} \approx 0.249$

8 **a** $r \approx 0.898$

There is a strong correlation between the age of contestants and the time taken to complete the task.

b   **i** $y \approx 0.930x - 1.56$

    ii   We expect that an increase of one year in age will add 0.93 minutes to the time to complete the task.

9 **a** $y \approx 1.09x - 0.781$ {using technology}

b $r \approx 0.883$

c There is a strong positive correlation between the times taken to complete the obstacle course of mice without adrenaline and the times of mice with adrenaline.

d Subject D is an outlier.

e $y \approx 1.094x - 0.7813$

Substituting in $y = 48$ gives

$$48 \approx 1.094x - 0.7813$$
$$\therefore \quad 48.7813 \approx 1.094x$$
$$\therefore \quad x \approx 44.6$$

So, we expect that an adrenaline injection would reduce the mouse's time to 44.6 s, a reduction of about 3.4 seconds.

10 **a** $r \approx 0.995$

b There appears to be a very strong, positive correlation between monthly rainfall and crop yield.

c The least squares regression line is $y \approx 0.606x + 9.4$.

d   **i**   If $x = 0$,   then $y \approx 0.606(0) + 9.4$

                            ≈ 9.4

      So, the expected yield is approximately 9.4 tonnes.

    ii   If $x = 12$,   then $y \approx 0.606(12) + 9.4$

                            ≈ 16.7

      So, the expected yield is approximately 16.7 tonnes.

e The estimate in **i** is an extrapolation as it is outside the data range; we expect it to be unreliable, especially as it predicts such a large yield when there is no rain at all. In contrast, the estimate in **ii** is an interpolation, and we would expect the estimate to be reliable.

11 $P(A \cup B) = P(A) + P(B) - P(A \cap B)$

But A and B are independent, so $P(A \cap B) = P(A)\,P(B)$.

Hence, $P(A \cup B) = P(A) + P(B) - P(A)\,P(B)$.

Let $P(A) = x$

$$\therefore \quad 0.63 = x + 0.36 - 0.36x$$
$$\therefore \quad 0.27 = 0.64x$$
$$\therefore \quad x = P(A) \approx 0.422$$

12 $P(A \cup B) = 1 - P((A \cup B)') = 1 - \frac{1}{12} = \frac{11}{12}$

$P(A \cup B) = P(A) + P(B) - P(A \cap B)$

$\therefore \quad \frac{11}{12} = 0.46 + \frac{5}{7} - P(A \cap B)$

$\therefore \quad P(A \cap B) = 0.46 + \frac{5}{7} - \frac{11}{12}$

$\therefore \quad P(A \cap B) \approx 0.258$

13 **a**

                                  2nd draw

               1st draw $\frac{6}{9}$ → P

                      P

             $\frac{7}{10}$ $\frac{3}{9}$ → R

            $\frac{3}{10}$ $\frac{7}{9}$ → P

                   R

                         $\frac{2}{9}$ → R

b   **i**   P(at least one red ticket)

$$= 1 - P(\text{no red tickets})$$
$$= 1 - P(PP)$$
$$= 1 - \frac{7}{10} \times \frac{6}{9}$$
$$= 1 - \frac{42}{90}$$
$$= \frac{48}{90} = \frac{8}{15}$$

    ii   P(one ticket of each colour)

$$= P(PR \text{ or } RP)$$
$$= \frac{7}{10} \times \frac{3}{9} + \frac{3}{10} \times \frac{7}{9}$$
$$= \frac{21}{90} + \frac{21}{90}$$
$$= \frac{42}{90} = \frac{7}{15}$$

    iii   P(purple ticket second)

$$= P(PP \text{ or } RP)$$
$$= \frac{7}{10} \times \frac{6}{9} + \frac{3}{10} \times \frac{7}{9}$$
$$= \frac{42}{90} + \frac{21}{90}$$
$$= \frac{63}{90} = \frac{7}{10}$$

14

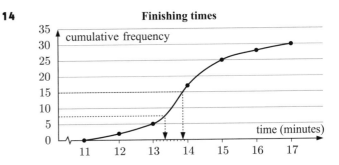

Finishing times

a median $\approx$ 15th score ≈ 13.8 (or 13.9) minutes

b $Q_1 \approx 7\frac{1}{2}$th score ≈ 13.3 min.

So, any time less than 13.3 minutes.

c 2 finished within 12 minutes and 25 finished within 15 min

$\therefore$ 23 finished between 12 and 15 minutes.

d 5 runners out of 30 finished within 13 minutes.

$\therefore$ P(a runner finished in less than 13 min) $= \frac{5}{30} = \frac{1}{6}$

15 $\mu = 310$ mL, $\sigma = 5$ mL

a $P(300 < X < 310) \approx 0.477$

$\therefore$ 47.7% lie between 300 mL and 310 mL.

b $P(X \geqslant 304) \approx 0.885$

$\therefore$ 88.5% are at least 304 mL.

c $P(X < 300) \approx 0.0228$

16 a i For English, $P(X > 80) \approx 0.266$

$\therefore$ 26.6% scored higher than Ashleigh

ii For History, $P(X > 72) \approx 0.212$

$\therefore$ 21.2% scored higher than Ashleigh

b z-score for English $\dfrac{80 - 75}{8} = 0.625$

z-score for History $\dfrac{72 - 60}{15} = 0.800$

$\therefore$ Ashleigh achieved a higher standard in History.

17 $X \sim N(\mu, \sigma^2)$

Now $P(X > 90) = 0.12$

$\therefore$ $P(X \leqslant 90) = 0.88$

$\therefore$ $P\left(\dfrac{X - \mu}{\sigma} \leqslant \dfrac{90 - \mu}{\sigma}\right) = 0.88$

$\therefore$ $P\left(Z \leqslant \dfrac{90 - \mu}{\sigma}\right) = 0.88$

$\therefore$ $\dfrac{90 - \mu}{\sigma} \approx 1.1750$

$90 - \mu \approx 1.1750\sigma$ .... (1)

Also, $P(X < 60) = 0.20$

$\therefore$ $P\left(\dfrac{X - \mu}{\sigma} < \dfrac{60 - \mu}{\sigma}\right) = 0.20$

$\therefore$ $P\left(Z < \dfrac{60 - \mu}{\sigma}\right) = 0.20$

$\therefore$ $\dfrac{60 - \mu}{\sigma} \approx -0.8416$

$\therefore$ $60 - \mu \approx -0.8416\sigma$ .... (2)

Solving (1) and (2):

$90 - \mu \approx 1.1750\sigma$

$-60 + \mu \approx 0.8416\sigma$

Adding, $30 \approx 2.0166\sigma$

$\therefore$ $\sigma \approx \dfrac{30}{2.0166} \approx 14.88$

and $90 - \mu \approx 1.1750 \times 14.88$

$\therefore$ $\mu \approx 72.5$

Thus $\mu \approx 72.5$ and $\sigma \approx 14.9$

18 $p = \frac{4}{5} = 0.8$

Let X be the number of people sampled who oppose the traffic lights.

$X \sim B(20, 0.8)$

a $P(X = 16) \approx 0.218$ **b** $P(X \geqslant 16) = 1 - P(X \leqslant 15)$

$\approx 1 - 0.370$

≈ 0.630

19 a i $r \approx -0.647$ **ii** $y \approx -0.555x + 71.3$

b The outlier is $(50, 12)$.

With the outlier removed:

i $r \approx -0.986$ **ii** $y \approx -0.637x + 80.5$

c i The gradient of the line is steeper (has become more negative).

ii The relationship has changed from moderate to very strong.

20 a $y \approx 2.43x + 32.0$

b If $y = 70$, $70 \approx 2.43x + 32$

$\therefore$ $38 \approx 2.43x$

$\therefore$ $x \approx 15.6$

So, we estimate that Tony revised for 15.6 hours.

c The y-intercept (32%) is the estimate of the result for a student who did not do any revision.

The gradient of the line indicates that the result will increase by 2.43% for each additional hour studied.

21 If Robert gets the 5 known correct then there are 10 answers he guesses.

Let X be the number he correctly guesses, so

$X \sim B(10, 0.25)$

a $P(\text{Robert fails})$ **b** $P(\text{answers exactly 8 correctly})$

$= P(X \leqslant 2)$ $= P(X = 3)$

≈ 0.526 ≈ 0.250

c $P(\text{achieves a C or better})$

$= P(X \geqslant 5)$

$= 1 - P(X \leqslant 4)$

$\approx 1 - 0.9219$

≈ 0.0781

22 $\mu = 0$, $\sigma = 1$, and $X \sim N(0, 1^2)$.

a $P(X \leqslant 1) \approx 0.841$

b $P(-0.5 \leqslant X \leqslant 0.5) \approx 0.383$

c $P(X > 2) \approx 0.0228$

$\therefore$ we can expect that $0.0228 \times 850 \approx 19$ speeds measured will exceed the actual speed by more than 2 km h^{-1}.

23 $\mu = 40$, $\sigma = 5$, and $X \sim N(40, 5^2)$.

a i $P(X > 45) \approx 0.159$

ii $P(35 < X < 50) \approx 0.819$

b We need to find k such that

$P(X > k) = 0.1$

$\therefore$ $P(X \leqslant k) = 0.9$

$\therefore$ $k \approx 46.4$

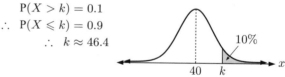

So, the minimum length of the longest 10% of fish is 46.4 cm.

24 $\mu = 500$, $\sigma = 2.5$

a $P(X < 495) \approx 0.0228$

b $0.0228 \times 10\,000 \approx 228$ bottles will require extra sauce.

25 $\mu = 38.4$, $\sigma = 4.6$

a i $P(X > 43.5) \approx 0.134$ **ii** $P(X \leqslant 36.4) \approx 0.332$

iii $P(30 \leqslant X \leqslant 40) \approx 0.602$

b We need to find k such that

$P(X > k) = 0.9$

$\therefore$ $P(X \leqslant k) = 0.1$

$\therefore$ $k \approx 32.5$

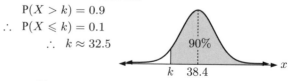

So, 90% will reduce their oxygen consumption by more than 32.5 mL.

26 a $P(X < 56) = 0.8$ means that

$$P\left(Z < \frac{56 - \mu}{\sigma}\right) = 0.8$$

$$\therefore \quad \frac{56 - \mu}{\sigma} \approx 0.8416$$

$$\therefore \quad 56 - \mu \approx 0.8416\sigma$$

So, a score of 56 is 0.842 standard deviations from the mean.

b If $\sigma = 4$ then from **a**, $56 - \mu \approx 0.8416(4)$

$$\therefore \quad 56 - \mu \approx 3.366$$

$$\therefore \quad \mu \approx 52.6$$

27 $\mu = 1020$, $\sigma = 15$

a $P(X < 1000) \approx 0.0912$

b Containers that overflow have more than 1050 mL added to them.

Now $P(X > 1050) \approx 0.0228$

$\therefore$ 2.28% of the containers overflow.

c $P(1000 \leqslant X \leqslant 1030) \approx 0.6563$

So, in a sample of 1500, we expect $0.6563 \times 1500 \approx 984$ containers will hold between 1 litre and 1.03 litres.

28 $X \sim B(10, 0.88)$ so $n = 10$, $p = 0.88$.

a $P(X = 8) \approx 0.233$

b A student passes if they pass 8 or more of the tests.

$$P(X \geqslant 8) = 1 - P(X \leqslant 7)$$
$$\approx 1 - 0.109$$
$$\approx 0.891$$

29 $X \sim B(6, 0.05)$ so $n = 6$, $p = 0.05$.

The manufacturer must pay double money back if more than two items are defective.

$P(\text{more than 2})$

$\approx 1 - P(X \leqslant 2)$ So, the manufacturer will

$\approx 1 - 0.99777$ have to pay double money

≈ 0.00223 back on 0.223% of boxes.

30

	Defective	Not defective	Total
Corn	37	581	618
Pineapple	24	617	641
Total	61	1198	1259

a 1259 tins

b **i** 61 out of the 1259 tins are defective.

$\therefore$ $P(\text{defective}) \approx \frac{61}{1259} \approx 0.0485$

ii 37 of the 61 defective tins are corn.

$\therefore$ $P(\text{corn} \mid \text{defective}) \approx \frac{37}{61} \approx 0.607$

iii 37 out of 618 corn tins are defective.

$\therefore$ $P(\text{defective} \mid \text{corn}) \approx \frac{37}{618} \approx 0.0599$

31

	< 50	⩾ 50	Total
Male	136	469	605
Female	155	310	465
Total	291	779	1070

a 1070 patients

b **i** 605 of the 1070 patients were male.

$\therefore$ $P(\text{male}) = \frac{605}{1070} \approx 0.565$

ii 291 of the 1070 patients were younger than 50.

$\therefore$ $P(\text{younger than 50}) = \frac{291}{1070} \approx 0.272$

iii Of the 779 patients who were 50 or older, 469 were male.

$\therefore$ $P(\text{male} \mid 50 \text{ or older}) = \frac{469}{779} \approx 0.602$

iv Of the 465 female patients, 310 were 50 or older.

$\therefore$ $P(50 \text{ or older} \mid \text{female}) = \frac{310}{465} \approx 0.667$

32 Let X be the number of allergic reactions.

$\therefore$ $X \sim B(5000, 0.1)$

$$P(X < 470) = P(X \leqslant 469)$$
$$\approx 0.0743$$

33 The length X cm of a chopstick is normally distributed with mean μ cm and standard deviation 0.5 cm.

Now $P(X < 24) = 0.01$

$$\therefore \quad P\left(\frac{X - \mu}{0.5} < \frac{24 - \mu}{0.5}\right) = 0.01$$

$$\therefore \quad P\left(Z < \frac{24 - \mu}{0.5}\right) = 0.01$$

$$\therefore \quad \frac{24 - \mu}{0.5} \approx -2.326$$

$$\therefore \quad 24 - \mu \approx -1.163$$

$$\therefore \quad \mu \approx 25.2 \text{ cm}$$

34 If X cm is the length of a steel rod then X is normally distributed with mean 13.8 cm.

Now $P(X < 13.2) = 0.015$

$$\therefore \quad P\left(\frac{X - 13.8}{\sigma} < \frac{13.2 - 13.8}{\sigma}\right) = 0.015$$

$$\therefore \quad P\left(Z < \frac{-0.6}{\sigma}\right) = 0.015$$

$$\therefore \quad \frac{-0.6}{\sigma} \approx -2.17009$$

$$\therefore \quad \sigma \approx 0.276 \text{ cm}$$

35 $P(x) = P(X = x) = \frac{1}{24}(x + 6)$, $x \in \{1, 2, 3\}$

a $P(1) = \frac{1}{24}(7) = \frac{7}{24}$

$P(2) = \frac{1}{24}(8) = \frac{8}{24}$

$P(3) = \frac{1}{24}(9) = \frac{9}{24}$

b $E(X) = \sum_{i=1}^{3} x_i \, P(X = x_i)$

$$= 1\left(\frac{7}{24}\right) + 2\left(\frac{8}{24}\right) + 3\left(\frac{9}{24}\right)$$

$$= \frac{50}{24}$$

$$= 2\frac{1}{12}$$

36 a $0.05 + k + 0.5 + 0.3 = 1$

$$\therefore \quad k + 0.85 = 1$$

$$\therefore \quad k = 0.15$$

b $E(X) = \sum x_i p_i$

$$= 0(0.05) + 1(0.15) + 2(0.5) + 3(0.3)$$

$$= 0.15 + 1 + 0.9$$

$$= 2.05$$

37 $0.3 + 0.2 + m + n = 1$

$$\therefore \quad m + n = 0.5$$

$$\therefore \quad n = 0.5 - m$$

Now $E(X) = \sum x_i p_i$

$$\therefore \quad 1.55 = 0(0.3) + 1(0.2) + 2m + 3n$$

$$\therefore \quad 1.35 = 2m + 3(0.5 - m)$$

$$\therefore \quad m = 0.15$$

38 **a** $r \approx -0.832$

b As the number of tomatoes in a bag increases, the median weight of tomatoes in the bag decreases.
There is a moderate negative linear correlation between the variables.

c $y \approx -8.21x + 224$

d **i** If $x = 13$, then $y \approx -8.21(13) + 224$
≈ 118
So, the median weight is approximately 118 g.

ii If $x = 20$, then $y \approx -8.21(20) + 224$
≈ 60.2
So, the median weight is approximately 60.2 g.

e The estimate in **i** is an interpolation whereas the estimate in **ii** is an extrapolation. The estimate in **i** is therefore more reliable.

39
$$P(X \leqslant 15) = 0.613$$
$$\therefore \ P\left(\frac{X - \mu}{\sigma} \leqslant \frac{15 - \mu}{\sigma}\right) = 0.613$$
$$\therefore \ P\left(Z \leqslant \frac{15 - 13}{\sigma}\right) = 0.613$$
$$\therefore \ \frac{2}{\sigma} \approx 0.287$$
$$\therefore \ \sigma \approx 6.97$$

40
$$P(X \leqslant 24) = 0.035$$
$$\therefore \ P\left(Z \leqslant \frac{24 - \mu}{\sigma}\right) = 0.035$$
$$\therefore \ \frac{24 - \mu}{\sigma} \approx -1.812$$
$$\therefore \ 24 - \mu \approx -1.812\sigma \ \ .... \ (1)$$

Also, $P(X \geqslant 33) = 0.262$
$$\therefore \ P(X < 33) = 0.738$$
$$\therefore \ P\left(Z < \frac{33 - \mu}{\sigma}\right) = 0.738$$
$$\therefore \ \frac{33 - \mu}{\sigma} \approx 0.6372$$
$$\therefore \ 33 - \mu \approx 0.6372\sigma \ \ .... \ (2)$$
$(1) - (2)$ gives
$$(24 - \mu) - (33 - \mu) \approx -1.812\sigma - 0.6372\sigma$$
$$\therefore \ -9 \approx -2.449\sigma$$
$$\therefore \ \sigma \approx 3.67$$
$$\therefore \ \mu \approx 24 + 1.812(3.67) \approx 30.7$$
So, the mean $\mu \approx 30.7$ and the standard deviation $\sigma \approx 3.67$.

SOLUTIONS TO TOPIC 6 (CALCULUS)

NO CALCULATORS

1 **a**
$$f(x) = 7x - x^2$$
$$\therefore \ f(x + h) = 7(x + h) - (x + h)^2$$
$$= 7x + 7h - (x^2 + 2xh + h^2)$$
$$= 7x + 7h - x^2 - 2xh - h^2$$

Now $f'(x) = \lim_{h \to 0} \dfrac{f(x + h) - f(x)}{h}$
$$= \lim_{h \to 0} \frac{7x + 7h - x^2 - 2xh - h^2 - 7x + x^2}{h}$$
$$= \lim_{h \to 0} \frac{7h - 2xh - h^2}{h}$$
$$= \lim_{h \to 0} \frac{\cancel{h}(7 - 2x - h)}{\cancel{h}_1} \quad \{\text{as } h \neq 0\}$$
$$= \lim_{h \to 0} (7 - 2x - h)$$
$$= 7 - 2x$$

b $f(1) = 7(1) - 1^2 = 6$
$\therefore$ the point of contact is $(1, 6)$.
Now $f'(1) = 7 - 2(1) = 5$
$\therefore$ the tangent has equation
$$\frac{y - 6}{x - 1} = 5$$
which is $y - 6 = 5x - 5$
or $y = 5x + 1$

2 **a** Let $y = f(x) = -2x^2 + 3$
$$\frac{dy}{dx} = \lim_{h \to 0} \frac{f(x + h) - f(x)}{h}$$
$$= \lim_{h \to 0} \frac{[-2(x + h)^2 + 3] - [-2x^2 + 3]}{h}$$
$$= \lim_{h \to 0} \frac{-2(x^2 + 2xh + h^2) \cancel{+3} + 2x^2 \cancel{-3}}{h}$$
$$= \lim_{h \to 0} \frac{\cancel{-2x^2} - 4xh - 2h^2 \cancel{+2x^2}}{h}$$
$$= \lim_{h \to 0} \frac{-2\cancel{h}(2x + h)}{\cancel{h}_1}$$
$$= \lim_{h \to 0} -2(2x + h) \quad \{\text{as } h \neq 0\}$$
$$= -4x$$

b When $x = -1$, $\dfrac{dy}{dx} = -4(-1) = 4$
$\therefore$ the tangent has gradient 4.

c When $x = -1$, $y = -2(-1)^2 + 3 = 1$
$\therefore$ the point of contact is $(-1, 1)$.
Since the gradient of the tangent is 4, the gradient of the normal is $-\frac{1}{4}$.
So, the equation of the normal is
$$\frac{y - 1}{x - (-1)} = -\frac{1}{4}$$
$$\therefore \ 4y - 4 = -(x + 1)$$
$$\therefore \ 4y = -x + 3$$
$$\therefore \ y = \frac{-x + 3}{4}$$

d The normal meets the curve where
$$\frac{-x + 3}{4} = -2x^2 + 3$$
$$\therefore \ -x + 3 = -8x^2 + 12$$
$$\therefore \ 8x^2 - x - 9 = 0$$
$$\therefore \ (8x - 9)(x + 1) = 0$$
$$\therefore \ x = -1 \text{ or } \tfrac{9}{8}$$
When $x = \frac{9}{8}$, $y = -2\left(\frac{9}{8}\right)^2 + 3$
$$= -2\left(\tfrac{81}{64}\right) + 3$$
$$= \tfrac{15}{32}$$
So, the normal meets the curve again at $\left(\frac{9}{8}, \frac{15}{32}\right)$.

3   **a** $y = \dfrac{3x+1}{\sqrt{x}} = 3x^{\frac{1}{2}} + x^{-\frac{1}{2}}$

$\therefore \ \dfrac{dy}{dx} = \dfrac{3}{2}x^{-\frac{1}{2}} - \dfrac{1}{2}x^{-\frac{3}{2}}$

$= \dfrac{3}{2\sqrt{x}} - \dfrac{1}{2x\sqrt{x}}$

b $y = (x^4 + 9)^{-1}$

$\therefore \ \dfrac{dy}{dx} = -(x^4 + 9)^{-2} \times (4x^3)$

c $y = x^2(1-x^2)^{\frac{1}{2}}$

$\therefore \ \dfrac{dy}{dx} = 2x(1-x^2)^{\frac{1}{2}} + x^2 \times \frac{1}{2}(1-x^2)^{-\frac{1}{2}} \times (-2x)$

$= 2x\sqrt{1-x^2} - \dfrac{x^3}{\sqrt{1-x^2}}$

d $y = (2x+3)^5$

$\therefore \ \dfrac{dy}{dx} = 5(2x+3)^4 \times 2$

$= 10(2x+3)^4$

4   **a** $g(x) = -x\cos x$

$\therefore \ g'(x) = -\cos x + (-x)(-\sin x)$

$= -\cos x + x\sin x$

b $g'(\frac{\pi}{3}) = -\cos(\frac{\pi}{3}) + \frac{\pi}{3}\sin(\frac{\pi}{3})$

$= -\frac{1}{2} + \frac{\pi}{3}\left(\frac{\sqrt{3}}{2}\right)$

$= \frac{\pi\sqrt{3}}{6} - \frac{1}{2}$

So, the tangent has gradient $\frac{\pi\sqrt{3}-3}{6}$.

5   **a** $f(x) = x^3 - 2x^2$

$\therefore \ f'(x) = 3x^2 - 4x$

b $f'(x) = 3x^2 - 4x$

$= x(3x-4)$

$\therefore \ f'(x) = 0$ when $x = 0$ or $\frac{4}{3}$

Sign diagram for $f'(x)$
on $-1 \leqslant x \leqslant 1$:

$f(0) = 0$, so the greatest value is 0 when $x = 0$.

Also, $f(-1) = (-1)^3 - 2(-1)^2 = -3$

and $f(1) = 1^3 - 2(1)^2 = -1$

$\therefore$ the least value is -3 when $x = -1$.

6   **a** $y = (2+x)\sqrt{3-x}$ is defined when $3 - x \geqslant 0$

$\therefore \ x \leqslant 3$

$\therefore$ the domain is $\{x \mid x \leqslant 3\}$.

b $y = (2+x)(3-x)^{\frac{1}{2}}$

$\therefore \ \dfrac{dy}{dx} = (1)(3-x)^{\frac{1}{2}} + (2+x)[\frac{1}{2}(-1)(3-x)^{-\frac{1}{2}}]$

$\{\text{product rule}\}$

$= (3-x)^{\frac{1}{2}} - \frac{1}{2}(2+x)(3-x)^{-\frac{1}{2}}$

$= \sqrt{3-x} - \dfrac{2+x}{2\sqrt{3-x}}$

c   If $\dfrac{dy}{dx} = 0$ then $\sqrt{3-x} - \dfrac{2+x}{2\sqrt{3-x}} = 0$

$\therefore \ \dfrac{2+x}{2\sqrt{3-x}} = \sqrt{3-x}$

$\therefore \ 2 + x = 2(3-x)$

$\therefore \ 2 + x = 6 - 2x$

$\therefore \ 3x = 4$

$\therefore \ x = \frac{4}{3}$

When $x = \frac{4}{3}, \quad y = (2 + \frac{4}{3})\sqrt{3 - \frac{4}{3}}$

$= \frac{10}{3}\sqrt{\frac{5}{3}}$

Sign diagram for $f'(x)$:

There is a local maximum at $(\frac{4}{3}, \frac{10}{3}\sqrt{\frac{5}{3}})$.

7   **a**   The curves meet where $\sqrt{3x+1} = \sqrt{5x - x^2}$

$\therefore \ 3x + 1 = 5x - x^2$

$\therefore \ x^2 - 2x + 1 = 0$

$\therefore \ (x-1)^2 = 0$

$\therefore \ x = 1$

When $x = 1, \quad y = \sqrt{3+1} = 2$.

$\therefore$ they meet at $(1, 2)$.

b   For $y = (3x+1)^{\frac{1}{2}}, \quad \dfrac{dy}{dx} = \frac{1}{2}(3x+1)^{-\frac{1}{2}}(3)$

$= \dfrac{3}{2\sqrt{3x+1}}$

$\therefore$ when $x = 1, \quad \dfrac{dy}{dx} = \frac{3}{4}$.

For $y = (5x - x^2)^{\frac{1}{2}}, \quad \dfrac{dy}{dx} = \frac{1}{2}(5x-x^2)^{-\frac{1}{2}}(5-2x)$

$\therefore$ when $x = 1, \quad \dfrac{dy}{dx} = \frac{1}{2}(4^{-\frac{1}{2}})3 = \frac{3}{4}$.

Both curves have the same gradient $\frac{3}{4}$ at their point of intersection.

c   The equation of the common tangent is

$\dfrac{y-2}{x-1} = \frac{3}{4}$ which is $4y - 8 = 3x - 3$

or $3x - 4y = -5$

8   **a** $h(t) = 100 + 32t - 4t^2$

$\therefore \ h'(t) = 32 - 8t$

b $h'(t) = 0$ when $32 = 8t$

$\therefore \ t = 4$

Sign diagram for $h'(t)$:

So, the height is maximised when $t = 4$ s.

Now $h(4) = 100 + 32(4) - 4(4)^2 = 164$

$\therefore$ the maximum height is 164 m.

9   **a** $y = \dfrac{1-2x}{\sqrt[3]{x}} = \dfrac{1-2x}{x^{\frac{1}{3}}} = x^{-\frac{1}{3}} - 2x^{\frac{2}{3}}$

$\therefore \ \dfrac{dy}{dx} = -\frac{1}{3}x^{-\frac{4}{3}} - \frac{4}{3}x^{-\frac{1}{3}}$

b $y = 2x(1+2x)^4$

$\therefore \ \dfrac{dy}{dx} = 2(1+2x)^4 + 2x(4)(1+2x)^3(2)$

$= 2(1+2x)^4 + 16x(1+2x)^3$

10 a $\quad y = \dfrac{3}{x^2} = 3x^{-2}$

$\therefore \quad \dfrac{dy}{dx} = -6x^{-3}$

$\therefore \quad \dfrac{d^2y}{dx^2} = 18x^{-4} = \dfrac{18}{x^4}$

b $\quad y = x^2 \sin 3x$

$\therefore \quad \dfrac{dy}{dx} = 2x \sin 3x + x^2(3\cos 3x) \quad \{\text{product rule}\}$

$\qquad = 2x \sin 3x + 3x^2 \cos 3x$

$\therefore \quad \dfrac{d^2y}{dx^2} = 2\sin 3x + 2x(3\cos 3x) + 6x \cos 3x$

$\qquad\qquad + 3x^2(-3\sin 3x)$

$\qquad = 12x \cos 3x + (2 - 9x^2)\sin 3x$

11 a $\quad f(x) = \dfrac{x-4}{x+2}$ is undefined when $x = -2$, so $x = -2$ is a vertical asymptote.

$f(x) = \dfrac{x-4}{x+2} = \dfrac{1 - \frac{4}{x}}{1 + \frac{2}{x}}$

As $x \to \infty$, $f(x) \to \dfrac{1}{1} = 1$, so $y = 1$ is a horizontal asymptote.

b $\quad f'(x) = \dfrac{1(x+2) - (x-4)1}{(x+2)^2} \quad \{\text{quotient rule}\}$

$\qquad = \dfrac{6}{(x+2)^2}$

c Since $f(3) = \dfrac{-1}{5}$, the point of contact is $\left(3, -\frac{1}{5}\right)$.

Now $\quad f'(3) = \dfrac{6}{(3+2)^2} = \dfrac{6}{25}$

$\therefore$ the tangent has equation

$\qquad \dfrac{y - \left(-\frac{1}{5}\right)}{x - 3} = \dfrac{6}{25}$

$\therefore \quad 25\left(y + \frac{1}{5}\right) = 6x - 18$

$\therefore \quad 25y + 5 = 6x - 18$

$\therefore \quad 6x - 25y = 23$

12 a $\quad y = \left(x + \dfrac{1}{x}\right)^4$ is undefined when $x = 0$, so $x = 0$ is a vertical asymptote.

As $x \to \infty$, $\quad y \to \infty$

As $x \to -\infty$, $\quad y \to \infty$

$\therefore$ there are no horizontal asymptotes.

b $\qquad y = \left(x + \dfrac{1}{x}\right)^4 = \left(x + x^{-1}\right)^4$

$\therefore \quad \dfrac{dy}{dx} = 4\left(x + x^{-1}\right)^3 \left(1 - x^{-2}\right)$

$\qquad = 4\left(x + \dfrac{1}{x}\right)^3 \left(1 - \dfrac{1}{x^2}\right)$

c Since $\dfrac{d^2y}{dx^2} > 0$ for all $x \neq 0$, the curve is concave upwards either side of its asymptote.

d $\dfrac{dy}{dx} = 4\left(x + \dfrac{1}{x}\right)^3 \left(1 - \dfrac{1}{x^2}\right)$

$\therefore \quad \dfrac{dy}{dx} = 0$ when

$\left(x + \dfrac{1}{x}\right)^3 = 0 \quad$ or when $\quad 1 - \dfrac{1}{x^2} = 0$

$\therefore \quad x = -\dfrac{1}{x} \qquad$ or $\qquad x^2 = 1$

$\therefore \quad x^2 = -1 \qquad$ or $\qquad x = \pm 1$

Sign diagram of $\dfrac{dy}{dx}$ is:

For $x > 0$, there is a local minimum at $x = 1$.

When $x = 1$, $\quad y = \left(1 + \frac{1}{1}\right)^4 = 16$.

So, the minimum value of the function for $x > 0$ is at $(1, 16)$.

13 a $\quad v(t) = t^3 - 9t^2 + 24t \ \text{m s}^{-1}$ where $t \geqslant 0$

$\therefore \quad a(t) = v'(t)$

$\qquad = 3t^2 - 18t + 24 \ \text{m s}^{-2}$

b $v'(t) = 3t^2 - 18t + 24 = 3(t^2 - 6t + 8)$

$\qquad = 3(t - 4)(t - 2)$

Sign diagram for $v'(t)$:

$v_{\max}$ is the larger of $v(2)$ or $v(6)$

Now $\quad v(2) = 8 - 36 + 48 = 20 \ \text{m s}^{-1}$

$\qquad v(6) = 216 - 324 + 144 = 36 \ \text{m s}^{-1}$

$\therefore \quad v_{\max} = 36 \ \text{m s}^{-1}$ when $t = 6$ s.

14 a Let $f(x) = x^3 + 2x + 1$

$\therefore \quad f(-1) = (-1)^3 + 2(-1) + 1 = -2$

Now $\quad f'(x) = 3x^2 + 2$

$\therefore \quad f'(-1) = 3(-1)^2 + 2 = 5$

$\therefore$ the tangent at $(-1, -2)$ has gradient 5, and its equation is $\quad \dfrac{y - (-2)}{x - (-1)} = 5$

$\qquad \therefore \quad y + 2 = 5x + 5$

$\qquad\qquad \therefore \quad y = 5x + 3$

b $(x + 1)^2(x - 2) = (x^2 + 2x + 1)(x - 2)$

$\qquad = x^3 - 2x^2 + 2x^2 - 4x + x - 2$

$\qquad = x^3 - 3x - 2$

c Now $y = 5x + 3$ meets $y = x^3 + 2x + 1$ where

$\qquad x^3 + 2x + 1 = 5x + 3$

$\qquad \therefore \quad x^3 - 3x - 2 = 0$

$\qquad \therefore \quad (x + 1)^2(x - 2) = 0 \quad \{\text{using } \mathbf{b}\}$

$\qquad\qquad \therefore \quad x = -1 \text{ or } 2$

When $x = 2$, $\quad y = 2^3 + 2(2) + 1 = 13$

So, the tangent meets the curve again at $(2, 13)$.

15 a $\quad s(t) = 12t - 3t^3 + 1$

$\therefore \quad v(t) = s'(t) = 12 - 9t^2$

$\therefore \quad a(t) = v'(t) = -18t$

b $v(t) = 12 - 9t^2$

$\qquad = 3(4 - 3t^2)$

$\qquad = 3(2 + t\sqrt{3})(2 - t\sqrt{3})$

which has sign diagram:

$a(t) = -18t$

which has sign diagram:

i Speed is decreasing when $v(t)$ and $a(t)$ have the opposite sign.

$\therefore$ the speed is decreasing for $0 \leqslant t \leqslant \dfrac{2}{\sqrt{3}}$.

ii Velocity is decreasing when $v'(t) \leqslant 0$.
Since $v'(t) = a(t) \leqslant 0$ for all $t \geqslant 0$, the velocity is decreasing for $t \geqslant 0$.

16 a i $\quad g(x) = x^2 e^{-(x+2)}$

$\therefore \ g'(x) = 2xe^{-(x+2)} + x^2 e^{-(x+2)}(-1)$

$\qquad = 2xe^{-(x+2)} - x^2 e^{-(x+2)}$

$\qquad = (2x - x^2)e^{-(x+2)}$

ii $g''(x) = (2 - 2x)e^{-(x+2)} + (2x - x^2)e^{-(x+2)}(-1)$

$\qquad = (2 - 2x - 2x + x^2)e^{-(x+2)}$

$\qquad = (x^2 - 4x + 2)e^{-(x+2)}$

b i $g'(x) = (2x - x^2)e^{-(x+2)}$

$g'(x) = 0$ when $2x - x^2 = 0$

$\qquad \therefore \ x(2 - x) = 0$

$\qquad \therefore \ x = 0$ or 2

Sign diagram of $g'(x)$ is:

$$\xleftarrow{\qquad \overset{-}{\quad} \underset{0}{\mid} \overset{+}{\quad} \underset{2}{\mid} \overset{-}{\quad} \qquad} x$$

So, $y = g(x)$ is increasing for $0 \leqslant x \leqslant 2$.

ii $g''(x) = (x^2 - 4x + 2)e^{-(x+2)}$

$g''(x) = 0$ when $x^2 - 4x + 2 = 0$

$\qquad \therefore \ x = \dfrac{4 \pm \sqrt{16 - 4(2)}}{2}$

$\qquad \therefore \ x = 2 \pm \sqrt{2}$

Sign diagram of $g''(x)$ is:

$$\xleftarrow{\quad \overset{+}{\quad} \underset{2-\sqrt{2}}{\mid} \overset{-}{\quad} \underset{2+\sqrt{2}}{\mid} \overset{+}{\quad} \quad} x$$

So, $y = g(x)$ is concave up for $x \leqslant 2 - \sqrt{2}$ and $x \geqslant 2 + \sqrt{2}$.

17 a $\quad y = x(x^2 - 12x + 45)$

$\qquad = x^3 - 12x^2 + 45x$

$\therefore \ \dfrac{dy}{dx} = 3x^2 - 24x + 45$

and $\dfrac{d^2y}{dx^2} = 6x - 24$

b $\dfrac{dy}{dx} = 3x^2 - 24x + 45$

$\qquad = 3(x^2 - 8x + 15)$

$\qquad = 3(x - 3)(x - 5)$

Sign diagram for $\dfrac{dy}{dx}$:

$$\xleftarrow{\quad \overset{+}{\quad} \underset{3}{\mid} \overset{-}{\quad} \underset{5}{\mid} \overset{+}{\quad} \quad} x$$

When $x = 3$, $y = (3)^3 - 12(3)^2 + 45(3)$

$\qquad = 27 - 108 + 135$

$\qquad = 54$

and when $x = 5$, $y = (5)^3 - 12(5)^2 + 45(5)$

$\qquad = 125 - 300 + 225$

$\qquad = 50$

$\therefore$ there is a local maximum at $(3, 54)$ and a local minimum at $(5, 50)$.

c $\dfrac{d^2y}{dx^2} = 6x - 24$

$\therefore \ \dfrac{d^2y}{dx^2} = 0$ when $x = 4$

Sign diagram of $\dfrac{d^2y}{dx^2}$ is:

$$\xleftarrow{\quad \overset{-}{\quad} \underset{4}{\mid} \overset{+}{\quad} \quad} x$$

When $x = 4$, $y = 4^3 - 12(4)^2 + 45(4)$

$\qquad = 64 - 192 + 180$

$\qquad = 52$

So, there is a non-stationary inflection point at $(4, 52)$.

d The graph cuts the x and y-axes at 0.

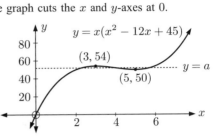

e The equation $x^3 - 12x^2 + 45x - a = 0$ has 3 real roots if $x(x^2 - 12x + 45) = a$ has 3 real roots.

This occurs provided $y = x(x^2 - 12x + 45)$ meets $y = a$ in 3 places.

$\therefore \ 50 < a < 54$

18 $\qquad f(x) = 8x^{-2}$

$\therefore \ f(2) = 8 \times 2^{-2} = 2$

Now $f'(x) = -16x^{-3} = \dfrac{-16}{x^3}$

$\qquad \therefore \ f'(2) = \dfrac{-16}{8} = -2$

$\therefore$ the gradient of the normal at $(2, 2)$ is $\frac{1}{2}$.

$\therefore$ the equation of normal is $\dfrac{y - 2}{x - 2} = \frac{1}{2}$

$\qquad$ which is $2y - 4 = x - 2$

$\qquad$ or $x - 2y = -2$

19 a i $\qquad y = \dfrac{x}{e^x}$

$\therefore \ \dfrac{dy}{dx} = \dfrac{1(e^x) - xe^x}{e^{2x}} = \dfrac{e^x(1 - x)}{e^{2x}} = \dfrac{1 - x}{e^x}$

ii $\qquad y = \dfrac{e^{2x} + 1}{e^{2x} - 1}$

$\therefore \ \dfrac{dy}{dx} = \dfrac{(e^{2x})(2)(e^{2x} - 1) - (e^{2x} + 1)(e^{2x})(2)}{(e^{2x} - 1)^2}$

b $\int (x^2 + e^{2x+1}) \, dx = \dfrac{x^3}{3} + \frac{1}{2}e^{2x+1} + c$

20 a $\qquad p(x) = x^3 + ax^2 + b$

$\therefore \ p'(x) = 3x^2 + 2ax$

$\qquad = x(3x + 2a)$

$\therefore \ p'(x) = 0$ when $x = 0$ or $x = \dfrac{-2a}{3}$

Thus $p(x)$ has a stationary point at $x = 0$ for all a and b.

b i If $(-2, 6)$ is a second stationary point, then

$\qquad \dfrac{-2a}{3} = -2$

$\qquad \therefore \ -2a = -6$

$\qquad \therefore \ a = 3$

Also, $p(-2) = 6$, so $(-2)^3 + 3(-2)^2 + b = 6$

$\qquad \therefore \ -8 + 12 + b = 6$

$\qquad \therefore \ b = 2$

ii $p'(x) = 3x^2 + 2ax$

$\therefore \ p'(x) = 3x(x+2)$

Sign diagram for $p'(x)$:

$\therefore$ there is a local maximum at $(-2, 6)$ and a local minimum at $(0, 2)$.

c If (h, k) is the second stationary point,

then $\dfrac{-2a}{3} = h$

$\therefore \ a = -\dfrac{3h}{2}$

Also, $p(h) = k$, so $h^3 + ah^2 + b = k$

$\therefore \ h^3 + \left(-\dfrac{3h}{2}\right)h^2 + b = k$

$\therefore \ h^3 - \dfrac{3h^3}{2} + b = k$

$\therefore \ -\dfrac{h^3}{2} + b = k$

$\therefore \ b = k + \dfrac{h^3}{2}$

21 **a** Perimeter $P = 48 = 3.6x + 2y$

$\therefore \ y = \dfrac{48 - 3.6x}{2}$

b Area $A = xy + (0.6)x^2$

$\therefore \ A = x\left(\dfrac{48 - 3.6x}{2}\right) + 0.6x^2$

$= 24x - 1.8x^2 + 0.6x^2$

$= 24x - 1.2x^2$

$\therefore \ \dfrac{dA}{dx} = 24 - 2.4x = 2.4(10 - x)$

$\therefore \ \dfrac{dA}{dx} = 0$ when $x = 10$

Sign diagram for $\dfrac{dA}{dx}$:

The maximum area occurs when $x = 10$.

$\therefore$ the maximum area $= 24(10) - 1.2(10)^2 = 120$ m^2.

22 **a** $y = x\ln(x+1), \ x > -1$

$\therefore \ \dfrac{dy}{dx} = (1)\ln(x+1) + x\left(\dfrac{1}{x+1}\right), \quad x > -1$

$= \ln(x+1) + \dfrac{x}{x+1}$

b $y = x\ln x^2 = 2x\ln x$ as $x > 0$

$\therefore \ \dfrac{dy}{dx} = (2)\ln x + 2x\left(\dfrac{1}{x}\right) = 2\ln x + 2, \quad x > 0$

c $y = \dfrac{e^{2x}}{2x+1} \qquad \therefore \ \dfrac{dy}{dx} = \dfrac{e^{2x}(2)(2x+1) - e^{2x}(2)}{(2x+1)^2}$

$= \dfrac{e^{2x}[4x + 2 - 2]}{(2x+1)^2}$

$= \dfrac{4xe^{2x}}{(2x+1)^2}, \quad x \neq -\tfrac{1}{2}$

d $y = \ln\left(\dfrac{x-4}{x^2+4}\right) = \ln(x-4) - \ln(x^2+4), \quad x > 4$

$\therefore \ \dfrac{dy}{dx} = \dfrac{1}{x-4} - \dfrac{2x}{x^2+4}, \quad x > 4$

23 **a** $f(x) = \ln\left(\dfrac{1-2x}{x^2+2}\right)$

$= \ln(1-2x) - \ln(x^2+2)$

$\therefore \ f'(x) = \dfrac{-2}{1-2x} - \dfrac{2x}{x^2+2}$

$= \dfrac{-2x^2 - 4 - 2x(1-2x)}{(1-2x)(x^2+2)}$

$= \dfrac{2x^2 - 2x - 4}{(1-2x)(x^2+2)}$

b $f'(x) = \dfrac{2(x-2)(x+1)}{(1-2x)(x^2+2)}$

Now $x^2 + 2 > 0$ always, so $f(x)$ is defined when $1 - 2x > 0$ or in other words $x < \tfrac{1}{2}$.

So, $f'(x)$ has sign diagram:

$f(x)$ is decreasing on the interval where $f'(x) \leqslant 0$.

$\therefore \ f(x)$ is decreasing for $-1 \leqslant x < \tfrac{1}{2}$.

24 **a** Total surface area

$= 2(\tfrac{1}{2}x \times x) + 2xy$ {area of $\triangle = \tfrac{1}{2}$ base $\times$ height}

$= x^2 + 2xy$

Thus $x^2 + 2xy = 27$.

b $V = $ area of end $\times$ length

$= \tfrac{1}{2}x \times x \times y$

$= \tfrac{1}{2}x^2 y$ m^3

From **a**, $x^2 + 2xy = 27$

$\therefore \ y = \dfrac{27 - x^2}{2x}$

$\therefore \ V = \tfrac{1}{2}x^2\left(\dfrac{27 - x^2}{2x}\right)$

$= \dfrac{27}{4}x - \dfrac{x^3}{4}$

c $\dfrac{dV}{dx} = \dfrac{27}{4} - \dfrac{3x^2}{4}$ Sign diagram for $\dfrac{dV}{dx}$:

$= \tfrac{3}{4}(9 - x^2)$

$= \tfrac{3}{4}(3+x)(3-x)$

$\therefore \ V$ is maximised when $x = 3$ and $y = \dfrac{27 - 3^2}{2(3)} = 3$

So, $x = y = 3$ metres.

25

	$f'(x)$	$f''(x)$
A	0	+
B	0	0
C	+	0
D	+	−

26 **a** $y = f(x) = x + 5 + \dfrac{4}{x}$ is undefined when $x = 0$, so $x = 0$ is a vertical asymptote.

As $x \to \infty$, $\quad f(x) \to \infty$

As $x \to -\infty$, $\quad f(x) \to -\infty$

$\therefore$ there are no horizontal asymptotes.

b $f(x) = x + 5 + \dfrac{4}{x}$

$\therefore\ f(x) = 0$ when $x + 5 + \dfrac{4}{x} = 0$

$\qquad\qquad\quad \therefore\ x^2 + 5x + 4 = 0$

$\qquad\qquad\quad \therefore\ (x+1)(x+4) = 0$

$\qquad\qquad\qquad\quad \therefore\ x = -1$ or -4

c $\quad f(x) = x + 5 + 4x^{-1}$

$\therefore\ f'(x) = 1 - 4x^{-2}$

$\qquad\quad = 1 - \dfrac{4}{x^2}$

$\qquad\quad = \dfrac{x^2 - 4}{x^2}$

$\qquad\quad = \dfrac{(x+2)(x-2)}{x^2}$

$\therefore\ f'(x) = 0$ when $x = \pm 2$

Sign diagram for $f'(x)$:

Now $f(-2) = -2 + 5 + \frac{4}{-2} = 1$

and $f(2) = 2 + 5 + \frac{4}{2} = 9$

So, there is a local maximum at $(-2,\ 1)$ and a local minimum at $(2,\ 9)$.

d

$y = x + 5 + \dfrac{4}{x}$

$(2, 9)$

$(-2, 1)$

$x = 0$

27 a

i $y = 4x^3 - 3x^4$ cuts the x-axis when $y = 0$

$\therefore\ 4x^3 - 3x^4 = 0$

$\therefore\ x^3(4 - 3x) = 0$

$\qquad\quad \therefore\ x = 0$ or $\frac{4}{3}$

$\therefore$ the x-intercepts are 0 and $\frac{4}{3}$, and the y-intercept is 0.

ii $\dfrac{dy}{dx} = 12x^2 - 12x^3 = 12x^2(1 - x)$

which has sign diagram:

When $x = 0$, $y = 0$

and when $x = 1$, $y = 4 - 3 = 1$

$\therefore$ there is a stationary inflection at $(0, 0)$ and a local maximum at $(1, 1)$.

iii $\dfrac{d^2 y}{dx^2} = 24x - 36x^2 = 12x(2 - 3x)$

which has sign diagram:

When $x = \frac{2}{3}$, $y = 4\left(\frac{2}{3}\right)^3 - 3\left(\frac{2}{3}\right)^4$

$\qquad\qquad\qquad = \frac{32}{27} - \frac{16}{27}$

$\qquad\qquad\qquad = \frac{16}{27}$

$\therefore$ there is a non-stationary inflection at $\left(\frac{2}{3}, \frac{16}{27}\right)$.

b

non-stationary inflection $\left(\frac{2}{3}, \frac{16}{27}\right)$

$(1,1)$ local max

$y = k$

$\left(\frac{4}{3}, 0\right)$

stationary inflection

$y = 4x^3 - 3x^4$

c If $4x^3 - 3x^4 = k$ has exactly two distinct positive solutions then the horizontal line $y = k$ meets the graph of $y = 4x^3 - 3x^4$ in two different points with x-coordinate > 0.

Thus $0 < k < 1$.

28 a $f(x) = 1 - \dfrac{4x}{x^2 + 4}$

$f(0) = 1$, so the y-intercept $= 1$

$f(x) = 0$ when $\qquad 1 - \dfrac{4x}{x^2 + 4} = 0$

$\qquad\qquad\qquad\quad \therefore\ \dfrac{4x}{x^2 + 4} = 1$

$\qquad\qquad\qquad\qquad \therefore\ 4x = x^2 + 4$

$\qquad\qquad\quad \therefore\ x^2 - 4x + 4 = 0$

$\qquad\qquad\qquad \therefore\ (x - 2)^2 = 0$

$\qquad\qquad\qquad\qquad\quad \therefore\ x = 2$

So, the x-intercept is 2.

b $f'(x) = 0 - \left(\dfrac{4(x^2 + 4) - 4x(2x)}{(x^2 + 4)^2} \right)$

$\qquad\quad = \dfrac{8x^2 - 4x^2 - 16}{(x^2 + 4)^2}$

$\qquad\quad = \dfrac{4x^2 - 16}{(x^2 + 4)^2}$

$\qquad\quad = \dfrac{4(x + 2)(x - 2)}{(x^2 + 4)^2}$

$f'(x)$ has sign diagram:

$f(-2) = 1 - \left(\frac{-8}{8}\right) = 2$

$f(2) = 1 - \left(\frac{8}{8}\right) = 0$

$\therefore$ there is a local maximum at $(-2,\ 2)$ and a local minimum at $(2,\ 0)$.

c

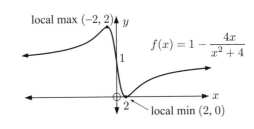

local max $(-2, 2)$

$f(x) = 1 - \dfrac{4x}{x^2 + 4}$

local min $(2, 0)$

29 a $\quad f(x) = 3 \sin(x - 4)$

$\therefore\ f'(x) = 3 \cos(x - 4) \times 1$

$\qquad\qquad = 3 \cos(x - 4)$

b $\quad f(x) = 12x - 2 \cos\left(\frac{x}{3}\right)$

$\therefore\ f'(x) = 12 - 2\left(-\sin\left(\frac{x}{3}\right)\right) \times \frac{1}{3}$

$\qquad\qquad = 12 + \frac{2}{3} \sin\left(\frac{x}{3}\right)$

Mathematics SL – Exam Preparation & Practice Guide (3ʳᵈ edition)

c $f(x) = \dfrac{\sin 2x}{1 + 2x}$

$\therefore\ f'(x) = \dfrac{2\cos 2x \times (1 + 2x) - \sin 2x \times 2}{(1 + 2x)^2}$

$\qquad = \dfrac{2(1 + 2x)\cos 2x - 2\sin 2x}{(1 + 2x)^2}$

d $f(x) = [\sin(2x + 1)]^{\frac{1}{2}}$

$\therefore\ f'(x) = \frac{1}{2}[\sin(2x + 1)]^{-\frac{1}{2}} \times 2\cos(2x + 1)$

$\qquad = \dfrac{\cos(2x + 1)}{\sqrt{\sin(2x + 1)}}$

e $f(x) = e^{2\sin x}$

$\therefore\ f'(x) = e^{2\sin x} \times 2\cos x$

$\qquad = 2e^{2\sin x}\cos x$

f $f(x) = \tan(3x - 4)$

$\therefore\ f'(x) = \dfrac{\frac{d}{dx}(3x - 4)}{\cos^2(3x - 4)}$

$\qquad = \dfrac{3}{\cos^2(3x - 4)}$

30   **a** $f(x) = \dfrac{x + 2}{\sqrt{x - 1}}$ is defined if $x - 1 > 0$, so $x > 1$.

b $f(x) = \dfrac{x + 2}{(x - 1)^{\frac{1}{2}}}$

$\therefore\ f'(x) = \dfrac{(1)(x - 1)^{\frac{1}{2}} - (x + 2)(\frac{1}{2})(x - 1)^{-\frac{1}{2}}(1)}{x - 1}$

$\therefore\ f'(10) = \dfrac{9^{\frac{1}{2}} - 12(\frac{1}{2})9^{-\frac{1}{2}}}{9} = \dfrac{3 - 6(\frac{1}{3})}{9} = \dfrac{1}{9}$

$\therefore$ the gradient of the normal at $x = 10$ is $\frac{-9}{1} = -9$

Now $f(10) = \frac{12}{\sqrt{9}} = 4$ so the point of contact is $(10, 4)$.

$\therefore$ the equation of the normal is $\dfrac{y - 4}{x - 10} = -9$

$\qquad\qquad\qquad$ which is $y - 4 = -9x + 90$

$\qquad\qquad\qquad\qquad$ or $9x + y = 94$

31 C follows the curve $y = x^2$,
so C is (x, x^2).

a $s^2 = x^2 + (x^2 - 2)^2$ {Pythagoras}

$\therefore\ s^2 = x^2 + x^4 - 4x^2 + 4$

$\therefore\ s^2 = x^4 - 3x^2 + 4$

$\therefore\ s = \sqrt{x^4 - 3x^2 + 4}$ {as $s > 0$}

b Since $s > 0$, s is minimised when s^2 is minimised.

Now $s^2 = x^4 - 3x^2 + 4$

$\therefore\ \dfrac{d[s^2]}{dx} = 4x^3 - 6x$

$\qquad = 2x(2x^2 - 3)$

$\qquad = 2x(\sqrt{2}x + \sqrt{3})(\sqrt{2}x - \sqrt{3})$

Sign diagram for $\dfrac{d[s^2]}{dx}$:

Now by symmetry,

$s\left(-\dfrac{\sqrt{3}}{\sqrt{2}}\right) = s\left(\dfrac{\sqrt{3}}{\sqrt{2}}\right) = \sqrt{\dfrac{9}{4} - 3(\dfrac{3}{2}) + 4}$

$\qquad\qquad\qquad\qquad = \sqrt{\dfrac{9}{4} - \dfrac{9}{2} + 4}$

$\qquad\qquad\qquad\qquad = \dfrac{\sqrt{7}}{2}$ units

$\therefore$ the minimum distance is $\dfrac{\sqrt{7}}{2}$ units when $x = \pm\dfrac{\sqrt{3}}{\sqrt{2}}$.

The maximum distance occurs either when $x = 0$ or at one of the endpoints of the domain.

$s(-2) = s(2) = \sqrt{16 - 12 + 4} = \sqrt{8}$

$\quad$ and $s(0) = \sqrt{4} = 2$

$\therefore$ the maximum distance is $\sqrt{8}$ units when $x = \pm 2$.

32   **a** Let sides be x m and y m long, as shown.

Now $xy = 48$, so $y = \dfrac{48}{x}$

$\therefore$ the total cost $C = 18(2y + x) + 30x$

$\qquad\qquad\qquad = 36y + 48x$

$\qquad\qquad\qquad = 36\left(\dfrac{48}{x}\right) + 48x$

$\qquad\qquad\qquad = 48\left(\dfrac{36}{x} + x\right)$ dollars

b Since $C = 48(36x^{-1} + x)$, $\dfrac{dC}{dx} = 48(-36x^{-2} + 1)$

$\qquad\qquad\qquad\qquad = 48\left(1 - \dfrac{36}{x^2}\right)$

$\qquad\qquad\qquad\qquad = 48\left(\dfrac{x^2 - 36}{x^2}\right)$

$\qquad\qquad\qquad\qquad = \dfrac{48(x + 6)(x - 6)}{x^2}$

$\therefore\ \dfrac{dC}{dx}$ has sign diagram:

$\therefore\ C$ is a minimum when $x = 6$
$\qquad\qquad\qquad$ and $y = 8$.

33   **a** $RQ = \sqrt{x^2 + 64}$ km
$\qquad\qquad$ {Pythagoras}

$\therefore$ the total cost $C(x)$
$\quad$ = cost under sea + cost on land
$\quad = 5\sqrt{x^2 + 64} + 3(11 - x)$
$\quad = 5\sqrt{x^2 + 64} + 33 - 3x$
$\qquad\qquad$ millions of dollars

b $C(x) = 5(x^2 + 64)^{\frac{1}{2}} + 33 - 3x$

$\therefore\ C'(x) = \dfrac{5}{2}(x^2 + 64)^{-\frac{1}{2}}(2x) - 3$

$\qquad = \dfrac{5x}{\sqrt{x^2 + 64}} - 3$

$\therefore\ C'(x) = 0$ when $\dfrac{5x}{\sqrt{x^2 + 64}} = 3$

$\qquad\qquad\qquad \therefore\ 5x = 3\sqrt{x^2 + 64}$

$\qquad\qquad\qquad \therefore\ 25x^2 = 9(x^2 + 64)$

$\qquad\qquad\qquad \therefore\ 25x^2 = 9x^2 + 9 \times 64$

$\qquad\qquad\qquad \therefore\ 16x^2 = 9 \times 64$

$\qquad\qquad\qquad \therefore\ x^2 = 9 \times 4 = 36$

$\qquad\qquad\qquad \therefore\ x = 6$ {as $x > 0$}

Sign diagram for $C'(x)$:

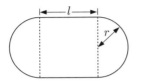

Now $C(6) = 5\sqrt{36 + 64} + 33 - 3 \times 6$
$$= 5\sqrt{100} + 33 - 18$$
$$= 50 + 15 = 65$$

∴ the minimum cost is \$65 million.

34

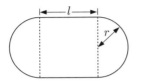

Let l be the length of the straight section.
Let r be the radius of the semi-circular sections.
The area $A = \pi r^2 + 2rl$ which is a constant

$$\therefore \quad l = \frac{A - \pi r^2}{2r} \quad .... (1)$$

Let p be the cost per unit length of straight wall.
∴ the total cost is
$$C = (2l + 2\pi r(\tfrac{5}{4}))p$$
$$= \left(\frac{A}{r} - \pi r + \frac{5\pi r}{2}\right)p \quad \{\text{using (1)}\}$$
$$= \left(\frac{A}{r} + \frac{3\pi}{2}r\right)p$$
$$= \left(Ar^{-1} + \frac{3\pi}{2}r\right)p$$
$$\therefore \quad \frac{dC}{dr} = \left(-\frac{A}{r^2} + \frac{3\pi}{2}\right)p$$
$$\therefore \quad \frac{dC}{dr} = 0 \text{ when } r^2 = \frac{2A}{3\pi}$$

$\dfrac{dC}{dr}$ has sign diagram:

So, the minimum cost is

when $r = \sqrt{\dfrac{2A}{3\pi}}$

∴ the area of the shaded portion $= \pi r^2 = \pi\left(\dfrac{2A}{3\pi}\right) = \tfrac{2}{3}A$

35 a $\int_2^5 f(x)\,dx = 6$ **b** $\int_5^8 f(x)\,dx = -4$

c $\int_2^8 f(x)\,dx = \int_2^5 f(x)\,dx + \int_5^8 f(x)\,dx$
$$= 6 + (-4)$$
$$= 2$$

36 Since $\int_0^a f(x)\,dx = 4$, the shaded area $= 4$
$$\therefore \quad \tfrac{1}{4}\pi a^2 = 4$$
$$\therefore \quad a^2 = \frac{16}{\pi}$$
$$\therefore \quad a = \frac{4}{\sqrt{\pi}} \quad \{a > 0\}$$

37 a $\int (2x^2 + x - 3)\,dx = \dfrac{2x^3}{3} + \dfrac{x^2}{2} - 3x + c$

b $\int_0^1 (5x+4)^{\frac{1}{2}}\,dx = \left[\dfrac{1}{5} \times \dfrac{(5x+4)^{\frac{3}{2}}}{\frac{3}{2}}\right]_0^1$
$$= \tfrac{2}{15}\left[(5x+4)^{\frac{3}{2}}\right]_0^1$$
$$= \tfrac{2}{15}\left(9^{\frac{3}{2}} - 4^{\frac{3}{2}}\right)$$
$$= \tfrac{2}{15}(27 - 8)$$
$$= \tfrac{38}{15}$$

c $\int \left(x + \dfrac{1}{x}\right)^2 dx$
$$= \int \left[x^2 + 2x\left(\dfrac{1}{x}\right) + \left(\dfrac{1}{x}\right)^2\right] dx$$
$$= \int (x^2 + 2 + x^{-2})\,dx \qquad \text{provided } x \neq 0$$
$$= \frac{x^3}{3} + 2x + \frac{x^{-1}}{-1} + c$$
$$= \tfrac{1}{3}x^3 + 2x - \frac{1}{x} + c$$

d $\int_0^1 \dfrac{1}{2x+1}\,dx = \left[\tfrac{1}{2}\ln|2x+1|\right]_0^1$
$$= \tfrac{1}{2}\ln 3 - \tfrac{1}{2}\ln 1$$
$$= \tfrac{1}{2}\ln 3 - 0$$
$$= \tfrac{1}{2}\ln 3$$

e $\int (e^x - 1)^2\,dx = \int (e^{2x} - 2e^x + 1)\,dx$
$$= \tfrac{1}{2}e^{2x} - 2e^x + x + c$$

f $\int_0^4 \dfrac{1}{\sqrt{x+4}}\,dx = \int_0^4 (x+4)^{-\frac{1}{2}}\,dx = \left[\dfrac{(x+4)^{\frac{1}{2}}}{\frac{1}{2}}\right]_0^4$
$$= \left[2\sqrt{x+4}\right]_0^4$$
$$= 2\sqrt{8} - 2\sqrt{4}$$
$$= 4\sqrt{2} - 4$$

38 $g'(x) = 2\cos 3x$
$$\therefore \quad g(x) = \int 2\cos 3x\,dx$$
$$= 2 \times \tfrac{1}{3}\sin 3x + c$$
$$= \tfrac{2}{3}\sin 3x + c$$

But $g(\tfrac{\pi}{2}) = 4$,

so $\tfrac{2}{3}\sin(\tfrac{3\pi}{2}) + c = 4$
$$\therefore \quad -\tfrac{2}{3} + c = 4$$
$$\therefore \quad c = 4\tfrac{2}{3}$$
$$\therefore \quad g(x) = \tfrac{2}{3}\sin 3x + \tfrac{14}{3}$$

39 $f'(x) = (x^2 + 2)^2$
$$\therefore \quad f(x) = \int (x^2 + 2)^2\,dx$$
$$= \int (x^4 + 4x^2 + 4)\,dx$$
$$= \frac{x^5}{5} + \frac{4x^3}{3} + 4x + c$$

But $f(1) = \tfrac{8}{15}$,

so $\tfrac{1}{5} + \tfrac{4}{3} + 4 + c = \tfrac{8}{15}$
$$\therefore \quad c = -5$$
$$\therefore \quad f(x) = \frac{x^5}{5} + \frac{4x^3}{3} + 4x - 5$$

40 $f'(x) = \sqrt{4x+5}, \quad f(0) = 0$

a $f'(x) = \sqrt{4x+5}$ is defined when $4x + 5 \geqslant 0$
$$\therefore \quad x \geqslant -\tfrac{5}{4}$$

b $f(x) = \int \sqrt{4x+5}\,dx$
$$= \int (4x+5)^{\frac{1}{2}}\,dx$$
$$= \tfrac{1}{4}\frac{(4x+5)^{\frac{3}{2}}}{\frac{3}{2}} + c$$
$$= \tfrac{1}{6}(4x+5)^{\frac{3}{2}} + c$$

But $\quad f(0) = -\frac{\sqrt{5}}{6}$

so $\quad \frac{1}{6}(5)^{\frac{3}{2}} + c = -\frac{\sqrt{5}}{6}$

$\therefore \quad c = -\frac{5\sqrt{5}}{6} - \frac{\sqrt{5}}{6} = -\sqrt{5}$

$\therefore \quad f(x) = \frac{1}{6}(4x+5)^{\frac{3}{2}} - \sqrt{5}$

41 $f(x) = x(3-2x)^{\frac{1}{2}}$

$\therefore \quad f'(x) = (1)(3-2x)^{\frac{1}{2}} + x(\frac{1}{2})(3-2x)^{-\frac{1}{2}}(-2)$

$= \dfrac{\sqrt{3-2x}}{1} - \dfrac{x}{\sqrt{3-2x}}$

$= \dfrac{3-2x-x}{\sqrt{3-2x}}$

$= \dfrac{3(1-x)}{(3-2x)^{\frac{1}{2}}}$

Thus $\quad 3\displaystyle\int \dfrac{1-x}{(3-2x)^{\frac{1}{2}}}\,dx = x(3-2x)^{\frac{1}{2}} + c_1$

$\therefore \quad \displaystyle\int \dfrac{x-1}{(3-2x)^{\frac{1}{2}}}\,dx = -\frac{1}{3}x(3-2x)^{\frac{1}{2}} + c$

42 a $\displaystyle\int \dfrac{2x^2 - x - 3}{x^2}\,dx = \int \left(2 - \dfrac{1}{x} - 3x^{-2}\right)\,dx$

$= 2x - \ln|x| - \dfrac{3x^{-1}}{-1} + c$

$= 2x - \ln|x| + \dfrac{3}{x} + c$

b $\displaystyle\int_1^5 \dfrac{2x^3 + 1}{x^2}\,dx = \int_1^5 (2x + x^{-2})\,dx$

$= \left[x^2 - \dfrac{1}{x}\right]_1^5$

$= \left(5^2 - \dfrac{1}{5}\right) - (1^2 - 1)$

$= 24\frac{4}{5}$

43 $\displaystyle\int \sin^2 3x\,dx = \int \left(\frac{1}{2} - \frac{1}{2}\cos 6x\right)\,dx$

$= \frac{1}{2}x - \frac{1}{2}(\frac{1}{6})\sin 6x + c$

$= \frac{1}{2}x - \frac{1}{12}\sin 6x + c$

44 $y = 1 - x^2$ meets $y = -3$

where $\quad 1 - x^2 = -3$

$\therefore \quad 4 = x^2$

$\therefore \quad x = \pm 2$

Area $= \displaystyle\int_{-2}^2 \left((1-x^2) - (-3)\right)\,dx$

$= \displaystyle\int_{-2}^2 (4 - x^2)\,dx$

$= \left[4x - \frac{1}{3}x^3\right]_{-2}^2$

$= 8 - \frac{8}{3} - (-8 + \frac{8}{3})$

$= 16 - \dfrac{16}{3}$

$= 10\frac{2}{3}$ units^2

45 $y = x\sqrt{4-x} = x(4-x)^{\frac{1}{2}}$

$\dfrac{dy}{dx} = 1(4-x)^{\frac{1}{2}} + x(\frac{1}{2})(4-x)^{-\frac{1}{2}}(-1)$ {product rule}

$= \sqrt{4-x} - \dfrac{x}{2\sqrt{4-x}}$

$= \dfrac{2(4-x) - x}{2\sqrt{4-x}}$

$= \dfrac{8 - 3x}{2\sqrt{4-x}}$

Hence $\displaystyle\int_0^2 \dfrac{8-3x}{\sqrt{4-x}}\,dx = 2\int_0^2 \dfrac{8-3x}{2\sqrt{4-x}}\,dx$

$= 2\left[x\sqrt{4-x}\right]_0^2$

$= 2(2\sqrt{2} - 0\sqrt{4})$

$= 4\sqrt{2}$

46 a $\displaystyle\int_{-2}^2 f(x)\,dx = \int_{-2}^2 (x^3 - x^2 - 4x + 4)\,dx$

$= \left[\dfrac{x^4}{4} - \dfrac{x^3}{3} - \dfrac{4x^2}{2} + 4x\right]_{-2}^2$

$= \left(4 - \frac{8}{3} - 8 + 8\right) - \left(4 + \frac{8}{3} - 8 - 8\right)$

$= \dfrac{32}{3}$

b No, the shaded portion has area

$= \displaystyle\int_{-2}^1 f(x)\,dx - \int_1^2 f(x)\,dx$

whereas $\displaystyle\int_{-2}^2 f(x)\,dx = \int_{-2}^1 f(x)\,dx + \int_1^2 f(x)\,dx$

47 a $v = \dfrac{10}{\sqrt{5t+4}} = 10(5t+4)^{-\frac{1}{2}}$ m s^{-1}

$\therefore \quad s = \displaystyle\int v\,dt = 10\left(\frac{1}{5} \times \dfrac{(5t+4)^{\frac{1}{2}}}{\frac{1}{2}}\right) + c$

$= 4(5t+4)^{\frac{1}{2}} + c$ m

When $t = 0$, $s = 0$, so $\quad 0 = 4\sqrt{4} + c$

$\therefore \quad c = -8$

$\therefore \quad s = 4\sqrt{5t+4} - 8$ m

b $a = \dfrac{dv}{dt} = 10(-\frac{1}{2})(5t+4)^{-\frac{3}{2}}(5)$

$= \dfrac{-25}{(5t+4)^{\frac{3}{2}}}$ m s^{-2}

48 a $\displaystyle\int_0^\pi \sin x\,dx$

$= [-\cos x]_0^\pi$

$= (-\cos \pi) - (-\cos 0)$

$= -(-1) + 1$

$= 2$

b $\displaystyle\int_{-\frac{\pi}{4}}^{\frac{\pi}{4}} \cos 2x\,dx$

$= \left[\frac{1}{2}\sin 2x\right]_{-\frac{\pi}{4}}^{\frac{\pi}{4}}$

$= \frac{1}{2}\sin(\frac{\pi}{2}) - \frac{1}{2}\sin(-\frac{\pi}{2})$

$= \frac{1}{2}(1) - \frac{1}{2}(-1)$

$= 1$

49 $\dfrac{d}{dx}(x^2 \ln x) = 2x\ln x + x^2\left(\dfrac{1}{x}\right)$

$= 2x\ln x + x$

$\therefore \quad \displaystyle\int(2x\ln x + x)\,dx = x^2\ln x + c_1$

$\therefore \quad \displaystyle\int 2x\ln x\,dx + \int x\,dx = x^2\ln x + c_1$

$\therefore \quad 2\displaystyle\int x\ln x\,dx + \frac{1}{2}x^2 + c_2 = x^2\ln x + c_1$

$\therefore \quad 2\displaystyle\int x\ln x\,dx = x^2\ln x - \frac{1}{2}x^2 + c_3$

$\therefore \quad \displaystyle\int x\ln x\,dx = \frac{1}{2}x^2\ln x - \frac{1}{4}x^2 + c$

50 $y = x^2 e^{-x^2}$

$\therefore \quad \dfrac{dy}{dx} = (2x)e^{-x^2} + x^2(e^{-x^2})(-2x)$ {product rule}

$= 2xe^{-x^2}(1 - x^2)$

$= 2x(1 - x^2)e^{-x^2}$

Thus $\displaystyle\int 2x(1-x^2)e^{-x^2}\,dx = x^2 e^{-x^2} + c_1$

$\therefore \quad 2\displaystyle\int x(1-x^2)e^{-x^2}\,dx = x^2 e^{-x^2} + c_1$

$\therefore \quad \displaystyle\int x(1-x^2)e^{-x^2}\,dx = \frac{1}{2}x^2 e^{-x^2} + c$

51 **a** $y = x^2 + 2x - 3$ meets $y = x - 1$ where

$$x^2 + 2x - 3 = x - 1$$
$$\therefore \quad x^2 + x - 2 = 0$$
$$\therefore \quad (x + 2)(x - 1) = 0$$
$$\therefore \quad x = -2 \text{ or } 1$$

When $x = -2$, $y = -3$.
When $x = 1$, $y = 0$.
$\therefore$ the graphs meet at $(-2, -3)$ and $(1, 0)$.

b Area $= \int_{-2}^{1} ((x - 1) - (x^2 + 2x - 3))\, dx$

$$= \int_{-2}^{1} \left(x - 1 - x^2 - 2x + 3 \right) dx$$
$$= \int_{-2}^{1} \left(2 - x - x^2 \right) dx$$
$$= \left[2x - \tfrac{1}{2}x^2 - \tfrac{1}{3}x^3 \right]_{-2}^{1}$$
$$= 2 - \tfrac{1}{2} - \tfrac{1}{3} - \left(2(-2) - \tfrac{1}{2}(-2)^2 - \tfrac{1}{3}(-2)^3 \right)$$
$$= 2 - \tfrac{1}{2} - \tfrac{1}{3} + 4 + 2 - \tfrac{8}{3}$$
$$= 4\tfrac{1}{2} \text{ units}^2$$

52 **a** $y = 4 - x^2$ meets $y = -2x - 4$ where

$$-2x - 4 = 4 - x^2$$
$$\therefore \quad x^2 - 2x - 8 = 0$$
$$\therefore \quad (x + 2)(x - 4) = 0$$
$$\therefore \quad x = -2 \text{ or } 4$$

When $x = -2$, $y = 0$.
When $x = 4$, $y = -12$.
$\therefore$ the graphs meet at $(-2, 0)$ and $(4, -12)$.

b Area $= \int_{-2}^{4} \left((4 - x^2) - (-2x - 4) \right) dx$

$$= \int_{-2}^{4} \left(-x^2 + 2x + 8 \right) dx$$
$$= \left[-\tfrac{1}{3}x^3 + x^2 + 8x \right]_{-2}^{4}$$
$$= \left(-\tfrac{64}{3} + 16 + 32 \right) - \left(\tfrac{8}{3} + 4 - 16 \right)$$
$$= 36 \text{ units}^2$$

53 **a** $\quad a(t) = \dfrac{dv}{dt} = 2 - 3t \text{ m s}^{-2}$

$$\therefore \quad v(t) = \int (2 - 3t)\, dt = 2t - \frac{3t^2}{2} + c \text{ m s}^{-1}$$

Now when $t = 1$, $v = 0$

$$\therefore \quad 0 = 2 - \tfrac{3}{2} + c$$
$$\therefore \quad 0 = \tfrac{1}{2} + c$$
$$\therefore \quad c = -\tfrac{1}{2}$$
$$\therefore \quad v(t) = 2t - \frac{3t^2}{2} - \tfrac{1}{2} \text{ m s}^{-1}$$

b Now $v = 0$ when $2t - \dfrac{3t^2}{2} - \tfrac{1}{2} = 0$

$$\therefore \quad 4t - 3t^2 - 1 = 0$$
$$\therefore \quad 3t^2 - 4t + 1 = 0$$
$$\therefore \quad (3t - 1)(t - 1) = 0$$
$$\therefore \quad t = \tfrac{1}{3} \text{ or } t = 1$$

$\therefore \quad t = \tfrac{1}{3}$ s is the other time.

c $s(t) = \int v\, dt = \int \left(2t - \dfrac{3t^2}{2} - \tfrac{1}{2} \right) dt$

$$= \frac{2t^2}{2} - \frac{3t^3}{2(3)} - \tfrac{1}{2}t + d$$
$$= t^2 - \tfrac{1}{2}t^3 - \tfrac{1}{2}t + d \text{ m}$$

But when $t = 0$, $s = 3$ $\quad \therefore \quad d = 3$
$$\therefore \quad s(t) = t^2 - \tfrac{1}{2}t^3 - \tfrac{1}{2}t + 3 \text{ m}$$

54 **a** $v = 2t - 3t^2 \text{ m s}^{-1}$

Now $s = \int v\, dt = \int (2t - 3t^2)\, dt$

$$= \frac{2t^2}{2} - \frac{3t^3}{3} + c$$
$$= t^2 - t^3 + c$$
$$\therefore \quad s(0) = c \text{ and } s(1) = c$$

So, the change in displacement is 0 m.

b $v = 2t - 3t^2 = t(2 - 3t)$

Sign diagram of v:

$\therefore$ a change in direction occurs at $t = \tfrac{2}{3}$ s.

$s(0) = c$, $\quad s(\tfrac{2}{3}) = \tfrac{4}{27} + c$, $\quad s(1) = c$

The total distance travelled $= \tfrac{4}{27} + \tfrac{4}{27} = \tfrac{8}{27}$ m.

55 **a** $(x - 1)^2(x + 2) = (x^2 - 2x + 1)(x + 2)$

$$= x^3 + 2x^2 - 2x^2 - 4x + x + 2$$
$$= x^3 - 3x + 2$$

b $y = x - 2$ meets $y = x^3 - 2x$

where $\quad x^3 - 2x = x - 2$
$$\therefore \quad x^3 - 3x + 2 = 0$$
$$\therefore \quad (x - 1)^2(x + 2) = 0$$

Since the factor $(x - 1)$ is squared, $y = x - 2$ is a tangent to the curve when $x = 1$.
The line meets the curve again when $x = -2$.
When $x = 1$, $y = -1$.
When $x = -2$, $y = -4$.
$\therefore$ T is $(1, -1)$ and P is $(-2, -4)$.

c Consider $y = x^3 - 2x$.
When $x = 0$, $y = 0$, so the y-intercept is 0.
When $y = 0$, $x^3 - 2x = 0$
$$\therefore \quad x(x^2 - 2) = 0$$
$$\therefore \quad x(x + \sqrt{2})(x - \sqrt{2}) = 0$$
$\therefore$ the x-intercepts are $\pm\sqrt{2}$ and 0.

d

e Area $= \int_{-2}^{1} \left((x^3 - 2x) - (x - 2) \right) dx$

$\qquad = \int_{-2}^{1} (x^3 - 3x + 2) \, dx$

$\qquad = \left[\dfrac{x^4}{4} - \dfrac{3x^2}{2} + 2x \right]_{-2}^{1}$

$\qquad = (\tfrac{1}{4} - \tfrac{3}{2} + 2) - (4 - 6 - 4)$

$\qquad = 6\tfrac{3}{4}$ units^2

56
$$\int_{a}^{a+1} x^2 \, dx = \tfrac{1}{2}$$

$\therefore \left[\dfrac{x^3}{3} \right]_{a}^{a+1} = \tfrac{1}{2}$

$\therefore (a+1)^3 - a^3 = \tfrac{3}{2}$

$\therefore \cancel{a^3} + 3a^2 + 3a + 1 - \cancel{a^3} = \tfrac{3}{2}$

$\therefore 3a^2 + 3a - \tfrac{1}{2} = 0$

$\therefore 6a^2 + 6a - 1 = 0$

$\therefore a = \dfrac{-6 \pm \sqrt{36 - 4(6)(-1)}}{12}$

$\therefore a = \dfrac{-6 \pm \sqrt{60}}{12}$

But $a > 0$, so $a = \dfrac{\sqrt{60} - 6}{12}$

57 a $\quad f(\theta) = \dfrac{2 - \cos \theta}{\sin \theta}$

$\therefore f'(\theta) = \dfrac{\sin \theta \times \sin \theta - (2 - \cos \theta) \cos \theta}{\sin^2 \theta}$

$\qquad = \dfrac{\sin^2 \theta - 2\cos \theta + \cos^2 \theta}{\sin^2 \theta}$

$\qquad = \dfrac{1 - 2\cos \theta}{\sin^2 \theta}$

b $f'(\theta) = 0$ when $\cos \theta = \tfrac{1}{2}$ $\therefore$ $\theta = \tfrac{\pi}{3}$

Sign diagram for $f'(\theta)$:

$\therefore$ $f(\theta)$ is a minimum when $\theta = \tfrac{\pi}{3}$

Now $f(\tfrac{\pi}{3}) = \dfrac{2 - \tfrac{1}{2}}{\tfrac{\sqrt{3}}{2}} = \dfrac{\tfrac{3}{2}}{\tfrac{\sqrt{3}}{2}} = \sqrt{3}$

$\therefore$ the minimum value is $\sqrt{3}$ when $\theta = \tfrac{\pi}{3}$.

58 a $f(\theta) = \cos \theta \times [\sin \theta]^2$

$\therefore f'(\theta) = -\sin \theta [\sin \theta]^2 + \cos \theta \times 2[\sin \theta]^1 \times \cos \theta$

$\qquad = -\sin^3 \theta + 2\sin \theta \cos^2 \theta$

$\qquad = \sin \theta [2\cos^2 \theta - \sin^2 \theta]$

$\qquad = \sin \theta [2\cos^2 \theta - (1 - \cos^2 \theta)]$

$\qquad = \sin \theta (3\cos^2 \theta - 1)$

b $f'(\theta) = 0$ when $\sin \theta = 0$ or $\cos^2 \theta = \tfrac{1}{3}$

But $0 < \theta \leqslant \tfrac{\pi}{2}$, so $\cos \theta > 0$ and $\sin \theta > 0$

$\therefore$ $f'(\theta) = 0$ when $\cos \theta = \tfrac{1}{\sqrt{3}}$

Sign diagram for $f'(\theta)$:

$\therefore$ $f(\theta)$ is a maximum when $\cos \theta = \tfrac{1}{\sqrt{3}}$

At this time, $\sin^2 \theta = 1 - \cos^2 \theta = 1 - \tfrac{1}{3} = \tfrac{2}{3}$

$\therefore$ the maximum value of $f(\theta)$ is $\tfrac{1}{\sqrt{3}} \times \tfrac{2}{3} = \tfrac{2}{3\sqrt{3}}$

59 a Any odd function has rotational symmetry about O.

b $\int_{-1}^{1} f(x) \, dx = \int_{-1}^{0} f(x) \, dx + \int_{0}^{1} f(x) \, dx$

$\qquad = (-A_2) + A_1$

$\qquad = A_1 - A_2$

But by symmetry, $A_1 = A_2$ for any odd function.

$\therefore$ $\int_{-1}^{1} f(x) \, dx = 0$

c If $f(x) = x^3 \cos 2x$ then

$f(-x) = (-x)^3 \cos(-2x)$

$\qquad = -(x^3 \cos(-2x))$

$\qquad = -(x^3 \cos 2x) \quad \{\cos(-\theta) = \cos \theta \text{ for all } \theta\}$

$\qquad = -f(x) \quad$ for all x

$\therefore$ $f(x)$ is an odd function.

d $\int_{-1}^{1} (e^{-2x} + x^3 \cos 2x) \, dx$

$= \int_{-1}^{1} e^{-2x} \, dx + \int_{-1}^{1} x^3 \cos 2x \, dx$

$= [-\tfrac{1}{2} e^{-2x}]_{-1}^{1} + 0 \quad \{\text{using } \textbf{b}, \text{ since } x^3 \cos 2x \text{ is odd}\}$

$= (-\tfrac{1}{2} e^{-2}) - (-\tfrac{1}{2} e^2)$

$= \tfrac{1}{2}(e^2 - \dfrac{1}{e^2})$

60 a **i** $x = \sin t + \tfrac{1}{2} \sin 2t$ cm

Velocity $v = \dfrac{dx}{dt} = \cos t + \tfrac{1}{2} \times 2 \cos 2t$

$\qquad = \cos t + \cos 2t$ cm s^{-1}

When $t = 0$, $x = \sin 0 + \tfrac{1}{2} \sin 0 = 0$ cm

$\qquad v = \cos 0 + \cos 0 = 2$ cm s^{-1}

When $t = 2\pi$, $x = \sin 2\pi + \tfrac{1}{2} \sin 4\pi = 0$ cm

$\qquad v = \cos 2\pi + \cos 4\pi = 2$ cm s^{-1}

ii The point comes to rest when $v = 0$ cm s^{-1}

$\therefore$ $\cos t + \cos 2t = 0$

$\therefore$ $\cos t + (2\cos^2 t - 1) = 0$

$\therefore$ $2\cos^2 t + \cos t - 1 = 0$

$\therefore$ $(2\cos t - 1)(\cos t + 1) = 0$

$\cos t = \tfrac{1}{2}$ or -1

$\therefore$ $t = \tfrac{\pi}{3}, \pi, \tfrac{5\pi}{3}$

Sign diagram for v is:

Acceleration $a = \dfrac{dv}{dt} = -\sin t - 2\sin 2t$ cm s^{-2}

$\therefore$ $a(\tfrac{\pi}{3}) = -\tfrac{\sqrt{3}}{2} - 2(\tfrac{\sqrt{3}}{2}) = -\tfrac{3\sqrt{3}}{2}$ cm s^{-2},

$\qquad a(\pi) = 0$ cm s^{-2},

and $a(\tfrac{5\pi}{3}) = \tfrac{\sqrt{3}}{2} + \tfrac{2\sqrt{3}}{2} = \tfrac{3\sqrt{3}}{2}$ cm s^{-2}

b At the time $t = 0$, the point is moving with velocity 2 cm s^{-1} in the positive direction. It moves in this direction for $\frac{\pi}{3}$ seconds, before coming to rest. It then moves back to its initial position, arriving there after π seconds. It momentarily stops, then continues to move in the negative direction until $t = \frac{5\pi}{3}$ seconds. At this time it changes direction and moves back to the initial position, arriving there at $t = 2\pi$ seconds.

61 **a** $f(x) = \sin\left(x + \frac{\pi}{6}\right)$ is a translation of $y = \sin x$ through $\begin{pmatrix} -\frac{\pi}{6} \\ 0 \end{pmatrix}$.

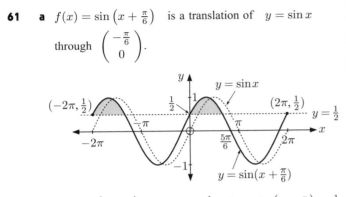

b $y = \sin\left(x + \frac{\pi}{6}\right)$ meets $y = \frac{1}{2}$ when $\sin\left(x + \frac{\pi}{6}\right) = \frac{1}{2}$

∴ on the given interval, $x = -2\pi,\ -\frac{4\pi}{3},\ 0,\ \frac{2\pi}{3}$, and 2π.

The total shaded area $= 2\int_0^{\frac{2\pi}{3}} \left(\sin(x + \frac{\pi}{6}) - \frac{1}{2}\right) dx$

$= 2\left[-\cos(x + \frac{\pi}{6}) - \frac{1}{2}x\right]_0^{\frac{2\pi}{3}}$

$= 2\left((-\cos\frac{5\pi}{6} - \frac{\pi}{3}) - (-\cos\frac{\pi}{6})\right)$

$= 2\left(\frac{\sqrt{3}}{2} - \frac{\pi}{3} + \frac{\sqrt{3}}{2}\right)$

$= 2\sqrt{3} - \frac{2\pi}{3}$ units^2

62 $\int_0^{\frac{\pi}{2}} (\sin 3x + 5\cos x)\, dx$

$= \left[-\frac{1}{3}\cos 3x + 5\sin x\right]_0^{\frac{\pi}{2}}$

$= (-\frac{1}{3}\cos(\frac{3\pi}{2}) + 5\sin(\frac{\pi}{2})) - (-\frac{1}{3}\cos 0 + 5\sin 0)$

$= (0 + 5) - (-\frac{1}{3} + 0)$

$= 5\frac{1}{3}$

63 **a** $y = \ln(\tan x)$

∴ $\dfrac{dy}{dx} = \dfrac{1}{\tan x} \times \dfrac{1}{\cos^2 x}$

$= \dfrac{\cos x}{\sin x} \times \dfrac{1}{\cos^2 x}$

$= \dfrac{1}{\sin x \cos x}$

$= \dfrac{2}{2\sin x \cos x}$

$= \dfrac{2}{\sin 2x}$

∴ $k = 2$

b Shaded area

$= \int_{\frac{\pi}{6}}^{\frac{\pi}{3}} \dfrac{1}{\sin 2x}\, dx$

$= \frac{1}{2} \int_{\frac{\pi}{6}}^{\frac{\pi}{3}} \dfrac{2}{\sin 2x}\, dx$

$= \frac{1}{2}[\ln(\tan x)]_{\frac{\pi}{6}}^{\frac{\pi}{3}}$

$= \frac{1}{2}(\ln\sqrt{3} - \ln(\frac{1}{\sqrt{3}}))$

$= \frac{1}{2}(\ln\sqrt{3} + \ln\sqrt{3})$

$= \frac{1}{2}\ln(\sqrt{3} \times \sqrt{3})$

$= \frac{1}{2}\ln 3$ units^2

64 **a** $V = \pi \int_0^1 (2x + 3)^2\, dx$

$= \pi \left[\frac{1}{2}\dfrac{(2x + 3)^3}{3}\right]_0^1$

$= \frac{\pi}{6}(5^3 - 3^3)$

$= \frac{49\pi}{3}$ units^3

b $V = \pi \int_1^3 (e^{2x})^2\, dx$

$= \pi \int_1^3 e^{4x}\, dx$

$= \pi \left[\frac{1}{4}e^{4x}\right]_1^3$

$= \frac{\pi}{4}(e^{12} - e^4)$ units^3

65 The parabola has x-intercepts $\pm\pi$, so its equation is $y = k(x - \pi)(x + \pi)$ for some k.

The y-intercept is α, so $k(-\pi)\pi = \alpha$

∴ $k = -\dfrac{\alpha}{\pi^2}$

∴ $y = -\dfrac{\alpha}{\pi^2}(x^2 - \pi^2)$

$= -\dfrac{\alpha}{\pi^2}x^2 + \alpha$

We need to consider two possible cases:

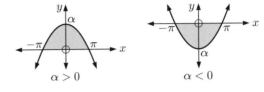

$\alpha > 0$ $\alpha < 0$

Consider the case $\alpha > 0$.

Using symmetry, the shaded area is $2\int_0^\pi \left(-\dfrac{\alpha}{\pi^2}x^2 + \alpha\right) dx$.

∴ $2\int_0^\pi \left(-\dfrac{\alpha}{\pi^2}x^2 + \alpha\right) dx = 4$

∴ $\left[-\dfrac{\alpha}{3\pi^2}x^3 + \alpha x\right]_0^\pi = 2$

∴ $-\dfrac{\alpha\pi}{3} + \alpha\pi + 0 - 0 = 2$

∴ $\frac{2}{3}\alpha\pi = 2$

∴ $\alpha = \dfrac{3}{\pi}$

By symmetry, the other possible solution is $\alpha = -\dfrac{3}{\pi}$.

So, $\alpha = \pm\dfrac{3}{\pi}$.

66 $x^2 - 2x = x(x - 2)$

∴ the x-intercepts are 0 and 2.

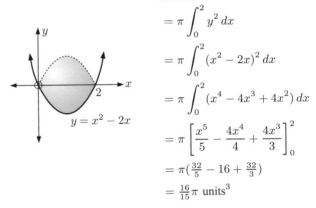

$y = x^2 - 2x$

The volume of the solid of revolution

$= \pi \int_0^2 y^2\, dx$

$= \pi \int_0^2 (x^2 - 2x)^2\, dx$

$= \pi \int_0^2 (x^4 - 4x^3 + 4x^2)\, dx$

$= \pi \left[\dfrac{x^5}{5} - \dfrac{4x^4}{4} + \dfrac{4x^3}{3}\right]_0^2$

$= \pi(\frac{32}{5} - 16 + \frac{32}{3})$

$= \frac{16}{15}\pi$ units^3

67 **a** **i** $f'(x) = \dfrac{1}{x}$ with domain $x > 0$.

ii $F'(x) = (1)\ln x + x\left(\dfrac{1}{x}\right) - 1$ provided $x > 0$

$= \ln x$ provided $x > 0$

b From **ii**, $\int \ln x\, dx = x\ln x - x + c$

∴ $\int f(x)\, dx = F(x) + c$

$F(x)$ is the antiderivative of $f(x)$.

c

$y = \ln x$

d **i** Let P be a point on the curve C with x-coordinate t, $1 \leqslant t \leqslant e$.

The shaded area A

$= $ area $\triangle OPQ - \int_1^t \ln x \, dx, \quad 1 < t \leqslant e$

$= \frac{1}{2} t \ln t - \int_1^t \ln x \, dx$

$= \frac{1}{2} t \ln t - [x \ln x - x]_1^t$

$= \frac{1}{2} t \ln t - t \ln t + t - 1$

$= t - \frac{1}{2} t \ln t - 1$ units^2

$\dfrac{dA}{dt} = 1 - \left(\frac{1}{2} \ln t + \frac{1}{2} t \left(\frac{1}{t} \right) \right) = \frac{1}{2}(1 - \ln t)$

$\therefore \quad \dfrac{dA}{dt} = 0$ when $t = e$

$\therefore$ the area is a maximum when $t = e$.

ii $y = \ln x \quad \therefore \quad \dfrac{dy}{dx} = \dfrac{1}{x}$

$\therefore$ at $(t, \ln t)$, $\dfrac{dy}{dx} = \dfrac{1}{t}$

$\therefore$ the tangent has equation $\dfrac{y - \ln t}{x - t} = \dfrac{1}{t}$

which is $\quad ty - t \ln t = x - t$

or $\quad x - ty = t - t \ln t$.

The tangent passes through $(0, 0)$ if

$t - t \ln t = 0$

$\therefore \quad t(1 - \ln t) = 0$

$\therefore \quad \ln t = 1 \quad \{ \text{as } t > 1 \}$

$\therefore \quad t = e$

Conclusion: The shaded region is maximised in area when [OP] is a tangent to C.

68 **a, b**

$\left(\frac{\pi}{4}, 1 \right) \quad \left(\frac{\pi}{2}, 1 \right)$

$f(x) = \sin x$

$g(x) = \sin 2x$

$\left(\frac{3\pi}{4}, -1 \right)$

c The graphs meet where $\quad \sin 2x = \sin x$

$\therefore \quad 2 \sin x \cos x - \sin x = 0$

$\therefore \quad \sin x (2 \cos x - 1) = 0$

$\therefore \quad \sin x = 0 \quad \text{or} \quad \cos x = \frac{1}{2}$

$\therefore \quad x = 0, \frac{\pi}{3}, \pi$

Area $A = \int_0^{\frac{\pi}{3}} (\sin 2x - \sin x) \, dx$

$= \left[-\frac{1}{2} \cos 2x + \cos x \right]_0^{\frac{\pi}{3}}$

$= \left(-\frac{1}{2} \cos(\frac{2\pi}{3}) + \cos(\frac{\pi}{3}) \right) - \left(-\frac{1}{2} \cos 0 + \cos 0 \right)$

$= \left(-\frac{1}{2}(-\frac{1}{2}) + \frac{1}{2} \right) - \left(-\frac{1}{2} + 1 \right)$

$= \frac{1}{4}$ unit^2

Area $B = \int_{\frac{\pi}{3}}^{\pi} (\sin x - \sin 2x) \, dx$

$= \left[-\cos x + \frac{1}{2} \cos 2x \right]_{\frac{\pi}{3}}^{\pi}$

$= \left(-\cos \pi + \frac{1}{2} \cos 2\pi \right)$

$\quad - \left(-\cos(\frac{\pi}{3}) + \frac{1}{2} \cos(\frac{2\pi}{3}) \right)$

$= \left(1 + \frac{1}{2} \right) - \left(-\frac{1}{2} + \frac{1}{2}(-\frac{1}{2}) \right)$

$= 2\frac{1}{4}$ units^2

69 **a** $OP + OQ + PQ = 40$ cm

$\therefore \quad x + x + s = 40$

$\therefore \quad s = 40 - 2x$

b $A = \frac{1}{2} \theta x^2$ where $s = \theta x$

$\therefore \quad A = \frac{1}{2} \left(\frac{s}{x} \right) x^2$

$= \frac{1}{2} xs$

$= \frac{1}{2} x(40 - 2x)$

$\therefore \quad A = 20x - x^2$ cm^2

c $\dfrac{dA}{dx} = 20 - 2x$

$\dfrac{dA}{dx}$ has sign diagram:

$\therefore$ the area is a maximum when $x = 10$.

d When $x = 10$, $s = 40 - 2x = 20$

Using $s = \theta x$, $\quad 20 = \theta(10)$

$\therefore \quad \theta = 2$ radians.

70 **a** $v(t) = e^{2t} - 3e^t$ m s^{-1}

$\therefore \quad v(0) = e^0 - 3e^0 = 1 - 3 = -2$ m s^{-1}

$\therefore$ the initial velocity is -2 m s^{-1}.

b Now $\quad v(t) = e^t(e^t - 3)$

Since $e^t > 0$ for all t, $v(t) = 0$ when $e^t = 3$

which is when $t = \ln 3$

$\therefore$ the particle is stationary at $t = \ln 3$ seconds.

c $s(t) = \int v(t) \, dt = \int (e^{2t} - 3e^t) \, dt$

$\therefore \quad s(t) = \frac{1}{2} e^{2t} - 3e^t + c$ metres

But $\quad s(0) = 1$, so $\quad \frac{1}{2} e^0 - 3e^0 + c = 1$

$\therefore \quad \frac{1}{2} - 3 + c = 1$

$\therefore \quad c = 3\frac{1}{2}$

Thus $\quad s(t) = \frac{1}{2} e^{2t} - 3e^t + \frac{7}{2}$ metres

$\therefore \quad s(\ln 5) = \frac{1}{2} e^{2 \ln 5} - 3 e^{\ln 5} + \frac{7}{2}$

$= \frac{1}{2} e^{\ln 5^2} - 3(5) + \frac{7}{2}$

$= \frac{25}{2} - 15 + \frac{7}{2}$

$= 16 - 15$

$= 1$ m

So, the particle is 1 m to the right of O.

71 $f(x) = \dfrac{3x}{e^x} = 3x e^{-x}, \quad 0 \leqslant x \leqslant 4$

a $f'(x) = 3e^{-x} - 3x e^{-x}$

$\therefore \quad f''(x) = -3e^{-x} - 3e^{-x} + 3x e^{-x}$

$= \dfrac{3(x - 2)}{e^x}$

b **i** $f'(x) = \dfrac{3(1 - x)}{e^x} = 0$ when $x = 1$

Sign diagram of $f'(x)$:

$\therefore$ there is a maximum turning point at $x = 1$.

When $x = 1$, $y = \dfrac{3(1)}{e^1} = \dfrac{3}{e}$

So, the maximum turning point is at $\left(1, \dfrac{3}{e} \right)$.

ii $f''(x) = \dfrac{3(x-2)}{e^x} = 0$ when $x = 2$

Sign diagram of $f''(x)$:

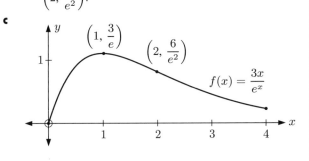

$\therefore$ there is a non-stationary inflection point at $x = 2$.

When $x = 2$, $y = \dfrac{3(2)}{e^2} = \dfrac{6}{e^2}$

So, there is a non-stationary inflection point at $\left(2, \dfrac{6}{e^2}\right)$.

c

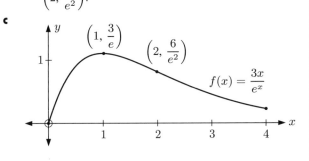

d If $F(x) = -\dfrac{3(x+1)}{e^x} = -3(x+1)e^{-x}$

then $F'(x) = -3e^{-x} + 3(x+1)e^{-x}$

$\qquad = 3xe^{-x}$

$\qquad = f(x)$

$\therefore$ $F(x)$ is the antiderivative of $f(x)$.

e The area $= \displaystyle\int_0^4 f(x)\,dx$

$\qquad = [F(x)]_0^4$

$\qquad = \left[-\dfrac{3(x+1)}{e^x}\right]_0^4$

$\qquad = -\dfrac{15}{e^4} + \dfrac{3}{e^0}$

$\qquad = 3 - \dfrac{15}{e^4}$ units^2

72 a $f(x) = -(x-2)^2 + 4$

The vertex is at $(2, 4)$.

When $x = 0$, $\quad y = -4 + 4 = 0$

When $y = 0$, $\quad -(x-2)^2 + 4 = 0$

$\qquad\qquad\qquad \therefore\ (x-2)^2 = 4$

$\qquad\qquad\qquad \therefore\ x - 2 = \pm 2$

$\qquad\qquad\qquad\qquad \therefore\ x = 0$ or 4

b $f(x) = -(x-2)^2 + 4$

$\qquad = -(x^2 - 4x + 4) + 4$

$\qquad = -x^2 + 4x$

$\therefore\ f'(x) = -2x + 4$

$\therefore\ f'(a) = -2a + 4$

So, the normal at $P(a,\ f(a))$ has

gradient $= -\dfrac{1}{-2a+4} = \dfrac{1}{2a-4}$

c When $x = a$, $\quad y = -a^2 + 4a$

The equation of the normal is

$\quad x - (2a-4)y = a - (2a-4)(-a^2 + 4a)$

$\therefore\ x - (2a-4)y = a - (-2a^3 + 8a^2 + 4a^2 - 16a)$

$\therefore\ x - (2a-4)y = 2a^3 - 12a^2 + 17a$

d The normal passes through the origin.

When $x = 0$ and $y = 0$,

$\qquad 2a^3 - 12a^2 + 17a = 0$

$\therefore\ a(2a^2 - 12a + 17) = 0$

Since $a \neq 0$, $\quad a = \dfrac{-(-12) \pm \sqrt{(-12)^2 - 4(2)(17)}}{2(2)}$

$\qquad\qquad\qquad = \dfrac{12 \pm \sqrt{144 - 136}}{4}$

$\qquad\qquad\qquad = \dfrac{12 \pm \sqrt{8}}{4}$

$\qquad\qquad\qquad = 3 \pm \dfrac{\sqrt{2}}{2}$

$\therefore\ a = 3 \pm \dfrac{1}{\sqrt{2}}$ as required

e When $a = 3 + \dfrac{1}{\sqrt{2}}$, the normal L has equation

$\quad x - \left(2(3 + \tfrac{1}{\sqrt{2}}) - 4\right)y = 0$

$\therefore\ x - \left(6 + \tfrac{2}{\sqrt{2}} - 4\right)y = 0$

$\therefore\ x - (2 + \sqrt{2})y = 0$

$\qquad\qquad \therefore\ y = \dfrac{x}{2 + \sqrt{2}}$

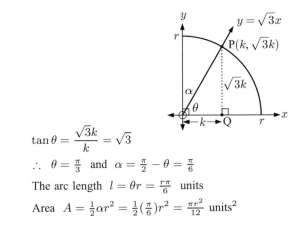

Area of shaded region

$= \displaystyle\int_0^{3 + \frac{1}{\sqrt{2}}} \left(-x^2 + 4x - \dfrac{x}{2 + \sqrt{2}}\right) dx$

$= \displaystyle\int_0^{3 + \frac{1}{\sqrt{2}}} \left(-x^2 + \left(4 - \dfrac{1}{2 + \sqrt{2}}\right)x\right) dx$

73 a Suppose the line and the arc meet at point P where $x = k$.

$\therefore$ P has coordinates $(k, \sqrt{3}k)$.

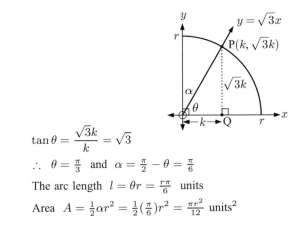

$\tan\theta = \dfrac{\sqrt{3}k}{k} = \sqrt{3}$

$\therefore\ \theta = \dfrac{\pi}{3}$ and $\alpha = \dfrac{\pi}{2} - \theta = \dfrac{\pi}{6}$

The arc length $l = \theta r = \dfrac{r\pi}{6}$ units

Area $A = \dfrac{1}{2}\alpha r^2 = \dfrac{1}{2}(\tfrac{\pi}{6})r^2 = \dfrac{\pi r^2}{12}$ units^2

b Using Pythagoras, $k^2 + (\sqrt{3}k)^2 = r^2$

$$\therefore \ k^2(1+3) = r^2$$

$$\therefore \ k^2 = \tfrac{1}{4}r^2$$

But $k > 0$, so $k = \tfrac{1}{2}r$

The equation of the arc is $y^2 = r^2 - x^2$

$\therefore$ since $y > 0$, $y = \sqrt{r^2 - x^2}$

Now $A = \int_0^{\frac{r}{2}} \left(\sqrt{r^2 - x^2} - \sqrt{3}x \right) dx$

$\qquad = \int_0^{\frac{r}{2}} \sqrt{r^2 - x^2}\, dx - \sqrt{3} \int_0^{\frac{r}{2}} x\, dx$

$\qquad = \int_0^{\frac{r}{2}} \sqrt{r^2 - x^2}\, dx - \sqrt{3} \left[\tfrac{1}{2}x^2 \right]_0^{\frac{r}{2}}$

$\qquad = \int_0^{\frac{r}{2}} \sqrt{r^2 - x^2}\, dx - \sqrt{3} \times \tfrac{1}{2} \left(\tfrac{r}{2} \right)^2$

$\qquad = \int_0^{\frac{r}{2}} \sqrt{r^2 - x^2}\, dx - \frac{\sqrt{3}r^2}{8}$ as required

c Using **a** and **b**, $A = \dfrac{\pi r^2}{12} = \displaystyle\int_0^{\frac{r}{2}} \sqrt{r^2 - x^2}\, dx - \dfrac{\sqrt{3}r^2}{8}$

$\therefore \displaystyle\int_0^{\frac{r}{2}} \sqrt{r^2 - x^2}\, dx = \dfrac{\pi r^2}{12} + \dfrac{\sqrt{3}r^2}{8}$

d Letting $r = 2$ in **c**,

$$\int_0^1 \sqrt{4 - x^2}\, dx = \frac{\pi(4)}{12} + \frac{\sqrt{3}(4)}{8}$$

$$= \frac{\pi}{3} + \frac{\sqrt{3}}{2}$$

$$\therefore \ 3\int_0^1 \sqrt{4 - x^2}\, dx = \pi + \frac{3\sqrt{3}}{2}$$

$$\therefore \ \int_0^1 \sqrt{36 - 9x^2}\, dx = \pi + \frac{3\sqrt{3}}{2}$$

74 a $S = \pi(1)^2 - \pi(x)^2 = \pi(1 - x^2)$

But in the right angled $\triangle$, $x^2 + y^2 = 1$

$$\therefore \ y^2 = 1 - x^2$$

$$\therefore \ S = \pi y^2$$

Also, $\sin\theta = \dfrac{y}{1} = y$, so $S = \pi \sin^2\theta$

b The shaded area below [AB]

$\quad$ = area of sector − area of triangle

$\quad = \tfrac{1}{2}r^2(2\theta - \sin 2\theta)$

$\quad = \theta - \tfrac{1}{2}\sin 2\theta$

c The shaded area *between* [AB] and [CD]

$$= S - 2\left(\theta - \tfrac{1}{2}\sin 2\theta \right)$$

$$= \pi \sin^2\theta - 2(\theta - \tfrac{1}{2}\sin 2\theta)$$

$$= \pi \sin^2\theta - 2\theta + \sin 2\theta$$

So, $f(\theta) = \pi \sin^2\theta + \sin 2\theta - 2\theta$

d Let $g(\theta) = \pi \sin 2\theta + 2\cos 2\theta$

Now $f'(\theta) = \pi(2)\sin\theta \cos\theta + \cos 2\theta(2) - 2$

$\qquad = 2\pi \sin\theta \cos\theta + 2\cos 2\theta - 2$

$\qquad = (\pi \sin 2\theta + 2\cos 2\theta) - 2$

$\qquad = g(\theta) - 2$

e i If $f'(\theta) = 0$ then $g(\theta) = 2$

$\therefore$ from the graph, $\theta \approx 1$ $\{0 < \theta < \tfrac{\pi}{2}\}$

ii Sign diagram for $f'(\theta) = g(\theta) - 2$:

$$\overset{+}{\underset{0}{\quad}} \curvearrowright \overset{1}{\quad} \overset{-}{\curvearrowright} \underset{\frac{\pi}{2}}{\quad} \theta$$

So, the maximum value of $f(\theta)$ is when $\theta \approx 1$.

CALCULATORS

1 a $f(x) = -x^2 + 4x$

$f'(x) = \displaystyle\lim_{h \to 0} \frac{f(x+h) - f(x)}{h}$

$\qquad = \displaystyle\lim_{h \to 0} \frac{-(x+h)^2 + 4(x+h) - (-x^2 + 4x)}{h}$

$\qquad = \displaystyle\lim_{h \to 0} \frac{-\cancel{x^2} - 2xh - h^2 + \cancel{4x} + 4h + \cancel{x^2} - \cancel{4x}}{h}$

$\qquad = \displaystyle\lim_{h \to 0} \frac{\cancel{h}(-2x - h + 4)}{\cancel{h}}$

$\qquad = -2x + 4$ $\{$as $h \neq 0\}$

$f'(x)$ is the gradient function of $y = f(x)$.

$f'(a)$ represents the gradient of the tangent to $y = f(x)$ at the point $(a, f(a))$.

b When $x = k$, $y = -k^2 + 4k$

So, the point of contact is $(k, -k^2 + 4k)$.

Since $f'(k) = -2k + 4$, the tangent has equation

$$\frac{y - (-k^2 + 4k)}{x - k} = -2k + 4$$

$$\therefore \ \frac{y + k^2 - 4k}{x - k} = -2k + 4$$

c The tangent passes through $(4, 9)$

$$\therefore \ \frac{9 + k^2 - 4k}{4 - k} = -2k + 4$$

$$\therefore \ k^2 - 4k + 9 = (-2k + 4)(4 - k)$$

$$= -8k + 2k^2 + 16 - 4k$$

$$= 2k^2 - 12k + 16$$

$$\therefore \ k^2 - 8k + 7 = 0$$

$$\therefore \ (k - 7)(k - 1) = 0$$

$$\therefore \ k = 1 \text{ or } 7$$

However, the tangent has positive gradient.

$$\therefore \ -2k + 4 > 0$$

$$\therefore \ 2k < 4$$

$$\therefore \ k < 2$$

So, $k = 1$.

2 a

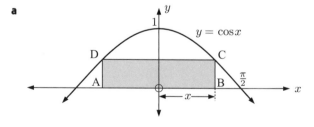

C has coordinates $(x, \cos x)$.

$\therefore$ rectangle ABCD has area $A = 2x \cos x$

b $\dfrac{dA}{dx} = 2\cos x + 2x(-\sin x)$ {product rule}

$\therefore \ \dfrac{dA}{dx} = 0$ when $2x\sin x = 2\cos x$

$\therefore \ x\tan x = 1$

$\therefore \ x \approx 0.860$ {using technology}

Sign diagram for $\dfrac{dA}{dx}$: ![sign diagram: + from 0 to 0.860, − from 0.860 to π/2]

$\therefore$ C has coordinates $(0.860, \ 0.652)$.

3 a The function is defined for $x > 0$.

b $f(x) = x - x^{-\frac{1}{2}}$

$\therefore \ f'(x) = 1 + \tfrac{1}{2}x^{-\frac{3}{2}} = 1 + \dfrac{1}{2x\sqrt{x}}$

$\therefore \ f'(x) > 0$ for $x > 0$ as each term is positive.

$\therefore$ the function is increasing over its whole domain.

c The function cuts the x-axis when $y = 0$.

$\therefore \ x - \dfrac{1}{\sqrt{x}} = 0$

$\therefore \ x = \dfrac{1}{\sqrt{x}}$

$\therefore \ x^{\frac{3}{2}} = 1$

$\therefore \ x = 1$ So, the x-intercept is 1.

The function does not cut the y-axis since $x > 0$.

d $f(x) = x - \dfrac{1}{\sqrt{x}}$ is undefined when $x = 0$, so $x = 0$ is a vertical asymptote.

As $x \to \infty$, $\dfrac{1}{\sqrt{x}} \to 0$ and $f(x) \to \infty$

$\therefore$ there is no horizontal asymptote.

e

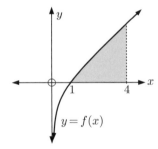

f Required area $= \int_1^4 (x - x^{-\frac{1}{2}}) \, dx$

$= 5\tfrac{1}{2}$ units^2 {using technology}

4 a $W(t) = 100e^{-\frac{t}{20}}$

$W(0) = 100e^0 = 100$ g

Initially there is 100 g of radioactive substance present.

b If $W = \tfrac{1}{2}W_0 = 50$ g then $50 = 100e^{-\frac{t}{20}}$

$\therefore \ e^{-\frac{t}{20}} = \tfrac{1}{2}$

$\therefore \ -\dfrac{t}{20} = \ln\tfrac{1}{2} = -\ln 2$

$\therefore \ t = 20\ln 2 \approx 13.86$

$\therefore$ it takes about 13.9 days for half of the mass to decay.

c $\dfrac{dW}{dt} = 100e^{-\frac{t}{20}}\left(-\tfrac{1}{20}\right) = -5e^{-\frac{t}{20}}$

Since $\dfrac{dW}{dt} < 0$ for all t, the weight of radioactive substance is always decreasing.

d As $t \to \infty$, $W \to 0$. The amount of radioactive substance decays to nothing.

e

![graph of W against t, curve from 100 decreasing, labelled $W_t = 100e^{-\frac{t}{20}}$; dashed lines at about 14 showing ½ mass decayed; axes W (20,40,60,80,100) and t (10,20,30,40)]

$\tfrac{1}{2}$ mass decayed

5 a $f(x) = xe^{-2x^2}$

$\therefore \ f'(x) = 1e^{-2x^2} + xe^{-2x^2}(-4x)$

$= e^{-2x^2}(1 - 4x^2)$

$= e^{-2x^2}(1 + 2x)(1 - 2x)$

where e^{-2x^2} is always positive.

$\therefore \ f'(x)$ has sign diagram: ![sign diagram: − for x<0... + from 0 to 1/2, − from 1/2 to 2]

There is a local maximum when $x = \tfrac{1}{2}$.

This is at $(\tfrac{1}{2}, \ \tfrac{1}{2}e^{-\frac{1}{2}})$ or $(\tfrac{1}{2}, \ 0.303)$.

b $f(0) = 0e^0 = 0$ and $f(2) = 2e^{-8} \approx 0.000\,671$

$\therefore$ the maximum value ≈ 0.303 and the minimum is 0.

c i Volume of revolution $= \pi \int_0^2 y^2 \, dx$

$= \pi \int_0^2 \left(xe^{-2x^2}\right)^2 dx$

$= \pi \int_0^2 \left(x^2 e^{-4x^2}\right) dx$

ii Volume of revolution ≈ 0.174 units^3 {using technology}

6 a The bin has capacity 500 litres

$= 0.5$ kL

$\therefore \ \pi r^2 h = 0.5$

$\therefore \ h = \dfrac{1}{2\pi r^2}$

Surface area $A = 2\pi rh + \pi r^2$

$= 2\pi r \left(\dfrac{1}{2\pi r^2}\right) + \pi r^2$

$\therefore \ A(r) = \dfrac{1}{r} + \pi r^2$ m^2

![diagram of a cylinder with height h m and radius r m]

b $\dfrac{dA}{dr} = -\dfrac{1}{r^2} + 2\pi r$

$\therefore \ \dfrac{dA}{dr} = 0$ when $2\pi r = \dfrac{1}{r^2}$

$\therefore \ r^3 = \dfrac{1}{2\pi}$

$\therefore \ r \approx 0.542$

$\therefore \ h \approx \dfrac{1}{2\pi r^2} \approx 0.542$

So, the surface area of the bin is minimised when the bin has a base radius and height of 54.2 cm.

7 $f(x) = 3x^3 + 3x^2 - 3x - 1$

a $f(0) = -1$, so the y-intercept is -1.

b $f'(x) = 9x^2 + 6x - 3$

$= 3(3x^2 + 2x - 1)$

$= 3(3x - 1)(x + 1)$

$\therefore \ f'(x) = 0$ when $x = -1$ or $\tfrac{1}{3}$

Sign diagram for $f'(x)$:

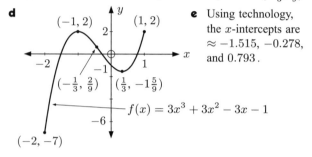

$f(-1) = 2$ and $f(\frac{1}{3}) = -\frac{14}{9}$

∴ there is a local maximum at $(-1,\ 2)$ and a local minimum at $(\frac{1}{3},\ -1\frac{5}{9})$.

c $f''(x) = 18x + 6$
$\qquad = 6(3x + 1)$
∴ $f''(x) = 0$ when $x = -\frac{1}{3}$

Sign diagram for $f''(x)$:

∴ there is a non-stationary inflection point at $x = -\frac{1}{3}$.
$f(-\frac{1}{3}) = \frac{2}{9}$
∴ there is a non-stationary inflection point at $(-\frac{1}{3},\ \frac{2}{9})$.

d

Points labelled: $(-1, 2)$, $(1, 2)$, $(-\frac{1}{3}, \frac{2}{9})$, $(\frac{1}{3}, -1\frac{5}{9})$, $(-2, -7)$
$f(x) = 3x^3 + 3x^2 - 3x - 1$

e Using technology, the x-intercepts are $\approx -1.515,\ -0.278,$ and 0.793.

8 a $f(x) = x \ln x + 1, \quad 0 < x \leqslant 2$

∴ $f'(x) = 1 \ln x + x \left(\frac{1}{x}\right) + 0 = \ln x + 1$

∴ $f'(x) = 0$ when $\ln x = -1$,
$\qquad$ which is when $x = e^{-1}$

Sign diagram for $f'(x)$:

∴ the minimum ability occurs when the child is
$\frac{1}{e} \approx 0.3679$ years ≈ 4.41 months
The minimum memorising ability occurs in the 5th month.

b Using technology we graph $y = f(x)$

$y = x \ln x + 1$

The maximum ability occurs at $x = 2$, or at the end of the 2 year interval.

9 a $f(t) = \dfrac{N}{1 + 2e^{-\frac{t}{2}}}$ where $N > 0$

∴ $f'(t) = \dfrac{0 - N\left(2e^{-\frac{t}{2}}\right)\left(-\frac{1}{2}\right)}{\left(1 + 2e^{-\frac{t}{2}}\right)^2}$

$\qquad = \dfrac{Ne^{-\frac{t}{2}}}{\left(1 + 2e^{-\frac{t}{2}}\right)^2}$

$N > 0$ is given. $e^{-\frac{t}{2}} > 0$ and $\left(1 + 2e^{-\frac{t}{2}}\right)^2 > 0$ for all t.
Thus $f'(t) > 0$ for all t.

b $f''(t) = \dfrac{\left(Ne^{-\frac{t}{2}}\left(-\frac{1}{2}\right)\left(1 + 2e^{-\frac{t}{2}}\right)^2 - Ne^{-\frac{t}{2}}2\left(1 + 2e^{-\frac{t}{2}}\right)\left(2e^{-\frac{t}{2}}\right)\left(-\frac{1}{2}\right)\right)}{\left(1 + 2e^{-\frac{t}{2}}\right)^4}$

$\qquad = \dfrac{\left(1 + 2e^{-\frac{t}{2}}\right)\left(\frac{1}{2}\right)Ne^{-\frac{t}{2}}\left[-1 - 2e^{-\frac{t}{2}} + 4e^{-\frac{t}{2}}\right]}{\left(1 + 2e^{-\frac{t}{2}}\right)^4}$

$\qquad = \dfrac{\frac{1}{2}Ne^{-\frac{t}{2}}\left(2e^{-\frac{t}{2}} - 1\right)}{\left(1 + 2e^{-\frac{t}{2}}\right)^3}$

∴ $f''(t) = 0$ when $e^{-\frac{t}{2}} = \frac{1}{2}$
$\qquad\qquad\qquad\quad$ ∴ $e^{\frac{t}{2}} = 2$
$\qquad\qquad\qquad\quad$ ∴ $t = \ln 4$

Sign diagram for $f''(t)$:

∴ $f'(t)$ is a maximum when $t = \ln 4$, and this occurs
when $f(t) = \dfrac{N}{1 + 2(\frac{1}{2})} = \dfrac{N}{2}$

So, the maximum rate of growth of the population occurs when $t = \ln 4$ and the size of the population is $\dfrac{N}{2}$ at this time.

c Now $f(0) = \dfrac{N}{1+2} = \dfrac{N}{3}$ and as $t \to \infty,\ f(t) \to N$

$f(2) \approx 0.58N, \quad f(4) \approx 0.79N,$
$f(6) \approx 0.91N, \quad f(8) \approx 0.96N$

Graph of $f(t)$ with horizontal asymptote at N, starting at $\frac{N}{3}$.

10 a $g(x) = \dfrac{\ln x}{x}$ for $0 < x \leqslant 5$

If $y = 0$ then $\ln x = 0$
$\qquad\qquad$ ∴ $x = 1$
So, the graph cuts the x-axis at $(1,\ 0)$.

b $g'(x) = \dfrac{\left(\frac{1}{x}\right)x - \ln x\,(1)}{x^2} = \dfrac{1 - \ln x}{x^2}$

∴ $g'(x) = 0$ when $\ln x = 1$ ∴ $x = e$

Sign diagram for $g'(x)$:

∴ the stationary point is a local maximum at $\left(e,\ \frac{1}{e}\right)$.

$g''(x) = \dfrac{\left(-\frac{1}{x}\right)x^2 - (1 - \ln x)2x}{x^4}$

$\qquad = \dfrac{-x - 2x + 2x \ln x}{x^4}$

$\qquad = \dfrac{2 \ln x - 3}{x^3}$

∴ $g''(x) = 0$ when $\ln x = \frac{3}{2}$
$\qquad\qquad\qquad$ ∴ $x = e^{\frac{3}{2}} \approx 4.482$

Sign diagram for $g''(x)$:

$$\begin{array}{c} \text{(sign diagram: shaded at } 0, \text{ then } - \text{ then } + \text{, with } e^{\frac{3}{2}} \text{ between } 0 \text{ and } 5, \text{ shaded at } 5) \end{array} \quad x$$

$\therefore$ there is a non-stationary inflection at $(4.48, 0.335)$.
At the point of inflection, the gradient of the graph is

$$g'(e^{\frac{3}{2}}) = \frac{1 - \ln e^{\frac{3}{2}}}{e^3} = \frac{1 - \frac{3}{2}}{e^3} = -\frac{1}{2e^3} \approx -0.0249 .$$

c As $x \to 0$ (right), $y \to -\infty$.

d

$$\text{graph with } (e, \tfrac{1}{e}), \ (4.48, 0.335), \ (5, 0.322), \ g(x) = \frac{\ln x}{x}$$

e Since there is a local maximum at $\left(e, \frac{1}{e}\right)$,

$$g(x) \leqslant \frac{1}{e} \quad \text{for all} \quad x > 0$$

$$\therefore \quad \frac{\ln x}{x} \leqslant \frac{1}{e}$$

$$\therefore \quad \ln x \leqslant \frac{x}{e} \quad \text{for} \quad x > 0$$

11 a $f(x) = \ln(x\sqrt{1 - 2x})$

$$= \ln x + \ln(1 - 2x)^{\frac{1}{2}} \quad \{\ln ab = \ln a + \ln b\}$$

$$= \ln x + \frac{1}{2}\ln(1 - 2x) \quad \{\ln a^n = n \ln a\}$$

$f(x)$ exists provided $x > 0$ and $1 - 2x > 0$

$$\therefore \quad x > 0 \quad \text{and} \quad x < \frac{1}{2}$$

$\therefore$ the domain is $\{x \mid 0 < x < \frac{1}{2}\}$.

b $f'(x) = \frac{1}{x} + \frac{1}{2}\left(\frac{-2}{1 - 2x}\right)$

$$= \frac{1}{x} - \frac{1}{1 - 2x}$$

$$= \frac{1 - 2x - x}{x(1 - 2x)}$$

$$= \frac{1 - 3x}{x(1 - 2x)}$$

c For points where the gradient of the normal is $-\frac{6}{5}$, $f'(x) = \frac{5}{6}$.

$$\frac{1 - 3x}{x(1 - 2x)} = \frac{5}{6}$$

$$\therefore \quad 6(1 - 3x) = 5x(1 - 2x)$$

$$\therefore \quad 6 - 18x = 5x - 10x^2$$

$$\therefore \quad 10x^2 - 23x + 6 = 0$$

$$\therefore \quad (x - 2)(10x - 3) = 0$$

$$\therefore \quad x = 2 \ \text{ or } \ \frac{3}{10}$$

But $0 < x < \frac{1}{2}$, so $x = \frac{3}{10}$

$f\left(\frac{3}{10}\right) = \ln\left(\frac{3}{10}\sqrt{1 - \frac{3}{5}}\right) = \ln\left(\frac{3}{10}\sqrt{\frac{2}{5}}\right) \approx -1.66$

So, the point is $(0.3, -1.66)$.

12 a Consider $f(x) = \left(2 - \frac{1}{x}\right)e^{-x}, \quad x > 0$

$$f(x) = 0 \quad \text{when} \quad 2 - \frac{1}{x} = 0 \quad \{\text{as } e^{-x} > 0 \text{ for all } x\}$$

$$\therefore \quad \frac{1}{x} = 2$$

$$\therefore \quad x = \frac{1}{2}$$

b As $x \to 0$ (right), $\frac{1}{x} \to \infty$ and $e^{-x} \to 1$

$$\therefore \quad f(x) \to -\infty$$

As $x \to \infty$, $e^{-x} \to 0$ and $2 - \frac{1}{x} \to 2$

$$\therefore \quad f(x) \to 0$$

c Since $f(x) = (2 - x^{-1})e^{-x}$,

$$f'(x) = x^{-2}e^{-x} + (2 - x^{-1})e^{-x}(-1)$$

$$= e^{-x}\left(x^{-2} - 2 + x^{-1}\right)$$

$$= e^{-x}\left(\frac{1}{x^2} - 2 + \frac{1}{x}\right)$$

$$= \frac{e^{-x}}{x^2}\left(1 - 2x^2 + x\right)$$

$\therefore \quad f'(x) = 0$ when $-2x^2 + x + 1 = 0$

$$\therefore \quad 2x^2 - x - 1 = 0$$

$$\therefore \quad (2x + 1)(x - 1) = 0$$

$$\therefore \quad x = -\frac{1}{2} \ \text{ or } \ 1$$

Now $f'\left(\frac{1}{2}\right) = 4e^{-\frac{1}{2}} > 0$ and $f'(2) = \frac{e^{-2}(-5)}{4} < 0$

So $f'(x)$ has sign diagram:

$$\text{(sign diagram: } + \text{ then } - \text{, change at } 1, \text{ starting at } 0) \quad x$$

$\therefore$ there is a local maximum at $\left(1, \frac{1}{e}\right)$.

d

$$\text{graph with max } \left(1, \tfrac{1}{e}\right), \ f(x) = \left(2 - \tfrac{1}{x}\right)e^{-x}$$

e $y = \left(2 - \frac{1}{x}\right)e^{-x}$ meets $y = x - 1$ where

$$\left(2 - \frac{1}{x}\right)e^{-x} = x - 1.$$

Using technology, the points of intersection are $(0.342, -0.658)$ and $(1.33, 0.330)$.

$$\text{Area} \approx \int_{0.342}^{1.33} \left[\left(2 - \frac{1}{x}\right)e^{-x} - (x - 1)\right] dx$$

$$\approx 0.373 \text{ units}^2 \quad \{\text{using technology}\}$$

13 a $f(x) = 1 + \frac{1}{2x - 1} = 1 + (2x - 1)^{-1}$

$$\therefore \quad f'(x) = -(2x - 1)^{-2}(2) = \frac{-2}{(2x - 1)^2}$$

$\therefore \quad f'(x)$ is never zero, and so $f(x)$ has no turning points.

b

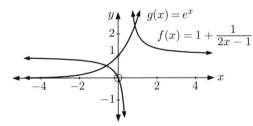

If $(2x-1)e^x - 2x = 0$

then $2x = (2x-1)e^x$

$\therefore \dfrac{2x}{2x-1} = e^x$

$\therefore \dfrac{(2x-1)+1}{2x-1} = e^x$

$\therefore 1 + \dfrac{1}{2x-1} = e^x$

The solutions of the equation correspond to the points of intersection of $y = f(x)$ and $y = g(x)$. There are hence two real solutions.

c Using technology, $x \approx -0.603$ or 0.864.

14 a $v(t) = 2\sqrt{t} - t = 2t^{\frac{1}{2}} - t$ ms^{-1}

$a(t) = v'(t)$

$= t^{-\frac{1}{2}} - 1$

$= \dfrac{1}{\sqrt{t}} - 1$ ms^{-2}, $t > 0$

b $v = 2t^{\frac{1}{2}} - t = t^{\frac{1}{2}}\left(2 - t^{\frac{1}{2}}\right)$, $t \geqslant 0$

$\therefore v = 0$ when $t = 0$ or when $t^{\frac{1}{2}} = 2$

$\therefore t = 0$ or $t = 4$

Sign diagram of v:

There is a reversal of direction at $t = 4$ s.

c The total distance travelled $= \int_0^9 |v(t)|\, dt$

$= \int_0^9 \left|2\sqrt{t} - t\right|\, dt$

$= 9\frac{5}{6}$ m

d $s = \int v\, d(t) = \int (2t^{\frac{1}{2}} - t)\, dt$

$= \dfrac{2t^{\frac{3}{2}}}{\frac{3}{2}} - \dfrac{t^2}{2} + c$

$= \frac{4}{3}t^{\frac{3}{2}} - \frac{1}{2}t^2 + c$

The particle starts at the origin.

$\therefore s(0) = 0$

$\therefore c = 0$

$\therefore s(t) = \frac{4}{3}t^{\frac{3}{2}} - \frac{1}{2}t^2$ m

15 a

Area $= \int_1^9 x^{-\frac{1}{2}}\, dx$

$= \left[\dfrac{x^{\frac{1}{2}}}{\frac{1}{2}}\right]_1^9$

$= \left[2\sqrt{x}\right]_1^9$

$= 6 - 2$

$= 4$ units^2

b Volume of revolution $= \pi \int_1^9 \left(\dfrac{1}{\sqrt{x}}\right)^2\, dx$

$= \pi \int_1^9 \dfrac{1}{x}\, dx$

$= \pi \left[\ln x\right]_1^9$

$= \pi(\ln 9 - \ln 1)$

≈ 6.90 units^3

16 a $f(x) = \dfrac{1}{x} - \dfrac{4}{x-2} = \dfrac{x - 2 - 4x}{x(x-2)} = \dfrac{-3x - 2}{x(x-2)}$

So, $f(x) = 0$ when $-3x - 2 = 0$

$\therefore x = -\frac{2}{3}$

b $f(x) = x^{-1} - 4(x-2)^{-1}$

$\therefore f'(x) = -x^{-2} + 4(x-2)^{-2}$

$= -\dfrac{1}{x^2} + \dfrac{4}{(x-2)^2}$

$= \dfrac{4x^2 - (x-2)^2}{x^2(x-2)^2}$

$= \dfrac{(2x + (x-2))(2x - (x-2))}{x^2(x-2)^2}$

$= \dfrac{(3x - 2)(x + 2)}{x^2(x-2)^2}$

$f'(x)$ has sign diagram:

$f(-2) = \frac{1}{2}$ and $f(\frac{2}{3}) = 4\frac{1}{2}$

$\therefore$ there is a local maximum at $(-2, \frac{1}{2})$ and a local minimum at $(\frac{2}{3}, 4\frac{1}{2})$.

c $f''(x) = 2x^{-3} - 8(x-2)^{-3} = \dfrac{2}{x^3} - \dfrac{8}{(x-2)^3}$

$\therefore f''(x) = 0$ when $\dfrac{2}{x^3} = \dfrac{8}{(x-2)^3}$

$\therefore (x-2)^3 = 4x^3$

$\therefore x \approx -3.4048$ {using technology}

$f(-3.4048) \approx 0.4464$

So, $f''(x) = 0$ at $(-3.40, 0.45)$.

d

e Area $= \int_{\frac{1}{2}}^{1\frac{1}{2}} \left(\dfrac{1}{x} - \dfrac{4}{x-2}\right)\, dx$

$= \int_{\frac{1}{2}}^{\frac{3}{2}} \left(\dfrac{1}{x} + \dfrac{4}{2-x}\right)\, dx$

$= \left[\ln x - 4\ln(2-x)\right]_{\frac{1}{2}}^{\frac{3}{2}}$

$= (\ln \frac{3}{2} - 4\ln \frac{1}{2}) - (\ln \frac{1}{2} - 4\ln \frac{3}{2})$

$= \ln \frac{3}{2} - 4\ln \frac{1}{2} - \ln \frac{1}{2} + 4\ln \frac{3}{2}$

$= 5\ln \frac{3}{2} - 5\ln \frac{1}{2}$

$= 5(\ln \frac{3}{2} - \ln \frac{1}{2})$

$= 5(\ln 3 - \ln 2 - \ln 1 + \ln 2)$

$= 5\ln 3$ units^2

17 a i $\dfrac{dy}{dx} = 2x - 3$

The gradient is 1 when $x = a$.
$\therefore \ 2a - 3 = 1$
$\quad \therefore \ 2a = 4$
$\qquad \therefore \ a = 2$

ii When $x = 2$, $y = 2^2 - 3(2) = -2$
So, the point of contact is $(2, -2)$.

Since $\dfrac{dy}{dx} = 1$ at $(2, -2)$, the normal has

gradient -1.

$\therefore$ the equation of the normal is
$$x + y = 2 + -2$$
$$\therefore \ y = -x$$

b $y = x^2 - 3x$ meets $y = x$ where

$x^2 - 3x = x$
$\therefore \ x^2 - 4x = 0$
$\therefore \ x(x - 4) = 0$
$\qquad \therefore \ x = 0$ or 4

Area $= \int_0^4 \left(x - (x^2 - 3x) \right) dx$

$= \int_0^4 \left(4x - x^2 \right) dx$

$= \left[\dfrac{4x^2}{2} - \dfrac{x^3}{3} \right]_0^4$

$= 32 - \dfrac{64}{3}$

$= \dfrac{32}{3}$ units^2

18 $\int_0^k \sin x \, dx = 0.42$

$\therefore \ [-\cos x]_0^k = 0.42$

$\therefore \ -\cos k + \cos 0 = 0.42$

$\therefore \ \cos k = 0.58$

$\therefore \ k \approx 0.952 \quad \{0 \leqslant k \leqslant \pi\}$

19 a

b Area $= \int_0^3 (3x^2 + 1) \, dx$

$= \left[x^3 + x \right]_0^3$

$= 27 + 3 - (0 + 0)$

$= 30$ units^2

c If $\int_0^k (3x^2 + 1) \, dx = 10$

then $\left[x^3 + x \right]_0^k = 10$

$\therefore \ k^3 + k - 10 = 0$

for which the only real solution is $k = 2$
{using technology}

20 a $a = 6t - 30$ cm s^{-2}

$\therefore \ v = \int a \, dt = \int (6t - 30) \, dt$

$= 3t^2 - 30t + c$ cm s^{-1}

Now when $t = 0$, $v = 27$ $\quad \therefore \ c = 27$

$\therefore \ v = 3t^2 - 30t + 27$ cm s^{-1}

b $s = \int v \, dt = \int (3t^2 - 30t + 27) \, dt$

$= t^3 - 15t^2 + 27t + d$ cm

But when $t = 0$, $s = 0$ $\quad \therefore \ d = 0$

$\therefore \ s = t^3 - 15t^2 + 27t$ cm

c Now $v = 3(t^2 - 10t + 9) = 3(t - 1)(t - 9)$

So, v has sign diagram:

$\therefore$ the particle changes direction at $t = 1$ and $t = 9$ s.

$s(0) = 0$, $\quad s(1) = 13$,
$s(9) = 729 - 1215 + 243 = -243$

$\therefore$ the total distance travelled $= 13 + 256 = 269$ cm

21 a $\int (x^3 + 2)^2 \, dx = \int (x^6 + 4x^3 + 4) \, dx$

$= \dfrac{x^7}{7} + x^4 + 4x + c$

b $x^3 + 2 = 0$

$\therefore \ x = -\sqrt[3]{2}$

c Volume of revolution $= \pi \displaystyle\int_{-\sqrt[3]{2}}^{0} \left(x^3 + 2 \right)^2 \, dx$

≈ 10.2 units^3

22 a $v(t) = e^{-2t}$ m s^{-1}

$a(t) = v'(t) = e^{-2t}(-2)$ m s^{-2}

$\therefore$ when $a = -\frac{1}{4}$ m s^{-2}, $e^{-2t}(-2) = -\frac{1}{4}$

$\therefore \ e^{-2t} = \frac{1}{8}$

$\therefore \ -2t = -\ln 8$

$\therefore \ t = \frac{1}{2} \ln 8 \approx 1.04$ s

b i $s(t) = \int v(t) \, dt = \int e^{-2t} \, dt = -\frac{1}{2} e^{-2t} + c$

When $t = 0$, $s = 2$

$\therefore \ 2 = -\frac{1}{2} e^0 + c$

$\therefore \ 2 = -\frac{1}{2} + c$

$\therefore \ c = 2\frac{1}{2}$

So, $s = -\frac{1}{2} e^{-2t} + 2.5$ m

ii When $t = 1$, $s = -\frac{1}{2} e^{-2} + 2.5 \approx 2.43$ m
The particle is 2.43 m to the right of O.

23 a $v(t) = 30 - 20e^{-0.2t}$ m s^{-1}

$\therefore \ v(0) = 30 - 20e^0 = 30 - 20(1) = 10$ m s^{-1}

b $v(2) = 30 - 20e^{-0.4} \approx 16.59$ m s^{-1}

c If $v = 20$ then $20 = 30 - 20e^{-0.2t}$

$\therefore \ 20e^{-0.2t} = 10$

$\therefore \ e^{-0.2t} = \frac{1}{2}$

$\therefore \ -0.2t = -\ln 2$

$\therefore \ t = 5 \ln 2 \approx 3.466$

$\therefore \ t \approx 3.47$ s

d As $t \to \infty$, $e^{-0.2t} \to 0$

$\therefore \ v \to 30$ m s^{-1} (below)

e $v'(t) = 0 - 20(e^{-0.2t})(-0.2) = 4e^{-0.2t}$

$\therefore \ a(t) = \dfrac{4}{e^{0.2t}}$ m s^{-2}

Both numerator and denominator are positive so $a(t)$ is positive for all $t \geqslant 0$.

f

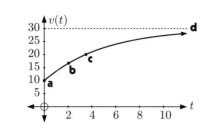

g
$$s(t) = \int v(t)\, dt = \int [30 - 20e^{-0.2t}]\, dt$$
$$= 30t - \frac{20e^{-0.2t}}{-0.2} + c$$
$$= 30t + 100e^{-0.2t} + c \ \text{m}$$

But $s(0) = 10$, so $0 + 100 + c = 10$
$$\therefore \quad c = -90$$

Hence $s(t) = 30t + 100e^{-0.2t} - 90 \ \text{m}$

24 a
$$\int_{a}^{2a} \sqrt{x}\, dx = 2$$
$$\therefore \quad \int_{a}^{2a} x^{\frac{1}{2}}\, dx = 2$$
$$\therefore \quad \left[\frac{x^{\frac{3}{2}}}{\frac{3}{2}} \right]_{a}^{2a} = 2$$
$$\therefore \quad \tfrac{2}{3}\left((2a)^{\frac{3}{2}} - a^{\frac{3}{2}} \right) = 2$$
$$\therefore \quad (2a)^{\frac{3}{2}} - a^{\frac{3}{2}} = 3$$

Using technology, $a \approx 1.391$

b When $x = a \approx 1.391$, $y \approx \sqrt{1.391}$
$$\approx 1.179$$

So, the point of contact is $(1.391, 1.179)$.
$$y = \sqrt{x} = x^{\frac{1}{2}}$$
$$\therefore \quad \frac{dy}{dx} = \tfrac{1}{2}x^{-\frac{1}{2}} = \frac{1}{2\sqrt{x}}$$

At $x \approx 1.391$, $\dfrac{dy}{dx} \approx \dfrac{1}{2\sqrt{1.391}} \approx 0.424$

$\therefore$ the normal at this point has gradient $\approx -\dfrac{1}{0.424}$
$$\approx -2.359$$

$\therefore$ the equation of the normal is
$$-2.359x - y \approx -2.359(1.391) - 1.179$$
$$\therefore \quad y \approx -2.36x + 4.46$$

25 a
$$C(x) = \frac{8}{x^2} + \frac{1}{(2-x)^2}$$
$$= 8x^{-2} + (2-x)^{-2}$$
$$\therefore \quad C'(x) = -16x^{-3} - 2(2-x)^{-3}(-1)$$
$$= -\frac{16}{x^3} + \frac{2}{(2-x)^3}$$

b $C'(x) = 0$ when $\dfrac{2}{(2-x)^3} = \dfrac{16}{x^3}$
$$\therefore \quad \frac{x^3}{(2-x)^3} = 8$$
$$\therefore \quad \left(\frac{x}{2-x} \right)^3 = 8$$

c Now when $\left(\dfrac{x}{2-x} \right)^3 = 8$, $\quad \dfrac{x}{2-x} = 2$
$$\therefore \quad x = 4 - 2x$$
$$\therefore \quad 3x = 4$$
$$\therefore \quad x = \tfrac{4}{3}$$

Sign diagram for $C'(x)$:

$\therefore$ the pollutants are minimised when $x = \tfrac{4}{3}$.

26 a
$$N = (8-t)e^{t-6}, \quad 0 \leqslant t \leqslant 8$$
$$\therefore \quad \frac{dN}{dt} = (-1)e^{t-6} + (8-t)e^{t-6}$$
$$= e^{t-6}(-1 + 8 - t)$$
$$= (7-t)e^{t-6}$$

b i $\dfrac{dN}{dt} = 0$ when $t = 7$

Sign diagram for $\dfrac{dN}{dt}$:

$N(7) = (1)e^1 = e$
$\therefore$ there is a local maximum at $(7, e)$.

ii
$$\frac{d^2N}{dt^2} = (-1)e^{t-6} + (7-t)e^{t-6}$$
$$= e^{t-6}(-1 + 7 - t)$$
$$= e^{t-6}(6 - t)$$
$$\therefore \quad \frac{d^2N}{dt^2} = 0 \quad \text{when} \quad t = 6$$

Sign diagram for $\dfrac{d^2N}{dt^2}$:

$N(6) = 2e^0 = 2(1) = 2$
$\therefore$ there is a non-stationary inflection point at $(6, 2)$.

iii The graph cuts the t-axis when $N = 0$
$$\therefore \quad (8-t)e^{t-6} = 0$$
$$\therefore \quad t = 8 \quad \text{as} \quad e^{t-6} > 0 \quad \text{for all } t.$$

c i When the bacteria are all dead, $N = 0$
$\therefore \quad t = 8$ hours

ii The maximum number of bacteria in the sample is
e million $\approx 2.72 \times 10^6$ bacteria.

iii The rate of increase is a maximum when $\dfrac{d^2N}{dt^2} = 0$.
This is at $t = 6$ hours.

d

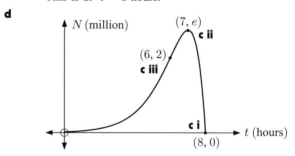

27 a $f(x) = a\cos bx, \quad -\pi \leqslant x \leqslant \pi$
The amplitude of the cosine curve is 3, so $a = 3$.
The period of the curve is $2 \times 2\pi = 4\pi$
$$\therefore \quad b = \frac{2\pi}{4\pi} = \tfrac{1}{2}$$

b **i** When $x = c$, $y = 3\cos\left(\frac{c}{2}\right)$

So, the point of contact is $\left(c, 3\cos\left(\frac{c}{2}\right)\right)$.

Now $y = 3\cos\left(\frac{x}{2}\right)$

so $\frac{dy}{dx} = 3\left(-\sin\left(\frac{x}{2}\right)\right)\left(\frac{1}{2}\right)$

$= -\frac{3}{2}\sin\left(\frac{x}{2}\right)$

When $x = c$, $\frac{dy}{dx} = -\frac{3}{2}\sin\left(\frac{c}{2}\right)$

∴ the normal has gradient $\dfrac{2}{3\sin\left(\frac{c}{2}\right)}$

∴ the equation of the normal is

$2x - 3\sin\left(\frac{c}{2}\right)y = 2c - \left(3\sin\left(\frac{c}{2}\right)\right)\left(3\cos\left(\frac{c}{2}\right)\right)$

∴ $2x - 3\sin\left(\frac{c}{2}\right)y = 2c - 9\sin\left(\frac{c}{2}\right)\cos\left(\frac{c}{2}\right)$

∴ $2x - 3\sin\left(\frac{c}{2}\right)y = 2c - \frac{9}{2}\sin c$

{using $\sin 2\theta = 2\sin\theta\cos\theta$}

ii If the normal also passes through the origin, then

$2c - \frac{9}{2}\sin c = 0$

∴ $\sin c = \frac{4}{9}c$

Using technology, $c \approx \pm 2.0234, 0$

c

28

$V = \pi \int_{\frac{\pi}{4}}^{\frac{5\pi}{6}} (\sin x)^2 \, dx$

$\approx 4.34 \text{ units}^3$ {using technology}

29 **a**

b Area $= \int_0^{\frac{\pi}{2}} (x + \sin x)\, dx$

$\approx 2.23 \text{ units}^2$ {using technology}

c We need to solve $x + \sin x = x^2$

Using technology, $x = 0$ or $x \approx 1.618$

So, $a \approx 1.618$

d

Area $= \int_0^a (x + \sin x - x^2)\, dx$

$\approx 0.944 \text{ units}^2$ {using technology}

30 **a**

b The graph meets the t-axis when $y = 0$

∴ $\sin^2 t - \sin t = 0$

∴ $\sin t(\sin t - 1) = 0$

∴ $\sin t = 0$ or 1

So, for $0 \leqslant t \leqslant 2$, $t = 0$ or $\frac{\pi}{2}$.

Area $= \int_0^2 \left[0 - (\sin^2 t - \sin t)\right] dt$

{$f(t)$ touches the t-axis at $t = \frac{\pi}{2}$}

$= \int_0^2 \left[\sin t - \sin^2 t\right] dt$

$\approx 0.227 \text{ units}^2$ {using technology}

31 Since $y = x^2 + 1$ is symmetric about the y-axis,

$\int_0^k (x^2 + 1)\, dx = 12$

∴ $\left[\frac{x^3}{3} + x\right]_0^k = 12$

∴ $\left(\frac{k^3}{3} + k\right) - (0) = 12$

∴ $k^3 + 3k = 36$

∴ $k^3 + 3k - 36 = 0$

Using technology, the only real solution is $k = 3$.

32 **a** $a = 4\cos t \text{ m s}^{-2}$

∴ $v = \int 4\cos t\, dt = 4\sin t + c \text{ m s}^{-1}$

But when $t = 0$, $v = 2$

∴ $2 = 4(0) + c$

∴ $c = 2$

∴ $v = 4\sin t + 2 \text{ m s}^{-1}$

∴ $v(4) \approx -1.03 \text{ m s}^{-1}$

b The total distance travelled $= \int_0^5 |v(t)|\, dt$

$= \int_0^5 |4\sin t + 2|\, dt$

$\approx 16.72 \text{ m}$

33 **a** $f(x) = 2\cos x - \sin x + 2x\sin x$

∴ $f'(x) = -2\sin x - \cos x + 2\sin x + 2x\cos x$

$= 2x\cos x - \cos x$

$= (2x - 1)\cos x$

b $f'(x) = 0$ when $2x - 1 = 0$ or $\cos x = 0$

∴ for $0 \leqslant x \leqslant 2$, $\quad x = \frac{1}{2}$ or $\quad x = \frac{\pi}{2}$

$f'(\frac{1}{4}) = -\frac{1}{2} \cos \frac{1}{4} < 0$

$f'(1) = \cos 1 > 0$

$f'(1.9) = 2.8 \times \cos 1.9 \approx -0.9052 < 0$

Sign diagram for $f'(x)$:

Now $f(\frac{1}{2}) \approx 1.755$

and $f(2) \approx 1.896$

∴ the smallest value is ≈ 1.76 when $x = \frac{1}{2}$.

34
$$\int_a^{a+2} \sin x \, dx = 0.3$$

∴ $\quad [-\cos x]_a^{a+2} = 0.3$

∴ $\quad -\cos(a+2) + \cos a = 0.3$

∴ $\quad \cos a - \cos(a+2) = 0.3$

So, $a \approx 1.96$ or 5.46 {using technology}

SOLUTIONS TO TRIAL EXAMINATION 1

Paper 1 - No calculators

Section A

1 a
$$\frac{x}{24} = \frac{6}{x}$$
∴ $x^2 = 144$
∴ $x = \pm 12$
But $x > 0$, ∴ $x = 12$

b $r = \frac{12}{24} = \frac{1}{2}$

c $u_5 = u_1 r^4$
$= 24 \times \left(\frac{1}{2}\right)^4$
$= \frac{24}{16}$
$= \frac{3}{2}$

d $S_\infty = \frac{u_1}{1-r}$
$= \frac{24}{1 - \frac{1}{2}}$
$= \frac{24}{\frac{1}{2}}$
$= 48$

2 a $h(x) = e^{-x} \cos x$
∴ $h'(x) = e^{-x}(-1)\cos x + e^{-x}(-\sin x)$
$= -e^{-x}(\cos x + \sin x)$

b $h'(\frac{\pi}{2}) = -e^{-\frac{\pi}{2}}\left(\cos \frac{\pi}{2} + \sin \frac{\pi}{2}\right)$
$= -e^{-\frac{\pi}{2}}(0 + 1)$
$= -e^{-\frac{\pi}{2}}$

c $h(\frac{\pi}{2}) = e^{-\frac{\pi}{2}} \cos \frac{\pi}{2}$
$= 0$
∴ the point of contact is $\left(\frac{\pi}{2}, 0\right)$.
∴ the tangent has equation $\frac{y - 0}{x - \frac{\pi}{2}} = -e^{-\frac{\pi}{2}}$
∴ $e^{\frac{\pi}{2}} y = -x + \frac{\pi}{2}$

3 a

∴ $x = \frac{2}{3}$, $y = \frac{1}{4}$, and $z = \frac{1}{2}$.

b $P(B) = P(A \cap B) + P(A' \cap B)$
$= \left(\frac{2}{3}\right)\left(\frac{3}{4}\right) + \left(\frac{1}{3}\right)\left(\frac{1}{2}\right)$
$= \frac{1}{2} + \frac{1}{6}$
$= \frac{2}{3}$

c $P(A' \mid B) = \frac{P(A' \cap B)}{P(B)}$
$= \frac{\left(\frac{1}{3}\right)\left(\frac{1}{2}\right)}{\frac{2}{3}}$
$= \frac{1}{4}$

4 a If $\sin 2\theta = \tan \theta$, then
$2 \sin \theta \cos \theta = \frac{\sin \theta}{\cos \theta}$
∴ $2 \sin \theta \cos^2 \theta = \sin \theta$
∴ $2 \sin \theta \cos^2 \theta - \sin \theta = 0$
∴ $\sin \theta (2 \cos^2 \theta - 1) = 0$
∴ $\sin \theta = 0$ or $\cos^2 \theta = \frac{1}{2}$
∴ $\sin \theta = 0$ or $\cos \theta = \pm \frac{1}{\sqrt{2}}$

b $\theta = 0, \pm \frac{\pi}{4}, \pm \frac{3\pi}{4}, \pm \pi$

5 a The vertex is at $(3, 7)$, so
$f(x) = a(x - 3)^2 + 7$
∴ $h = 3$, $k = 7$

b $f(0) = 2.5$ so $a(-3)^2 + 7 = 2.5$
∴ $9a = -4.5$
∴ $a = -\frac{1}{2}$

c $f(x) = -\frac{1}{2}(x - 3)^2 + 7$
∴ $f(x) = 0$ when $\frac{1}{2}(x - 3)^2 = 7$
∴ $(x - 3)^2 = 14$
∴ $x - 3 = \pm\sqrt{14}$
∴ $x = 3 \pm \sqrt{14}$
But $x > 0$ at A ∴ A is $(3 + \sqrt{14}, 0)$.

6 $f(x) = \int \left(2x - 3x^{-\frac{1}{2}}\right) dx$
$= \frac{2x^2}{2} - \frac{3x^{\frac{1}{2}}}{\frac{1}{2}} + c$
$= x^2 - 6\sqrt{x} + c$
But $f(4) = 3$
∴ $16 - 12 + c = 3$
∴ $c = -1$
∴ $f(x) = x^2 - 6\sqrt{x} - 1$

7 **a** $m + 0.15 + 2m + n = 1$

$\therefore \quad 3m + n = 0.85$

b $E(X) = m + 0.3 + 6m + 4n$

$= 7m + 4n + 0.3$

$= 7m + 4(0.85 - 3m) + 0.3 \quad \{\text{using } \mathbf{a}\}$

$= -5m + 3.7$

c If $E(X) = 2.7$, $-5m + 3.7 = 2.7$

$\therefore \quad -5m = -1$

$\therefore \quad m = 0.2$

Section B

8 **a** $\overrightarrow{BA} = \begin{pmatrix} 2 \\ -1 \\ 3 \end{pmatrix} - \begin{pmatrix} 1 \\ 2 \\ -4 \end{pmatrix} = \begin{pmatrix} 1 \\ -3 \\ 7 \end{pmatrix}$

b Suppose R lies on line L_1.

$\overrightarrow{OR} = \overrightarrow{OB} + t\,\overrightarrow{BA}$

$\therefore \quad \mathbf{r} = \begin{pmatrix} 1 \\ 2 \\ -4 \end{pmatrix} + t\begin{pmatrix} 1 \\ -3 \\ 7 \end{pmatrix}, \quad t \in \mathbb{R}$

c L_2 has direction vector $\begin{pmatrix} 4 \\ 2m \\ m \end{pmatrix}$ and $L_1 \perp L_2$.

$\therefore \quad \begin{pmatrix} 1 \\ -3 \\ 7 \end{pmatrix} \bullet \begin{pmatrix} 4 \\ 2m \\ m \end{pmatrix} = 0$

$\therefore \quad 4 - 6m + 7m = 0$

$\therefore \quad m = -4$

d L_2 has direction vector $\begin{pmatrix} 4 \\ -8 \\ -4 \end{pmatrix} = 4\begin{pmatrix} 1 \\ -2 \\ -1 \end{pmatrix}$

$\therefore$ a vector equation for L_2 is

$\mathbf{r} = \begin{pmatrix} 2 \\ 3 \\ k \end{pmatrix} + s\begin{pmatrix} 1 \\ -2 \\ -1 \end{pmatrix}, \quad s \in \mathbb{R}$

e L_1 meets L_2 where

$\begin{pmatrix} 2 \\ 3 \\ k \end{pmatrix} + s\begin{pmatrix} 1 \\ -2 \\ -1 \end{pmatrix} = \begin{pmatrix} 1 \\ 2 \\ -4 \end{pmatrix} + t\begin{pmatrix} 1 \\ -3 \\ 7 \end{pmatrix}$

$\therefore \quad 2 + s = 1 + t \quad \dots (1)$

$3 - 2s = 2 - 3t \quad \dots (2)$

$k - s = -4 + 7t \quad \dots (3)$

$4 + 2s = 2 + 2t \quad \{2 \times (1)\}$

$3 - 2s = 2 - 3t \quad \{(2)\}$

Adding, $\quad \overline{ 7 = 4 - t}$

$\therefore \quad t = -3$

$\therefore \quad 2 + s = -2$

$\therefore \quad s = -4$

So, in (3), $k + 4 = -4 - 21$

$\therefore \quad k = -29$

9 **a** $f(0) = -4\cos\left(-\frac{\pi}{4}\right) + 2$

$= -4\left(\frac{1}{\sqrt{2}}\right) + 2$

$= 2 - 2\sqrt{2}$

So, the y-intercept is $2 - 2\sqrt{2}$.

$\left(\frac{1}{\sqrt{2}}, -\frac{1}{\sqrt{2}}\right)$

b $f(x) = 0$ when

$-4\cos\left(\frac{\pi}{4}(x-1)\right) + 2 = 0$

$\therefore \quad \cos\left(\frac{\pi}{4}(x-1)\right) = \frac{1}{2}$

$\therefore \quad \frac{\pi}{4}(x-1) = \frac{\pi}{3}$

$\therefore \quad x - 1 = \frac{4}{3}$

$\therefore \quad x = 2\frac{1}{3}$

$\frac{1}{2}$

So, the x-intercept is $2\frac{1}{3}$.

c $f'(x) = -4\left[-\sin\left(\frac{\pi}{4}(x-1)\right)\right]\frac{\pi}{4} + 0$

$= \pi\sin\left(\frac{\pi}{4}(x-1)\right)$

d $f'(x) = 0$ when $\sin\left(\frac{\pi}{4}(x-1)\right) = 0$

$\therefore \quad \frac{\pi}{4}(x-1)$ is a multiple of π

$\therefore$ for the domain $0 \leqslant x \leqslant 6$, $x = 1$ or 5

$\therefore$ the x-coordinate of A is 1 and the x-coordinate of B is 5.

e Area $= \displaystyle\int_3^5 \left(-4\cos\left(\frac{\pi}{4}(x-1)\right) + 2\right) dx$

$= \left[-4\left(\frac{4}{\pi}\right)\sin\left(\frac{\pi}{4}(x-1)\right) + 2x\right]_3^5$

$= \left(-\frac{16}{\pi}\right)\sin\pi + 10 - \left[-\frac{16}{\pi}\sin\left(\frac{\pi}{2}\right) + 6\right]$

$= 10 + \frac{16}{\pi} - 6$

$= 4 + \frac{16}{\pi}$ units^2

10 **a** $(g \circ f)(x) = g(f(x))$

$= 3\left[f(x)\right]^2 - 1$

$= 3(2x - 1)^2 - 1$

$= 3(4x^2 - 4x + 1) - 1$

$= 12x^2 - 12x + 2$

b $y = 12x^2 - 12x + 2$ translated through $\begin{pmatrix} -1 \\ 4 \end{pmatrix}$ becomes

$y - 4 = 12(x+1)^2 - 12(x+1) + 2$

$\therefore \quad y - 4 = 12x^2 + 24x + 12 - 12x - 12 + 2$

$\therefore \quad y = 12x^2 + 12x + 6$

So, $h(x) = 12x^2 + 12x + 6$

c $h(x) = 12(x^2 + x) + 6$

$= 12\left(x^2 + x + \left(\frac{1}{2}\right)^2\right) + 6 - 12\left(\frac{1}{2}\right)^2$

$= 12\left(x + \frac{1}{2}\right)^2 + 3$

$= 12\left(x - \left(-\frac{1}{2}\right)\right)^2 + 3$

d **i** $g(x)$ has vertex $(0, -1)$.

ii $h(x)$ has vertex $\left(-\frac{1}{2}, 3\right)$.

e $y = 12x^2 - 12x + 6$ meets $y = 2x + c$

where $12x^2 - 12x + 6 = 2x + c$

$\therefore \quad 12x^2 - 14x + (6 - c) = 0$

In the case of a tangent, this equation has a repeated root.

$\therefore \quad \Delta = 0$

$\therefore \quad (-14)^2 - 4(12)(6 - c) = 0$

$\therefore \quad 196 - 288 + 48c = 0$

$\therefore \quad 48c = 92$

$\therefore \quad c = \frac{23}{12}$

Paper 2 - Calculators

Section A

1 a The reflex angle is $(2\pi - \theta)$

∴ arc length AXB $= r(2\pi - \theta)$

∴ $14.3 = 3.8(2\pi - \theta)$

∴ $2\pi - \theta = \dfrac{14.3}{3.8}$

∴ $\theta = 2\pi - \dfrac{14.3}{3.8}$

∴ $\theta \approx 2.52^c$

b Area $= \frac{1}{2}r^2\theta$

$\approx \frac{1}{2} \times 3.8^2 \times (2\pi - 2.520\,03)$

≈ 27.2 m^2

2 a The $(r+1)$th term is $T_{r+1} = \binom{n}{r}a^{n-r}b^r$

where $a = 2x^2$, $b = (-1)$, $n = 12$

∴ $T_{r+1} = \binom{12}{r}\left(2x^2\right)^{12-r}(-1)^r$

$= \binom{12}{r}2^{12-r}x^{24-2r}(-1)^r$

b If $24 - 2r = 10$ then $2r = 14$

∴ $r = 7$

Thus $T_8 = \binom{12}{7}2^5x^{10}(-1)^7$

∴ the coefficient of $x^{10} = -\binom{12}{7}2^5 = -25\,344$.

3 a mean $\overline{x} \approx 2.94$, median $= 3$

b standard deviation ≈ 1.43

c IQR $= Q_3 - Q_1$

$= 4 - 2$

$= 2$

4 a $u_1 = 17$, $u_2 = 15$, $u_3 = 13$, $u_4 = 11$, ...

The terms are decreasing by 2 each time. This pattern will continue because the general term has the form $u_n = u_1 - 2n$.

∴ the sequence is arithmetic.

b $d = -2$

c If $u_n = -55$, then $19 - 2n = -55$

∴ $2n = 74$

∴ $n = 37$

∴ -55 is the 37th term of the sequence.

d $S_n = \dfrac{n}{2}[2u_1 + (n-1)d]$

$= \dfrac{n}{2}[34 + (n-1)(-2)]$

$= \dfrac{n}{2}[34 - 2n + 2]$

$= \dfrac{n}{2}[36 - 2n]$

∴ $S_n = n(18 - n)$

5 Using $\mathbf{a} \bullet \mathbf{b} = |\mathbf{a}||\mathbf{b}|\cos\theta$,

$\begin{pmatrix} 1 \\ -1 \\ 2 \end{pmatrix} \bullet \begin{pmatrix} 3 \\ 1 \\ t \end{pmatrix} = \sqrt{1+1+4}\sqrt{9+1+t^2}\cos 60°$

∴ $3 - 1 + 2t = \sqrt{6}\sqrt{t^2 + 10}\left(\frac{1}{2}\right)$

∴ $4t + 4 = \sqrt{6t^2 + 60}$

∴ $16t^2 + 32t + 16 = 6t^2 + 60$

∴ $10t^2 + 32t - 44 = 0$

∴ $t \approx 1.038$ {as $t > 0$}

6 a Using A, $2(2)^3 + b(2)^2 + c(2) = 6$

∴ $16 + 4b + 2c = 6$

∴ $4b + 2c = -10$

∴ $2b + c = -5$ .... (1)

Using C, $2(-2)^3 + b(-2)^2 + c(-2) = -6$

∴ $-16 + 4b - 2c = -6$

∴ $4b - 2c = 10$

∴ $2b - c = 5$ .... (2)

Adding (1) and (2) gives $4b = 0$

∴ $b = 0$

Using (1), $c = -5$

b From **a**, $f(x) = 2x^3 - 5x$

But $f(k) = -2$, so $2k^3 - 5k = -2$ and we need a solution of this equation between $k = 0$ and $k = 2$.

Using technology, $k \approx 1.32$.

7 a As x increases, y increases also, so the correlation is positive.

b $y = 2.12x + 0.34$

c $r \approx 0.999\,79$

There is a very strong positive correlation between x and y.

d When $x = 7$, $y \approx 15.2$.

e $x = 12$ is outside the domain of the data used to find the regression line.

So, the result would be an extrapolation and therefore would not be reliable.

Section B

8 a Using technology, $a \approx -2.828$, $b \approx 2.828$

b $c \approx 2.27$ {technology}

c From the graph, the asymptotes appear to be $x = 3$ and $x = -3$.

As $x \to \pm 3$, $9 - x^2 \to 0$

Now $\ln 0$ is undefined, but as $\theta \to 0$, $\ln\theta \to -\infty$.

∴ as $x \to \pm 3$, $f(x) \to -\infty$

∴ $x = \pm 3$ are the vertical asymptotes.

d Shaded area $= \int_{-1}^{0} x^2 \ln(9 - x^2)\, dx$

≈ 0.709 units^2 {technology}

e Volume $= \pi\int_{-1}^{0}\left[x^2\ln(9 - x^2)\right]^2 dx$

≈ 2.81 units^3

9 a $2r + 3 = 123$ {max height}

∴ $2r = 120$

∴ $r = 60$

So, the radius is 60 m.

b The amplitude of the function is the radius of the wheel, so $a = 60$.

The average height corresponds to the principal axis, and this is the height of the centre of the wheel.

∴ $d = 63$.

c The period $= \dfrac{2\pi}{b} = 20$

∴ $b = \dfrac{2\pi}{20}$

∴ $b = \dfrac{\pi}{10}$

d When $t = 0$, $H(t)$ is at its minimum.

$\therefore \ 60\sin\left(\frac{\pi}{10}(0-c)\right) + 63 = 3$

$\therefore \ \sin\left(-\frac{c\pi}{10}\right) = -1$

$\therefore \ -\frac{c\pi}{10} = -\frac{\pi}{2}$

$\therefore \ c = 5$

e Thus $H(t) = 60\sin\left(\frac{\pi}{10}(t-5)\right) + 63$

$\therefore \ H(8) = 60\sin\left(\frac{3\pi}{10}\right) + 63$

$\therefore \ H(8) \approx 111.5$

The seat is 111.5 m above the ground.

f When $H(t) = 100$,

$60\sin\left(\frac{\pi}{10}(t-5)\right) + 63 = 100$

The first positive solution for t is

$t \approx 7.115 \quad \{\text{technology}\}$

The seat is 100 m above the ground about 7 min 7 s after the start.

10 a $y = 0$ appears to be the only asymptote.

b When $y = 0$, $\frac{1}{2}e^{-\frac{x}{2}}\left(4x - x^2\right) = 0$

$\therefore \ 4x - x^2 = 0$

$\therefore \ x(4 - x) = 0$

$\therefore \ x = 0 \text{ or } 4$

The x-intercepts are 0 and 4.

c Using technology:

A is a local maximum at $(1.17, 0.922)$.

C is a local minimum at $(6.83, -0.318)$.

d If $y = x^2 e^{-\frac{x}{2}}$, $\frac{dy}{dx} = 2xe^{-\frac{x}{2}} + x^2 e^{-\frac{x}{2}}\left(-\frac{1}{2}\right)$

$= \frac{1}{2}e^{-\frac{x}{2}}\left(4x - x^2\right)$

e From **d**, $\int \frac{1}{2}e^{-\frac{x}{2}}\left(4x - x^2\right) dx = x^2 e^{-\frac{x}{2}} + c_1$

$\therefore \ \int e^{-\frac{x}{2}}\left(4x - x^2\right) dx = 2x^2 e^{-\frac{x}{2}} + c$

SOLUTIONS TO TRIAL EXAMINATION 2

Paper 1 - No calculators

Section A

1 a

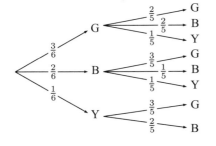

b $\text{P(G second)} = \text{P(GG or BG or YG)}$

$= \left(\frac{3}{6}\right)\left(\frac{2}{5}\right) + \left(\frac{2}{6}\right)\left(\frac{3}{5}\right) + \left(\frac{1}{6}\right)\left(\frac{3}{5}\right)$

$= \frac{1}{2}$

c $\text{P(B first} \mid \text{G second)} = \dfrac{\text{P(B first and G second)}}{\text{P(G second)}}$

$= \dfrac{\frac{6}{30}}{\frac{1}{2}}$

$= \frac{2}{5}$

2 a $(f \circ g)(x) = f(g(x))$

$= 3^{g(x)}$

$= 3^{x+1}$

b The inverse of $y = x + 1$ is $x = y + 1$

which is $y = x - 1$

$\therefore \ g^{-1}(x) = x - 1$

$(g^{-1} \circ f)(x) = g^{-1}(f(x))$

$= g^{-1}(3^x)$

$= 3^x - 1$

c $3^x - 1 = 8$

$\therefore \ 3^x = 9$

$\therefore \ x = 2$

3 a Let $u = x^2$

$\therefore \ du = 2x \, dx$

$\int xe^{-x^2} dx = \int \frac{1}{2}e^{-x^2}(2x) \, dx$

$= \int \frac{1}{2}e^{-u} \, du$

$= -\frac{1}{2}e^{-u} + c$

$= -\frac{1}{2}e^{-x^2} + c$

b $\int_0^m xe^{-x^2} dx = \dfrac{e-1}{2e}$

$\therefore \ \left[-\frac{1}{2}e^{-x^2}\right]_0^m = \dfrac{e-1}{2e}$

$\therefore \ -\frac{1}{2}e^{-m^2} + \frac{1}{2} = \frac{1}{2} - \frac{1}{2}e^{-1}$

$\therefore \ e^{-m^2} = e^{-1}$

$\therefore \ m^2 = 1$

$\therefore \ m = 1 \quad \{\text{as } m > 0\}$

4 a $4\cos^2 x = 3$

$\therefore \ \cos^2 x = \frac{3}{4}$

$\therefore \ \cos x = \pm\frac{\sqrt{3}}{2}$

But $\frac{\pi}{2} < x < \pi$, so $x = \frac{5\pi}{6}$

b i $\tan x = \tan\left(\frac{5\pi}{6}\right)$

$= -\frac{1}{\sqrt{3}}$

ii $\sin 2x = \sin\left(\frac{5\pi}{3}\right)$

$= -\frac{\sqrt{3}}{2}$

5 a i Since $12, a, 3, ...$ is a geometric sequence,

$\dfrac{a}{12} = \dfrac{3}{a}$

$\therefore \ a^2 = 36$

$\therefore \ a = 6 \quad \{\text{as } a > 0\}$

ii The common ratio $r = \dfrac{a}{12} = \frac{1}{2}$.

iii $u_{12} = u_1 r^{11}$

$= 12 \times \left(\frac{1}{2}\right)^{11}$

$= \dfrac{3 \times 2^2}{2^{11}}$

$= \dfrac{3}{2^9}$

$= \dfrac{3}{512}$

b $S_\infty = \dfrac{u_1}{1-r} = \dfrac{12}{\frac{1}{2}} = 24$

6 a A vector equation for L is $\mathbf{r} = \begin{pmatrix} 1 \\ 2 \\ -1 \end{pmatrix} + t \begin{pmatrix} 2 \\ 0 \\ -2 \end{pmatrix}$.

b $\overrightarrow{AB} = \begin{pmatrix} 3-1 \\ -2-2 \\ 1--1 \end{pmatrix} = \begin{pmatrix} 2 \\ -4 \\ 2 \end{pmatrix}$

$\overrightarrow{AB} \bullet \mathbf{v} = \begin{pmatrix} 2 \\ -4 \\ 2 \end{pmatrix} \bullet \begin{pmatrix} 2 \\ 0 \\ -2 \end{pmatrix}$

$= 4 + 0 - 4$

$= 0$

$\therefore$ $\overrightarrow{AB}$ is perpendicular to line L.

c Since $\overrightarrow{AB}$ is perpendicular to L, the shortest distance from B to line L is

$AB = \sqrt{2^2 + (-4)^2 + 2^2}$

$= \sqrt{24}$

$= 2\sqrt{6}$ units

7 a Using the cosine rule,

$5^2 = 4^2 + x^2 - 2(4)(x)\cos 60°$

$\therefore \quad 25 = 16 + x^2 - 8x\left(\tfrac{1}{2}\right)$

$\therefore \quad 9 = x^2 - 4x$

$\therefore \quad x^2 - 4x - 9 = 0$

b $x = \dfrac{4 \pm \sqrt{16 - 4(1)(-9)}}{2}$

$= \dfrac{4 \pm \sqrt{52}}{2}$

$= \dfrac{4 \pm 2\sqrt{13}}{2}$

$= 2 \pm \sqrt{13}$

But $x > 0$, so $x = 2 + \sqrt{13}$.

Section B

8 $f(x) = 1 - \dfrac{2}{1+x^2}$

a When $y = 0$, $1 - \dfrac{2}{1+x^2} = 0$

$\therefore \quad 1 + x^2 = 2$

$\therefore \quad x^2 = 1$

$\therefore \quad x = \pm 1$

$\therefore$ the x-intercepts are ± 1.

Also, $f(0) = 1 - \tfrac{2}{1} = -1$

$\therefore$ the y-intercept is -1.

b As $x \to \pm\infty$, $\dfrac{2}{1+x^2} \to 0^+$

$\therefore \quad f(x) \to 1^-$

c $f(x) = 1 - 2(1+x^2)^{-1}$

$\therefore \quad f'(x) = 0 + 2(1+x^2)^{-2}(2x)$

$= \dfrac{4x}{(1+x^2)^2}$

$\therefore \quad f'(x) = 0$ when $x = 0$

Sign diagram of $f'(x)$:

$\therefore$ there is a local minimum at $(0, -1)$.

d $f''(x) = \dfrac{4(1+x^2)^2 - 4x(2)(1+x^2)(2x)}{(1+x^2)^4}$

$= \dfrac{4(1+x^2)[1 + x^2 - 4x^2]}{(1+x^2)^4}$

$= \dfrac{4(1 - 3x^2)}{(1+x^2)^3}$

$\therefore \quad f''(x) = 0$ when $3x^2 = 1$

$\therefore \quad x^2 = \tfrac{1}{3}$

$\therefore \quad x = \pm\tfrac{1}{\sqrt{3}}$

So, $y = f(x)$ has points of inflection at $x = \pm\tfrac{1}{\sqrt{3}}$.

e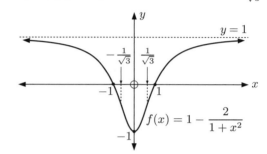

9 a $\mathbf{w} - 2\mathbf{v} = 3\mathbf{i} - \mathbf{j} - 2\mathbf{k} - 2(\mathbf{i} + 2\mathbf{j} - \mathbf{k})$

$= \mathbf{i} - 5\mathbf{j}$

$\therefore \quad |\mathbf{w} - 2\mathbf{v}| = \sqrt{1 + 25} = \sqrt{26}$

$\therefore$ the required vector is $\tfrac{2}{\sqrt{26}}(\mathbf{i} - 5\mathbf{j})$

b i L_1: $\mathbf{r} = \begin{pmatrix} 4 \\ -11 \\ 5 \end{pmatrix} + s \begin{pmatrix} 1 \\ 2 \\ -1 \end{pmatrix}$, $s \in \mathbb{R}$

L_2: $\mathbf{r} = \begin{pmatrix} 10 \\ k \\ -2 \end{pmatrix} + t \begin{pmatrix} 3 \\ -1 \\ -2 \end{pmatrix}$, $t \in \mathbb{R}$

ii L_1 meets L_2 when $x = 13$

$\therefore \quad 4 + s = 13$ and $10 + 3t = 13$

$\therefore \quad s = 9$ and $t = 1$

Using L_1, the point is $(13, 7, -4)$.

Using L_2, $k - 1 = 7$

$\therefore \quad k = 8$

iii If θ is the angle, $\cos\theta = \dfrac{|\mathbf{v} \bullet \mathbf{w}|}{|\mathbf{v}||\mathbf{w}|}$

$= \dfrac{|3 - 2 + 2|}{\sqrt{1 + 4 + 1}\sqrt{9 + 1 + 4}}$

$= \dfrac{3}{\sqrt{6}\sqrt{14}}$

$= \dfrac{3}{2\sqrt{21}}$

10 a i $\cos\left(\tfrac{\pi}{4}\right) = 1 - 2\sin^2\left(\tfrac{\pi}{8}\right)$ {double angle formula}

ii Now $\cos\left(\tfrac{\pi}{4}\right) = \tfrac{1}{\sqrt{2}}$

$\therefore \quad 1 - 2\sin^2\left(\tfrac{\pi}{8}\right) = \tfrac{1}{\sqrt{2}}$

$\therefore \quad 2\sin^2\left(\tfrac{\pi}{8}\right) = 1 - \tfrac{1}{\sqrt{2}}$

$\therefore \quad 2\sin^2\left(\tfrac{\pi}{8}\right) = \dfrac{\sqrt{2} - 1}{\sqrt{2}}$

$\therefore \quad \sin^2\left(\tfrac{\pi}{8}\right) = \dfrac{\sqrt{2} - 1}{2\sqrt{2}}$

$\therefore \quad \sin\left(\tfrac{\pi}{8}\right) = \sqrt{\dfrac{\sqrt{2} - 1}{2\sqrt{2}}}$

b **i**

$$\sin\left(\tfrac{\pi}{8}\right) = \frac{\tfrac{a}{2}}{r} = \frac{a}{2r}$$

$$\therefore \quad a = 2r\sin\left(\tfrac{\pi}{8}\right)$$

ii The area of the octagon is

$$A = 8\left(\frac{a}{2}\right)h$$

$$= 8r\sin\left(\tfrac{\pi}{8}\right)r\cos\left(\tfrac{\pi}{8}\right)$$

$$\left\{\cos\left(\tfrac{\pi}{8}\right) = \frac{h}{r}\right\}$$

$$= 4r^2\left(2\sin\left(\tfrac{\pi}{8}\right)\cos\left(\tfrac{\pi}{8}\right)\right)$$

$$= 4r^2\sin\left(\tfrac{\pi}{4}\right) \quad \{\text{double angle formula}\}$$

$$= 4r^2\left(\tfrac{1}{\sqrt{2}}\right)$$

$$= 2\sqrt{2}r^2$$

c **i** $\quad V = \tfrac{1}{3} \times 2\sqrt{2}r^2 \times 3r$

$$\therefore \quad V = 2\sqrt{2}r^3$$

ii $\dfrac{dV}{dr} = 6\sqrt{2}r^2$

iii The base area $A = 2\sqrt{2}r^2$

$$\therefore \quad \frac{dV}{dr} = 3A$$

Paper 2 - Calculators

Section A

1 **a** $\widehat{BAC} = 180° - 43° - 18° = 119°$

Using the sine rule, $\dfrac{a}{\sin 119°} = \dfrac{35.6}{\sin 43°}$

$$\therefore \quad a = \frac{35.6 \times \sin 119°}{\sin 43°}$$

$$\therefore \quad a \approx 45.7$$

So, the distance is about 45.7 cm.

b Area $= \tfrac{1}{2}ab\sin C$

$$\approx \tfrac{1}{2} \times 45.6547 \times 35.6 \times \sin 18°$$

$$\approx 251 \text{ cm}^2$$

2 The $(r+1)$th term of the expansion is

$$T_{r+1} = \binom{10}{r}(2x)^{10-r}5^r$$

$$= \binom{10}{r}2^{10-r}x^{10-r}5^r, \quad r = 0, 1, 2, ..., 10$$

The power of x is 6 when $\quad 10 - r = 6$

$$\therefore \quad r = 4$$

When $r = 4$, $\quad T_5 = \binom{10}{4}2^6 5^4 x^6$

So, the coefficient of x^6 is $\binom{10}{4}2^6 5^4$ or $8\,400\,000$.

3 **a** The vertical asymptotes occur when $\quad x^2 - 4 = 0$

$$\therefore \quad x^2 = 4$$

$\therefore$ the vertical asymptotes are $x = 2$ and $x = -2$.

b

c Range is $\{y \mid y \leqslant -\tfrac{1}{4} \text{ or } y \geqslant \tfrac{1}{5}\}$.

d $g(x) = -f\left(\tfrac{x}{2}\right)$

$$= -\frac{1}{\left(\tfrac{x}{2}\right)^2 - 4}$$

$$= \frac{4}{16 - x^2} \quad \text{with domain } -6 \leqslant x \leqslant 6$$

4 **a** E is $(0, 0, 6)$, M is $(5, 4, 0)$, and G is $(5, 8, 6)$.

b **i** $\overrightarrow{ME} = \begin{pmatrix} 0-5 \\ 0-4 \\ 6-0 \end{pmatrix} = \begin{pmatrix} -5 \\ -4 \\ 6 \end{pmatrix}$

ii $\overrightarrow{MG} = \begin{pmatrix} 5-5 \\ 8-4 \\ 6-0 \end{pmatrix} = \begin{pmatrix} 0 \\ 4 \\ 6 \end{pmatrix}$

c

Let the angle be θ.

$$\cos\theta = \frac{\overrightarrow{ME} \bullet \overrightarrow{MG}}{|\overrightarrow{ME}||\overrightarrow{MG}|}$$

$$= \frac{0 + (-16) + 36}{\sqrt{25 + 16 + 36}\sqrt{16 + 36}}$$

$$= \frac{20}{\sqrt{77 \times 52}}$$

$$\therefore \quad \theta \approx 71.6°$$

5 **a** $\quad \tfrac{9}{2} + \tfrac{3}{2}\cos 2\theta$

$$= \tfrac{9}{2} + \tfrac{3}{2}(2\cos^2\theta - 1)$$

$$= \tfrac{9}{2} + 3\cos^2\theta - \tfrac{3}{2}$$

$$= 3\cos^2\theta + 3$$

b $\quad \tfrac{3}{2}\cos 2\theta - 10\cos\theta + \tfrac{9}{2} = 0$

$$\therefore \quad 3\cos^2\theta - 10\cos\theta + 3 = 0 \quad \{\text{using } \mathbf{a}\}$$

$$\therefore \quad (3\cos\theta - 1)(\cos\theta - 3) = 0$$

$$\therefore \quad \cos\theta = \tfrac{1}{3} \quad \{\text{since } -1 \leqslant \cos\theta \leqslant 1\}$$

$$\therefore \quad \theta \approx 1.23 \quad \{0 \leqslant \theta \leqslant \pi\}$$

6 **a** When $t = 60$, $N \approx 50$.

$\therefore$ about 50 students took less than 60 seconds.

b $\frac{1}{2}(200) = 100$ and when $N = 100$, $t = 65$

So, the median is 65 seconds.

$\frac{3}{4}(200) = 150$, so $Q_3 = 70$

$\frac{1}{4}(200) = 50$, so $Q_1 = 60$

IQR $= Q_3 - Q_1 = 70 - 60 = 10$ s

c When $t = 75$, $N \approx 170$.

$\therefore$ about 30 students took more than 75 seconds.

$\therefore$ P(student took more than 75 s) $= \frac{30}{200} = \frac{3}{20}$

7 a $v(t) = \int a(t)\, dt$

$= \int 2(t+1)^{-\frac{1}{2}}\, dt$

$= 4(t+1)^{\frac{1}{2}} + c$

But $v(0) = 0$, so $4 + c = 0$

$\therefore c = -4$

$\therefore v(t) = 4\sqrt{t+1} - 4 \text{ ms}^{-1}$

b In the first 10 seconds, the distance travelled by the train is $\int_0^{10}(4\sqrt{t+1} - 4)\, dt \approx 54.6$ m.

Section B

8 a $f(x) = e^{3x} \sin 2x$

$\therefore f'(x) = e^{3x}(3) \sin 2x + e^{3x} \cos 2x(2)$

$= e^{3x}(3\sin 2x + 2\cos 2x)$

$\therefore f'(x) = 0$ when $3\sin 2x + 2\cos 2x = 0$

$\{$as $e^{3x} > 0$ for all $x\}$

$\therefore 3\sin 2x = -2\cos 2x$

$\therefore \frac{\sin 2x}{\cos 2x} = -\frac{2}{3}$

$\therefore \tan 2x = -\frac{2}{3}$

b i The graph cuts the x-axis when $y = 0$

$(-1, 0)$ $(1, 0)$

$\therefore e^{3x} \sin 2x = 0$

$\therefore \sin 2x = 0$

$\therefore 2x$ is a multiple of π

$\therefore x$ is a multiple of $\frac{\pi}{2}$

The x-coordinate of B is $\frac{\pi}{2}$

and the x-coordinate of C is π.

ii A is a local maximum, so $f'(x) = 0$ at A.

$\therefore \tan 2x = -\frac{2}{3}$

$\therefore 2x = \tan^{-1}(-\frac{2}{3})$

$\therefore 2x = \pi - \tan^{-1}(\frac{2}{3})$

$\therefore 2x \approx 2.5536$

$\therefore x \approx 1.28$

So, the x-coordinate of A ≈ 1.28.

c i $g(x) = \frac{1}{13}(3e^{3x} \sin 2x - 2e^{3x} \cos 2x)$

$= \frac{3}{13}e^{3x} \sin 2x - \frac{2}{13}e^{3x} \cos 2x$

$\therefore g'(x) = \frac{3}{13}\left[e^{3x}(3)\sin 2x + e^{3x}\cos 2x(2)\right]$

$\qquad - \frac{2}{13}\left[e^{3x}(3)\cos 2x + e^{3x}(-\sin 2x)(2)\right]$

$= e^{3x}\left(\frac{9}{13}\sin 2x + \frac{6}{13}\cos 2x\right.$

$\qquad \left. - \frac{6}{13}\cos 2x + \frac{4}{13}\sin 2x\right)$

$= e^{3x}\left(\frac{13}{13}\sin 2x\right)$

$= e^{3x}\sin 2x$

ii $g(x)$ is the antiderivative of $f(x)$.

d Area $= \int_0^{\frac{\pi}{2}} e^{3x} \sin 2x\, dx$

≈ 17.3 units^2 $\{$using technology$\}$

9 a i

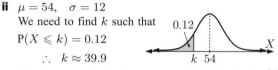

ii $\mu = 54$, $\sigma = 12$

We need to find k such that

P$(X \leqslant k) = 0.12$

$\therefore k \approx 39.9$

The greatest weight of any mouse in the lightest 12% of the population ≈ 39.9 grams.

iii If P$(X \geqslant k) = 0.08$

then P$(X < k) = 0.92$

$\therefore k \approx 70.9$

The lowest weight of a mouse in the top 8% of the population ≈ 70.9 grams.

b $\qquad \text{P}(X < 6) = 0.2$

$\therefore \text{P}\left(\frac{X-9}{\sigma} < \frac{6-9}{\sigma}\right) = 0.2$

$\therefore \text{P}\left(Z < -\frac{3}{\sigma}\right) = 0.2$

$\therefore -\frac{3}{\sigma} \approx -0.841\,62$

$\therefore \sigma \approx \frac{-3}{-0.841\,62} \approx 3.56$

c Let X be the number of times Pelé scores. $X \sim \text{B}(20, 0.8)$.

i $\text{E}(X) = np = 20 \times 0.8 = 16$

He expects success with 16 shots.

ii $\text{P}(X = 18) = \binom{20}{18}(0.8)^{18}(0.2)^2$

≈ 0.137

iii $\text{P}(X \geqslant 18) = 1 - \text{P}(X \leqslant 17)$

$\approx 1 - 0.794$

≈ 0.206

10 a $r \approx 0.984$

b The variables N and T have a very strong positive correlation. An increase in temperature results in more people using the pool.

c $N \approx 11.2T - 238$

d i When $T = 25$, $N \approx 11.2 \times 25 - 238$

≈ 42

We expect 42 people to be at the pool.

ii When $T = 40$, $N \approx 11.2 \times 40 - 238$

≈ 210

We expect 210 people to be at the pool.

e $T = 25$ lies within the domain of the collected data, whereas $T = 40$ does not.

Since the result for $T = 25$ is an interpolation, we expect it to be more reliable.

f When $T = 20$, $N \approx 11.2 \times 20 - 238$

≈ -14

which is not possible as $N \geqslant 0$

The model for N is not valid for lower temperatures outside the domain.

Paper 1 - No calculators

Section A

1 a

	Girls	Boys	Total
Computer Games	10	12	22
Sport	34	24	58
Total	44	36	80

b **i** $P(\text{prefers sport}) = \frac{58}{80} = \frac{29}{40}$

ii $P(\text{prefers sport} \mid \text{a girl}) = \frac{34}{44} = \frac{17}{22}$

2 a $f(x) = x^2 e^{-x}$

$\therefore\ f'(x) = 2xe^{-x} + x^2(-1)e^{-x}$
$= xe^{-x}(2 - x)$
$\therefore\ k = 2$

b $f'(-1) = (-1)e^1(2 - -1)$
$= -3e$

$f(-1) = (-1)^2 e^1$
$= e$

$\therefore$ the equation of the tangent is

$\dfrac{y - e}{x - -1} = -3e$

$\therefore\ y - e = -3e(x + 1)$
$\therefore\ y - e = -3ex - 3e$
$\therefore\ y = -3ex - 2e$

3 a Using the cosine rule in $\triangle ABD$,

$x^2 = 3^2 + 4^2 - 2(3)(4)\cos\alpha$

$\therefore\ \cos\alpha = \dfrac{25 - x^2}{24}$

b Using the cosine rule in $\triangle BCD$,

$x^2 = 1^2 + 5^2 - 2(1)(5)\cos\beta$

$\therefore\ \cos\beta = \dfrac{26 - x^2}{10}$

If $\alpha = \beta$ then $\cos\alpha = \cos\beta$

$\therefore\ \dfrac{25 - x^2}{\underset{12}{\cancel{24}}} = \dfrac{26 - x^2}{\underset{5}{\cancel{10}}}$

$\therefore\ 5(25 - x^2) = 12(26 - x^2)$
$\therefore\ 125 - 5x^2 = 312 - 12x^2$
$\therefore\ 7x^2 = 187$
$\therefore\ x^2 = \frac{187}{7}$

$\therefore$ since $x > 0,\ x = \sqrt{\frac{187}{7}}$

4 a **i** To obtain $y = f(x - 3)$ from $y = f(x)$, we translate 3 units to the right.

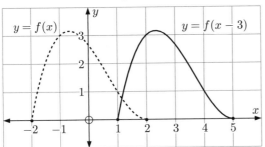

ii To obtain $y = f(-x)$ from $y = f(x)$, we reflect in the y-axis.

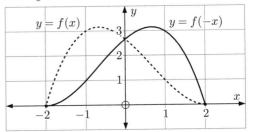

b **i** The area under $y = f(x)$ is reflected in the y-axis, so the area is unchanged.

$\therefore$ the area $= A$.

ii $\int_{-2}^{2} 2f(x)\,dx = 2\int_{-2}^{2} f(x)\,dx$

$\therefore$ the area $= 2A$

5 a $v(t) = 30 - 6t^2\ \text{m s}^{-1}$

$\therefore\ a(t) = \dfrac{dv}{dt} = -12t\ \text{m s}^{-2}$

$\therefore\ a(5) = -60\ \text{m s}^{-2}$

b $s(t) = \int v(t)\,dt = \int (30 - 6t^2)\,dt$

$= 30t - \dfrac{6t^3}{3} + c$

$= 30t - 2t^3 + c\ \text{m}$

But $s(0) = 15$, so $c = 15$

Hence $s(t) = 30t - 2t^3 + 15\ \text{m}$

6 The amplitude $= \dfrac{70 - 30}{2} = 20$

$\therefore\ a = 20$

The period $= \pi$

$\therefore\ \dfrac{2\pi}{b} = \pi$

$\therefore\ b = 2$

The principal axis is $y = 50$

$\therefore\ c = 50$

7 a $0.1 + 0.2 + p + 0.15 + 0.3 = 1$

$\therefore\ p = 0.25$

b $P(X \text{ is odd}) = P(X = 1) + P(X = 3) + P(X = 5)$
$= 0.1 + 0.25 + 0.3$
$= 0.65$

c $E(X) = \sum x_i\,P(X = x_i)$
$= 1 \times 0.1 + 2 \times 0.2 + 3 \times 0.25 + 4 \times 0.15$
$\qquad + 5 \times 0.3$
$= 0.1 + 0.4 + 0.75 + 0.6 + 1.5$
$= 3.35$

Section B

8 a $f(2) = 0$

$\therefore\ 2 \times 8 + a \times 4 + 4 \times 2 + 4 = 0$
$\therefore\ 4a = -28$
$\therefore\ a = -7$

b $f(-\tfrac{1}{2}) = 2 \times (-\tfrac{1}{2})^3 - 7 \times (-\tfrac{1}{2})^2 + 4 \times (-\tfrac{1}{2}) + 4$
$= -\tfrac{1}{4} - \tfrac{7}{4} - 2 + 4$
$= 0$

Point C has coordinates $(-\tfrac{1}{2}, 0)$.

c
$$f'(x) = 6x^2 - 14x + 4$$
$$= 2(3x^2 - 7x + 2)$$
$$= 2(x - 2)(3x - 1)$$
$\therefore\ f'(x) = 0$ when $x = \frac{1}{3}$ or 2
$\therefore$ B has x-coordinate $\frac{1}{3}$.

d $f(x)$ is increasing for $x \leqslant \frac{1}{3}$ and for $x \geqslant 2$.

e
$$f''(x) = 12x - 14$$
$$= 2(6x - 7)$$
$f''(x)$ has sign diagram:

$\therefore$ $f(x)$ is concave down for $x \leqslant \frac{7}{6}$.

f Area $= \int_{-\frac{1}{2}}^{2} (2x^3 - 7x^2 + 4x + 4)\, dx$

9 a $f(x) = \sqrt{\ln x}$ is defined provided $\ln x \geqslant 0$
$$\therefore\ x \geqslant 1$$
$\therefore$ the domain is $\{x \mid x \geqslant 1\}$.
As $x \to \infty,\ \ln x \to \infty$
$\therefore$ the range is $\{y \mid y \geqslant 0\}$.

b $f'(x) = \frac{1}{2}(\ln x)^{-\frac{1}{2}} \times \frac{1}{x} = \frac{1}{2x\sqrt{\ln x}}$

$\therefore\ f'(e) = \frac{1}{2e\sqrt{\ln e}} = \frac{1}{2e}$

So, the tangent has gradient $\frac{1}{2e}$.

c
$$\frac{d}{dx}(x \ln x) = \ln x + \frac{x}{x}$$
$$= \ln x + 1$$
$$\int \ln x\, dx = \int (\ln x + 1 - 1)\, dx$$
$$= \int (\ln x + 1)\, dx - \int 1\, dx$$
$$= x \ln x - x + c$$

d Volume
$$= \pi \int_1^e y^2\, dx$$
$$= \pi \int_1^e \ln x\, dx$$
$$= \pi \left[x \ln x - x \right]_1^e \quad \{\text{using } \mathbf{c}\}$$
$$= \pi (e \ln e - e - (\cancel{\ln 1} - 1))$$
$$= \pi (e - e + 1)$$
$$= \pi \text{ units}^3$$

$y = \sqrt{\ln x}$

10 a $\mathbf{r}_A = \begin{pmatrix} 1 \\ 0 \\ 0 \end{pmatrix} + s \begin{pmatrix} 1 \\ 3 \\ 5 \end{pmatrix}, \quad s \geqslant 0$

b $\mathbf{r}_A = \begin{pmatrix} 1 + s \\ 3s \\ 5s \end{pmatrix}$ and $\mathbf{r}_B = \begin{pmatrix} 3 + t \\ 4 + t \\ -5t \end{pmatrix}$

$\therefore$ the beams meet when $\begin{cases} 1 + s = 3 + t & \text{.... (1)} \\ 3s = 4 + t & \text{.... (2)} \\ 5s = -5t & \text{.... (3)} \end{cases}$

Using (3), $t = -s$
Substituting into (2), $3s = 4 - s$
$$\therefore\ 4s = 4$$
$$\therefore\ s = 1 \text{ and } t = -1$$
and this checks in (1).

The beams meet when $\mathbf{r}_A = \begin{pmatrix} 2 \\ 3 \\ 5 \end{pmatrix}$, which is the point $(2, 3, 5)$.

c The distance from $(2, 3, 5)$ to $(4, 7, 9)$
$$= \sqrt{(4 - 2)^2 + (7 - 3)^2 + (9 - 5)^2}$$
$$= \sqrt{2^2 + 4^2 + 4^2}$$
$$= 6 \text{ units on the grid}$$
$$= 60 \text{ m}$$
$\therefore$ the speed of the bird is $\dfrac{60 \text{ m}}{2 \text{ s}} = 30 \text{ m s}^{-1}$

d If θ is the angle between the beams then
$$\cos\theta = \frac{\begin{pmatrix} 1 \\ 3 \\ 5 \end{pmatrix} \bullet \begin{pmatrix} 1 \\ 1 \\ -5 \end{pmatrix}}{\sqrt{1^2 + 3^2 + 5^2}\sqrt{1^2 + 1^2 + (-5)^2}}$$
$$= \frac{1 + 3 - 25}{\sqrt{35}\sqrt{27}}$$
$$= -\frac{21}{\sqrt{105 \times 9}}$$
$$= -\frac{7}{\sqrt{105}}$$

Paper 2 - Calculators

Section A

1 Let X be the height of a randomly selected tree.
$\mu = 3.18, \quad \sigma = 0.195$

a **i** $P(X > 3) \approx 0.822$
  ii $P(2.8 < X < 3.3) \approx 0.705$

b We need to find k such that
$$P(X \geqslant k) = 0.2$$
$$\therefore\ P(X \leqslant k) = 0.8$$
$$\therefore\ k \approx 3.344$$

So, a tree must be about 3.34 m high to be in the tallest 20%.

2 a A vertical stretch of $y = \dfrac{1}{x}$ with scale factor 3 is $y = \dfrac{3}{x}$.

A translation of $y = \dfrac{3}{x}$ through $\begin{pmatrix} 5 \\ -2 \end{pmatrix}$ is
$$y = \frac{3}{x - 5} - 2$$
$$\therefore\ y = \frac{3 - 2(x - 5)}{x - 5}$$
$$\therefore\ y = \frac{-2x + 13}{x - 5}$$
$$\therefore\ a = -2, \quad b = 13, \quad d = -5$$

b Since the translation was $\begin{pmatrix} 5 \\ -2 \end{pmatrix}$, the vertical asymptote is $x = 5$, and the horizontal asymptote is $y = -2$.

c $f(0) = -\frac{13}{5}$
$\therefore$ the y-intercept is $-\frac{13}{5}$.
$f(x) = 0$ when $-2x + 13 = 0$
$$\therefore\ x = \frac{13}{2}$$
$\therefore$ the x-intercept is $\frac{13}{2}$.

d

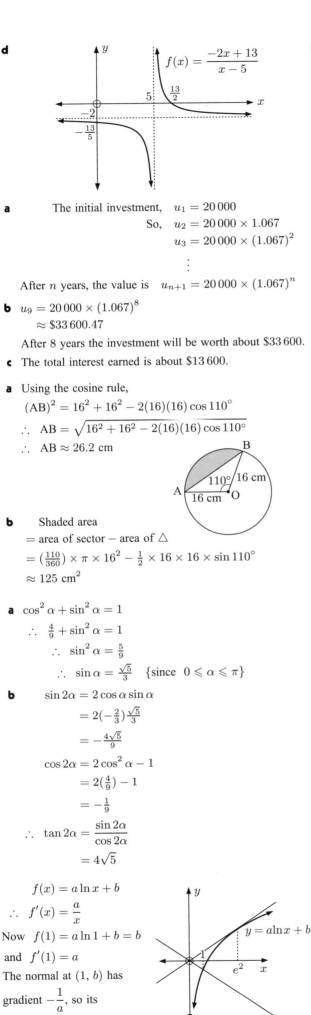

$f(x) = \dfrac{-2x+13}{x-5}$

3 a The initial investment, $u_1 = 20\,000$

So, $u_2 = 20\,000 \times 1.067$

$u_3 = 20\,000 \times (1.067)^2$

$\vdots$

After n years, the value is $u_{n+1} = 20\,000 \times (1.067)^n$

b $u_9 = 20\,000 \times (1.067)^8$

$\approx \$33\,600.47$

After 8 years the investment will be worth about $\$33\,600$.

c The total interest earned is about $\$13\,600$.

4 a Using the cosine rule,

$(AB)^2 = 16^2 + 16^2 - 2(16)(16)\cos 110°$

$\therefore \ AB = \sqrt{16^2 + 16^2 - 2(16)(16)\cos 110°}$

$\therefore \ AB \approx 26.2$ cm

b Shaded area

$=$ area of sector $-$ area of $\triangle$

$= \left(\frac{110}{360}\right) \times \pi \times 16^2 - \frac{1}{2} \times 16 \times 16 \times \sin 110°$

≈ 125 cm^2

5 a $\cos^2 \alpha + \sin^2 \alpha = 1$

$\therefore \ \frac{4}{9} + \sin^2 \alpha = 1$

$\therefore \ \sin^2 \alpha = \frac{5}{9}$

$\therefore \ \sin \alpha = \frac{\sqrt 5}{3}$ {since $0 \leqslant \alpha \leqslant \pi$}

b $\sin 2\alpha = 2\cos \alpha \sin \alpha$

$= 2(-\frac{2}{3})\frac{\sqrt 5}{3}$

$= -\frac{4\sqrt 5}{9}$

$\cos 2\alpha = 2\cos^2 \alpha - 1$

$= 2(\frac{4}{9}) - 1$

$= -\frac{1}{9}$

$\therefore \ \tan 2\alpha = \dfrac{\sin 2\alpha}{\cos 2\alpha}$

$= 4\sqrt 5$

6 $f(x) = a\ln x + b$

$\therefore \ f'(x) = \dfrac{a}{x}$

Now $f(1) = a\ln 1 + b = b$

and $f'(1) = a$

The normal at $(1, b)$ has

gradient $-\dfrac{1}{a}$, so its

equation is

$x + ay = 1 + ab$

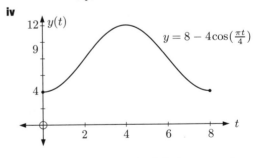

But this normal passes through O, so $1 + ab = 0$

$\therefore \ ab = -1 \ \dots (*)$

Also, $f(e^2) = a\ln e^2 + b = 2a + b$

and $f'(e^2) = \dfrac{a}{e^2}$

The tangent at $(e^2, \ 2a+b)$ has gradient $\dfrac{a}{e^2}$, so its equation

is $ax - e^2 y = ae^2 - e^2(2a + b)$

$= -e^2(a + b)$

This tangent also passes through O, so $-e^2(a + b) = 0$

$\therefore \ b = -a$

Using $(*)$, $-a^2 = -1$

$\therefore \ a^2 = 1$

We are given $a > 0$, so $a = 1$ and $b = -1$.

7 a

Length l (m)	0.30	0.40	0.50	0.60	0.80
Period T (s)	1.10	1.27	1.42	1.56	1.80
$\sqrt l$	0.548	0.632	0.707	0.775	0.894

b $r \approx 1.00$. There is an almost perfect positive linear association between the variables.

c $\overline{\sqrt l} \approx 0.711$

$\overline{T} = 1.43$

$\therefore \ m \approx \dfrac{1.43}{0.711} \approx 2.01$

d When $l = 0.7$, $T \approx 2.01\sqrt{0.70}$

≈ 1.68 seconds

Section B

8 a i $y(t) = 8 - 4\cos(\frac{\pi t}{4})$ has period $\dfrac{2\pi}{\frac{\pi}{4}} = 8$

ii $y(t)$ is a minimum when $\cos(\frac{\pi t}{4}) = 1$

On the given domain, this is when $t = 0$ and $t = 8$.

The minimum value is $8 - 4 = 4$.

iii $y(t)$ has a maximum value of $8 - 4(-1) = 12$

when $\cos(\frac{\pi t}{4}) = -1$, which is when $t = 4$.

iv

$y = 8 - 4\cos(\frac{\pi t}{4})$

b i Since the mean water depth is 6 m, $p = 6$.

Since the difference between high and low tides is 4 m, the amplitude is 2 m.

$\therefore \ q = 2$

Since the time between high and low tides is 6 hours, the period is 12 hours.

$\therefore \ \dfrac{2\pi}{\left(\frac{\pi}{r}\right)} = 12$

$\therefore \ r = 6$

ii Consider the 12 hour period $0 \leqslant t \leqslant 12$.
If the depth of the water is 7 m then

$$6 - 2\cos\left(\tfrac{\pi}{6}t\right) = 7$$

$$\therefore \quad 2\cos\left(\tfrac{\pi}{6}t\right) = -1$$

$$\therefore \quad \cos\left(\tfrac{\pi}{6}t\right) = -\tfrac{1}{2}$$

$$\therefore \quad \tfrac{\pi}{6}t = \tfrac{2\pi}{3} \text{ or } \tfrac{4\pi}{3}$$

$$\therefore \quad t = 4 \text{ or } 8$$

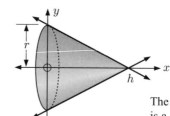

The depth of water is greater than 7 m if

$$\cos\left(\tfrac{\pi}{6}t\right) < -\tfrac{1}{2}$$

$$\therefore \quad 4 < t < 8$$

In each 12 hour period, the depth is at least 7 m for 4 hours.

∴ in a 24 hour day, it is at least 7 m for 8 hours.

∴ the ship can make its entry for $\tfrac{1}{3}$ of the day.

9 a i

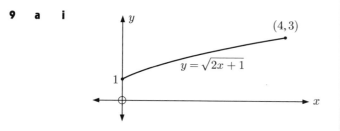

ii $\int f(x)\, dx$

$$= \int (2x + 1)^{\frac{1}{2}}\, dx$$

$$= \int \tfrac{1}{2}(2x + 1)^{\frac{1}{2}}\, 2\, dx \quad \{u = 2x + 1, \ du = 2\, dx\}$$

$$= \tfrac{1}{2} \int u^{\frac{1}{2}}\, du$$

$$= \tfrac{1}{2} \times \tfrac{2}{3} \times u^{\frac{3}{2}} + c$$

$$= \tfrac{1}{3} u^{\frac{3}{2}} + c$$

$$= \tfrac{1}{3}(2x + 1)^{\frac{3}{2}} + c$$

iii Area $= \int_0^4 f(x)\, dx$

$$= \left[\tfrac{1}{3}(2x + 1)^{\frac{3}{2}} \right]_0^4$$

$$= \tfrac{1}{3} \times 9^{\frac{3}{2}} - \tfrac{1}{3} \times 1^{\frac{3}{2}}$$

$$= 9 - \tfrac{1}{3}$$

$$= 8\tfrac{2}{3} \text{ units}^2$$

iv We need to find k such that

$$\pi \int_k^{2k} (2x + 1)\, dx = 30 \text{ units}^3$$

$$\therefore \quad \left[x^2 + x \right]_k^{2k} = \frac{30}{\pi}$$

$$\therefore \quad \left(4k^2 + 2k \right) - \left(k^2 + k \right) = \frac{30}{\pi}$$

$$\therefore \quad 3k^2 + k = \frac{30}{\pi}$$

Using technology, $\quad k \approx -1.959$ or 1.625

But $k > 0$, so $k \approx 1.63$

b i The line has gradient $= \dfrac{0 - r}{h - 0} = \dfrac{-r}{h}$

∴ its equation is $\quad y = -\dfrac{r}{h} x + r$

ii

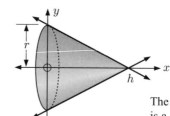

The solid of revolution is a cone of base radius r and height h.

iii Volume $= \pi \displaystyle\int_0^h \left(-\frac{r}{h} x + r \right)^2 dx$

$$= \pi r^2 \int_0^h \left(1 - \frac{x}{h} \right)^2 dx$$

$$= \pi r^2 \left[\frac{1}{-\frac{1}{h}} \frac{\left(1 - \frac{x}{h}\right)^3}{3} \right]_0^h$$

$$= \pi r^2 \left(-\frac{h}{3}(0) - \frac{-h}{3}(1) \right)$$

$$= \pi r^2 \times \frac{h}{3}$$

$$= \tfrac{1}{3}\pi r^2 h$$

10 a $A(2, -1, 0), \quad B(-10, 50, 1)$

$$\therefore \quad \overrightarrow{AB} = \begin{pmatrix} -10 - 2 \\ 50 - -1 \\ 1 - 0 \end{pmatrix} = \begin{pmatrix} -12 \\ 51 \\ 1 \end{pmatrix}$$

$$\therefore \quad |\overrightarrow{AB}| = \sqrt{144 + 2601 + 1} \approx 52.4$$

So, the aircraft is about 52.4 km away.

b The aircraft has direction vector $= \begin{pmatrix} 4 \\ -3 \\ 0 \end{pmatrix}$

which has length $\sqrt{16 + 9 + 0} = \sqrt{25} = 5$ km

Its speed is 200 km h^{-1}, so its velocity vector

$$= 40 \begin{pmatrix} 4 \\ -3 \\ 0 \end{pmatrix} = \begin{pmatrix} 160 \\ -120 \\ 0 \end{pmatrix}.$$

So, the position vector is

$$\mathbf{r} = \begin{pmatrix} x \\ y \\ z \end{pmatrix} = \underset{\substack{\uparrow \\ \text{position} \\ \text{at 10:00 am}}}{\begin{pmatrix} -10 \\ 50 \\ 1 \end{pmatrix}} + t \underset{\substack{\uparrow \\ \text{velocity} \\ \text{vector}}}{\begin{pmatrix} 160 \\ -120 \\ 0 \end{pmatrix}}$$

c At 10:30 am, $t = \tfrac{1}{2}$

$$\therefore \quad \begin{pmatrix} x \\ y \\ z \end{pmatrix} = \begin{pmatrix} -10 \\ 50 \\ 1 \end{pmatrix} + \begin{pmatrix} 80 \\ -60 \\ 0 \end{pmatrix} = \begin{pmatrix} 70 \\ -10 \\ 1 \end{pmatrix}$$

∴ the aircraft is at $(70, -10, 1)$.

d When $t = 0$, the helicopter has z-coordinate $= 0.5$

∴ it is flying 500 m above the ground.

e The velocity vector $= \begin{pmatrix} -120 \\ -50 \\ 0.5 \end{pmatrix}$

∴ the speed of the helicopter $= \sqrt{14\,400 + 2500 + 0.25}$

$$\approx 130 \text{ km h}^{-1}$$

f **i** The helicopter is directly below the airplane when

$$\begin{pmatrix} -10 \\ 50 \end{pmatrix} + t \begin{pmatrix} 160 \\ -120 \end{pmatrix} = \begin{pmatrix} 74 \\ 29 \end{pmatrix} + t \begin{pmatrix} -120 \\ -50 \end{pmatrix}$$

$$\therefore \quad -10 + 160t = 74 - 120t \text{ and}$$
$$50 - 120t = 29 - 50t$$
$$\therefore \quad 280t = 84 \text{ and } 70t = 21$$

Both equations are satisfied by $t = 0.3$ and so the time is 10:18 am.

ii $\mathbf{h} = \begin{pmatrix} x \\ y \\ z \end{pmatrix} = \begin{pmatrix} 74 \\ 29 \\ 0.5 \end{pmatrix} + 0.3 \begin{pmatrix} -120 \\ -50 \\ 0.5 \end{pmatrix}$

$$= \begin{pmatrix} 38 \\ 14 \\ 0.65 \end{pmatrix}$$

So, the helicopter is at $(38, 14, 0.65)$.

iii The distance from the helicopter to the airport

$$= \sqrt{(38 - 2)^2 + (14 - -1)^2 + (0.65 - 0)^2}$$
$$\approx 39.0 \text{ km}$$

$\therefore$ the helicopter will arrive at the airport

$\approx \frac{39.0}{130} \approx 0.3$ hours after 10:18 am,

which is 10:36 am.

NOTES